352.

Rossell
602

METEOROLOGICAL
INSTRUMENTS

METEOROLOGICAL INSTRUMENTS

BY

W. E. KNOWLES MIDDLETON, M.Sc.

Meteorologist in the Meteorological Service of Canada

THE UNIVERSITY OF TORONTO PRESS

TORONTO, CANADA

1942

First printed, September, 1941
Revised and reprinted, June, 1942
Revised and reprinted, Nov., 1942

London:
HUMPHREY MILFORD
Oxford University Press

TABLE OF CONTENTS

PREFACE

It is now fifty-three years since the appearance of the great *Treatise on Meteorological Apparatus and Methods* written by Cleveland Abbe. Since then there has been no general text-book on the subject in English, and no summary other than the excellent articles in the third volume of Glazebrook's *Dictionary of Applied Physics*, published in 1923.

Thus there would appear to be a need for such a book at this time. My apology for undertaking to write it is that the circumstances of my occupation have kept me in touch with both British and American practice, not to mention the numerous improvements in meteorological apparatus which have originated in the Meteorological Service of Canada under the guidance of the present Controller, Mr. John Patterson.

This unofficial function of liaison officer is assumed the more willingly because I believe that the practice in each country contains much that is good, and not a little that can be improved by a study of other methods. Nevertheless it should be made clear that the opinions expressed in this book are entirely personal, and not necessarily the official views of the Service.

The plan of the book follows that of the lectures on meteorological instruments that I have been giving for the past six years to graduate students in the course of meteorology at the University of Toronto. I have made no attempt to include every available instrument, not even every contemporary design. I have tried to emphasize the underlying principles; and I have also set down a number of practical matters that a practising meteorologist ought to know. The history of the subject has been omitted with regret, in order to bring the book within the compass desired by the publisher. Fortunately there are copies of Abbe's *Treatise* here and there, and the student who is interested in the history of meteorological instruments should borrow one and read it. The scope of the subject has also been artificially restricted to include only those instruments which are found at *meteorological* stations, omitting radiation instruments (an immense field) and instruments for the measurement of the electrical and optical state of the atmosphere, as well as instruments for the study of atmospheric pollution. These omissions are justified by the fact that only a small minority of meteorologists ever have occasion to operate such instruments.

Much more could have been written on radiosondes; but in the present state of the technique it seemed better to abstain from lengthy discussions which might be rendered irrelevant by some unforeseen improvement.

While the book is intended primarily as a text, I hope it will be of use to all who make or use meteorological instruments. To facilitate further study, a number of references to original papers have been selected from the enormous literature of the subject, but there has been no attempt to compile a bibliography.

In a few instances the mathematical demonstrations involve the simplest and most common differential equations, generally only elementary calculus. I believe that the non-mathematical parts of the book will be clear to those who do not wish to work through the theory.

The co-operation of several manufacturers has materially reduced the labour of preparing the illustrations. This is acknowledged in the captions of the illustrations concerned. In two cases (Figs. 60 and 125) it was thought better to make line tracings from the manufacturer's photographs. All the figures that appear without acknowledgment have been drawn or photographed by the author, in some instances using, with permission, drawings belonging to the Canadian Service.

I wish to thank the Chief of the United States Weather Bureau, and various American officials, especially Mr. A. H. Mears, Chief Engineer of the Instruments Division, for the most whole-hearted co-operation, without which the preparation of this book would have been very much more difficult. Finally I wish to thank Mr. J. Patterson, Controller of the Meteorological Service of Canada, Mr. A. Thomson, Assistant Controller, and my colleague Mr. R. C. Jacobsen, for helpful criticism of various parts of the manuscript.

Toronto,
July, 1941.

CHAPTER I

INTRODUCTION: PROPERTIES OF METEOROLOGICAL INSTRUMENTS

1. General Properties of Scientific Instruments

A scientific instrument is a machine or device for making a measurement; that is to say, for rendering the quantitative aspects of natural phenomena appreciable by our senses. Thus, although we may form the opinion that on a certain occasion the air is warm, we must have recourse to an instrument (the thermometer) if we are to express its degree of warmness in numerical terms. Other instruments measure quantities to which our senses do not respond at all, as for example the pressure of the atmosphere, or the electrical resistance of a piece of wire.

An instrument may be simple or complicated, according to the number of processes which intervene between the natural phenomenon and the senses of the user. The reader may multiply examples; but we may contrast an ordinary thermometer, in which the change in volume of a liquid due to change of its temperature is estimated directly by the length of a capillary column, and a photographically recording electrical resistance thermometer, in which no less than seven steps come between the temperature and its final reading by means of a scale of length.

The above examples suggest, and further consideration will show, that the final process leading directly to the senses of the user is almost always the observation by the eye of a coincidence in space, or else the estimation of a *small* distance. In special circumstances the ear or the touch may be used to observe a coincidence in time. The function of a scientific instrument, therefore, is primarily to convert the quantitative aspects of some natural phenomenon into a series of recognizable coincidences in time or space.

It is not our purpose to enter into the general subject of instrument design, more especially since meteorological instruments must frequently fulfil conditions different from those imposed on most scientific apparatus, and also because this book does not purport to be a treatise on the design of instruments.[1] It will nevertheless be well to emphasize some of the requirements of all good and serviceable instruments, in whatever field of scientific endeavour they may be used.

An instrument, then, should be as *accurate* as may be required for the problem in hand, as *sensitive* as needed to make full use of its accuracy, *robust* and *durable* enough to give the desired length of service, and as *convenient,*

---

[1] See WHITEHEAD, T. N., *The Design and Use of Instruments and Accurate Mechanism.* New York 1934, Macmillan.

simple, and *cheap* as may be compatible with the other requirements. The reader is specially desired to note the conditional nature of the above specifications, and in particular the qualifications attached to accuracy and sensitivity. These deserve some further comment.

There are still scientific workers who fully enjoy the stock laboratory joke about the student who measures the heat-conductivity of copper to ten decimal places, while themselves making impossible and totally unnecessary demands on the makers of instruments. This attitude is a result of a verbal confusion concerning *accuracy* and *sensitivity*. It is well to insist that a sensitive instrument may not be as accurate as another instrument with a lesser degree of sensitivity. For example, a large and well-constructed voltmeter would be sensitive, but not accurate, if its scale had unknown errors; a miniature instrument with a correct scale would be much less sensitive, but more accurate.

The requirements for accuracy can be reduced to two:

(1) The instrument should have and maintain a calibration under given conditions to within the desired precision.

(2) The errors under other conditions should be known and constant in time within required limits.

What, for instance, constitutes an accurate mercury thermometer? Without anticipating the discussion which is presented in chapter III, we may at once answer the question on the above bases: an accurate mercury thermometer is one made of stable materials in such a way as to change very little with the passage of time, provided with a calibration relating the readings of its scale at every point with an internationally recognized scale of temperature, and with known errors when used under conditions different from those under which it was calibrated. It is not necessary that the divisions of the scale should correspond exactly with the degrees of the international scale of temperature. Such a correspondence is, of course, highly desirable for many purposes; but its attainment adds only to the *convenience* of the instrument, and should be considered in that connection.

In a sensitive instrument a small change in the quantity being measured produces a large change in the final message to the senses. The optimum sensitivity is very seldom the greatest that can be obtained, and is always to be determined in connection with the desirable or possible precision. The thermometer will again serve as an example. Suppose we have to measure the temperature of a water-bath which can be controlled electrically within limits of ±0.5°F.; the extra cost and fragility of a thermometer which could be read to 0.01°F. would obviously not be justified; one graduated in whole degrees will not only be good enough, but actually better on account of the greater ease of reading it. The desirable precision of any observation can always be determined either theoretically or from practical experience with the phenomenon in question; and it is a good general rule that an instrument should be sensitive enough only to make it easy to read to that precision.

Durability and *robustness* are generally a matter of design and construction, and are often a function of cost, though less so now than formerly. In point of fact there are few instruments which cannot be made reasonably strong and durable—though some, it is true, need special precautions in packing and transport—and a piece of apparatus which needs undue care or delicate handling is generally badly designed. Nor, with modern materials, need an instrument be made heavy merely in order to give it strength.[2]

Convenience, simplicity, and *cost* are interrelated. Nowadays the first two are almost as much a matter of economics as is the last; to realize this one has only to compare the original drawings of some new instrument as published in a scientific periodical by its inventor, with the same instrument as finally manufactured in quantity. All the resources of stamping and die-casting, the precision of grinding, the marvellous properties of moulded plastics, are at the service of the instrument-maker if only the product can be sold in sufficient numbers. The result is the production of many simple, accurate, and convenient instruments at reasonable prices, doing without hand work except where it is essential, but—to the comfort of the conservative—employing the skilled instrument-maker wherever his employment is justified.

2. Special Characteristics of Meteorological Instruments

Meteorological instruments must have the properties of instruments in general, but the rather special conditions under which most of them are used render the emphasis somewhat different. Instruments used in the laboratory are commonly looked after by people with scientific training; they are protected from rain, snow, and dust; small defects can be repaired in a well-equipped workshop by competent mechanics. Meteorological instruments, on the other hand, are most frequently read and cared for by amateur or untrained observers; most of them are exposed to the weather; and they are often a thousand miles from where they can be repaired. Thus, supposing that it has a reasonable degree of accuracy and permanence of calibration (and we shall return to this matter), the most essential qualities of a meteorological instrument are simplicity and durability. Simplicity above all; if possible even to the point of being "fool-proof."

Meteorological instruments must have no delicate adjusting screws. Any adjustments that must be made at intervals by the observer should be provided for by large and easily manipulated screws or levers; other adjustments, which are to be made only by an inspector or at the head office, might well be effected by screws requiring a special wrench, to forestall the apparently irresistible temptation to adjust everything in sight whenever any trouble develops.

Instruments that are sensitive to ordinary vibration are to be avoided, as it is often difficult to find a suitable place to instal them. Most instruments for use indoors are arranged to stand on a table or shelf. In the writer's opinion this is a mistake; and the attention of the makers of such instruments as barographs and anemographs is invited to the possibility of making models to

---

[2]But for other reasons a heavy instrument may sometimes be desirable.

hang on a wall, their covers swinging downwards or sideways.[3] Every room has walls, which are likely to be at least as steady as shelves built upon them.

Simplicity of design usually leads to durability and convenience. But in meteorological practice there is more to convenience than mere facility in taking observations. Wherever possible, instruments should be provided which minimize the work of reducing the readings. Instruments requiring compli- cated tables or graphs of corrections are often necessary in the laboratory, but should be avoided at meteorological stations. Counting dots pricked in a chart is another labour which is now, happily, infrequently required.

Owing to the nature of atmospheric processes, the concept of accuracy in meteorological observations has a special meaning. This will be referred to again in later chapters; it will be sufficient to mention here that many simple instruments are capable of measuring phenomena under laboratory conditions with an accuracy much greater than can be attained in the open air.[4] Now- adays there is seldom any difficulty in obtaining ample accuracy when an instrument is new; the trouble often lies in maintaining it over long periods. This remark, it is freely admitted, does not apply to measurements of rain and certainly not to measurements of snow; but in these instances the exposure of the instrument provides the difficulty, rather than the instrument itself. Indeed, all meteorological instruments should be considered in connection with their exposures.

Enough has been said in this brief introduction, it is hoped, to provide the reader with some criteria for the estimation of the qualities of a meteorological instrument as an instrument. These criteria will be kept constantly in mind in later chapters. We shall close this chapter with some remarks on recording[5] instruments, all of which, with the exception of some types of sunshine record- ers and one or two balloon meteorographs, are provided with clocks.

3. Characteristics of Recording Instruments in General

The recording instruments used in meteorology may be classified under five headings, according to the way in which the record is produced:

(1) Instruments drawing a line by means of a pen on paper.

(2) Instruments drawing a line on a smoked or silvered surface by means of a sharp point.

(3) Photographic recorders, in which a spot of light leaves a latent image on sensitized photographic materials.

(4) Thread recorders, in which, at regular intervals, an inked thread is pressed down on paper by a bar which falls on the pointer of the instrument.

(5) Instruments in which the rays of the sun are focussed on a specially prepared card, in which they burn a trace.

---

[3]Some modern instruments, chiefly of German make, have this feature.

[4]See, for example, the discussion on the accuracy of thermometers in chapter III.

[5]The old term "self-recording instruments" is illogical and to be discouraged. Such instru- ments do not record themselves, but the variations of some physical quantity.

By far the majority of these instruments are in class (1). The other methods of recording are used chiefly where the available controlling forces are too small to ensure the smooth motion of a pen, class (2) also where a compressed scale makes the finest possible line essential, as in some meteorographs. Instruments of class (3) are seldom used except at large observatories, and then for special purposes, if we except certain forms of sunshine recorder which are in use in some countries. Thread recorders (class 4) are used to some extent at observatories in connection with electrical thermometers and other devices, but are probably less reliable than certain modern recording potentiometers which come in class (1). Class (5) is represented by the ubiquitous Campbell-Stokes sunshine recorder.

The remarks which follow will refer to instruments of the first two classes, since the third and fourth classes are special and uncommon, and the fifth will be treated fully in chapter IX.

All these instruments, then, with the exception of one or two balloon meteorographs, have clocks. The clock is used to revolve a drum on which a sheet of paper or a smoked foil is stretched or else to drive a sprocket which feeds paper continuously from a roll. A pen or stylus carried by an arm which is connected to the sensitive elements of the instrument draws a trace on the moving paper or foil.

Where there is a drum (as in most meteorological recorders), the clock may be inside it and revolve with it, or attached to the frame of the instrument and stationary. The former is the more common at the present time, but the stationary clock has two advantages: (a) backlash can be eliminated without trouble, (b) if the observer drops the drum when changing charts, the drum is all he drops. The clocks supplied by reputable makers in all countries have been developed to a high degree of excellence, and in England recently an attempt has been made to standardize their design by setting up an official specification,[6] in order that a very few types of clocks may fit all ordinary instruments.

In spite of excellent design and construction, however, there is a good deal of trouble with clocks in cold climates. In so far as this is due to the oil congealing, it may be avoided by soaking the clocks in gasoline (not in gasoline which contains tetraethyl lead) at the beginning of winter, and running them without oil. It is said to be essential to get all the oil out of the mainspring. But even clocks treated in this way may stop owing to differences in the thermal expansion of the materials; and it is annoying to lose a thermograph record on the coldest night of the year, when the course of the temperature is of special public interest. At stations served by an alternating-current network, this might be avoided by driving the drum by means of a synchronous motor, which will keep itself satisfactorily warm when in continuous operation. The very small synchronous clock motors are scarcely suitable for such rigorous conditions; but excellent motors of the shaded-pole type are available in ratings as low as 1/200 horse-power. A further advantage lies in the great

[6]Air Ministry, London, Meteorological Office, *Observer's Handbook*, 1938 ed.

accuracy of the time-scale, which has led to the adoption of synchronous motor drive in many industrial recorders.   The sole objection to this method is that the drum stops during interruptions of service; but in the large electrical networks of today this is commonly a matter of minutes in a year.

The paper is generally held on the drum by a spring clamp which holds down both ends of the sheet.   This makes it necessary to have the period of revolution about $7\frac{1}{2}$ days for a weekly chart, and about 25 to 26 hours for a daily chart, to allow for the width of the spring and to leave some latitude in the hour of attending to the instrument.   Daily charts are usually arranged for changing at about 0900, and weekly charts on Monday morning; but the writer has seen a daily chart, provided with a well-known instrument, on which the hour-lines were numbered from midnight to midnight—a really deplorable inhumanity on the part of the manufacturer!

Recently there has been a tendency to use clocks making a revolution in 78 or 102 hours, the charts being changed every three or four days.   This gives a very good scale, especially for barographs with drums of the usual proportions; and makes it feasible to have every hour indicated by an arc on the chart—a very great advantage.

In most instruments the pen is carried on a pivoted arm, commonly about 7.3 inches (18 cm) in length, so that the hour-lines on the chart are curved. It is very important that the pen arm should be supported at the proper height, and be of exactly the proper length, so that any instantaneous change in the reading of the instrument will cause the pen to describe an arc exactly parallel to the hour-lines.   Whenever a pen is changed the length of the arm should be checked, as an increase, for example, will expand the scale of the instrument in proportion, besides rendering the timing slightly inaccurate.   It should be remarked that, since the surface of the drum is not flat, it is impossible to get entirely uniform timing on all parts of the scale if the hour-lines are parts of circles; but this involves only a small error, and can usually be neglected.

It is seldom that instrument clocks keep exact time under all conditions of temperature; and in order to be able to ascertain the exact hour of significant points in the recorded curve, or to make an hourly abstract, it is absolutely necessary to make time-marks at several term-hours during the day.   This is accomplished by depressing the pen about $\frac{1}{8}''$ to $\frac{1}{4}''$ and releasing it.   Means are sometimes provided for doing this without opening the cover of the instrument.

The careless depression of the pen to make time-marks may disturb the calibration of an instrument, or even strain some of its parts beyond their elastic limit.   A simple and effective device to prevent this was designed in the Meteorological Office, Toronto, and is regularly applied to barographs used in Canada.   Its principle is shown in Fig. 1.   In a tube A works a plunger B, supported by a light helical spring C which rests on a stop D.   From B is hung a weight

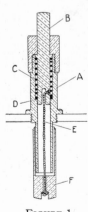

FIGURE 1
Time-marking
device.

F by a light chain E. The weight is heavy enough to depress the pen by about $\frac{1}{8}''$ when allowed to descend on one of the intermediate levers of the instrument; and since it is hung on a flexible chain, it is impossible to exert any further force, no matter how hard the plunger B is pushed down.

The pens used on small recording instruments are of two general types, shown in Fig. 2, (a) and (b); though a "crow-quill" mapping pen is used on some instruments such as pressure-tube anemometers. On larger instruments, especially recording electrical meters, a glass pen (Fig. 2c) is often used.

There is little to choose between types (a) and (b), though the latter can probably be made to give a slightly finer line. The performance of either type depends, first, on the correct shaping of the point, and second, on keeping the pen clean. This is on the assumption that the chart paper is of suitable quality. But a very superior line can be obtained by a metal pen such as that shown at (d), which is fitted with a fine platinum-iridium tube. An inner partition S makes a capillary space in which the ink will rise.

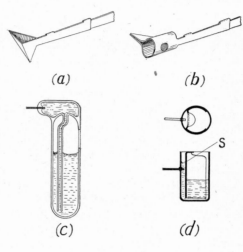

(a)   (b)

(c)   (d)

FIGURE 2
Pens for recording instruments.

So far we have discussed what might be called the "writing" parts of recording instruments. It remains to refer briefly to the mechanical system which transforms the displacement of the sensitive elements into the motion of the pen, often with greatly increased amplitude. The system usually consists of levers, but may include wheels, gears, or sprockets and chain. It is of the greatest importance that all bearings should be as nearly frictionless as possible, since the controlling forces are generally not very great. Pivot bearings are advisable; they should be made *and adjusted* with great care, often with some thought of the relative thermal expansion coefficients of the shafts and the frame. When a new instrument is received from the maker, the adjustment of the pivots should invariably be checked, as it may have been disturbed in transport. On some instruments, such as bimetallic thermographs (see page 71), journal bearings are satisfactory, as the controlling forces are adequate. When they can be used, they are decidedly more durable than pivots for use outdoors. Motions involving a cylinder sliding lengthwise in a sleeve should be avoided wherever possible unless comparatively great forces are available.[7]

---

[7]Recently a Swiss firm has put on the market a line of miniature ball bearings, which are more durable than jewels and offer even less friction, but must be given some protection from

Routine care of recording instruments.   Information regarding the daily care of recording instruments is given in the observers' hand-books of all Services, and we shall confine ourselves here to a simple list of the points which must be looked after (see Fig. 3).

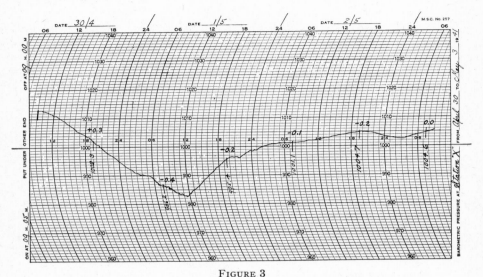

FIGURE 3

Typical barograph chart.   The barometer readings and the estimated corrections at the term-hours have been written near the time marks.

(1) *When changing charts:*

    (*a*) Clean the pen if necessary; if it is of type (2*a*), by passing a *thin* strong paper between the points. (Thick paper may spread them apart permanently.)

    (*b*) See that the ink is flowing freely enough to make a line that is clearly visible.

    (*c*) Wind the clock.

    (*d*) Write the date *and name of station* on the new chart. Observers may not realize that dozens of charts arrive at the central office each day, and that in consequence the paternity of a nameless chart may be difficult to establish.

    (*e*) Put the chart on the drum so that the outer end of the overlap points in the direction of motion of the pen relative to the chart.

    (*f*) Make sure that the edge of the chart is everywhere close up to the flange provided on the drum to retain it (e.g., at the bottom of a vertical drum).

---

moisture and dust.   The smallest of these are little more than a millimetre in outside diameter, and contain three balls.

(g) In setting the pen to the correct time, make the final adjustment by moving the drum in the direction opposite to its ordinary motion, to take up any backlash in the gears. If this is not done, it will be some time before the drum begins to turn, at least with many clocks.

(2) *At each terminal observation:*
(a) See that the instrument is recording properly.
(b) Read the instrument.
(c) Make the time-mark.
(The sequence of the last two operations should never be inverted.)

4. Control of Recording Instruments by Eye Readings of Non-Recording Instruments

Recording instruments are not easily made absolute; that is to say, they can seldom be calibrated from first principles. Neither can they be trusted to retain their calibration indefinitely. It is therefore the practice to control the readings of recording instruments by means of the term observations of indicating instruments, which are generally, if not absolute, at least much less subject to accidental errors. Thus the barograph is controlled by the mercury barometer, the thermograph by the thermometers, the hair hygrograph by the psychrometer. The following discussion applies to instruments of the first four of the classes mentioned above (page 4) with the exception of instruments for aerological purposes, which will be treated separately in chapter x. The fifth class will also be considered later (chapter ix).

Let us suppose that a barograph chart is being read off for the purpose of making an hourly abstract. The computer is provided with the barometer readings at term-hours over the corresponding period. The first step is to tabulate the readings of the barograph at the term-hours, if this has not already been done by the observer, and subtract each one from the corresponding barometer reading. The result is called the *correction*,

Correction = barometer − barograph,

and will be positive if the barograph is reading too low, negative if too high. The correction is thus the amount which must be added (algebraically) to the barograph reading to obtain the barometer reading. The results are written on the chart in pencil near the trace and above the time-marks (Fig. 3). When this has been done, the mean of all the corrections for each day (from midnight to 2359 h.) is found and written near the top of the chart, giving the correction to be applied to each hourly reading during that day. If the instrument is being run properly, the corrections will be so small that they can be applied mentally with very little effort. It may be remarked in passing that the actual process of abstracting charts, once the corrections have been established, can be performed much more than twice as fast by two people as by one alone, and with infinitely less fatigue; it is therefore uneconomical to assign only one computer to such work.

The process described above is logically unsound, as it introduces a discontinuity at each midnight. In practice, however, the change of correction from one day to the next is seldom greater than the probable error in reading the chart; indeed, a large change must invariably be investigated, and will often be due to an error in reading or correcting the indicating instrument. Abstracting the charts of recording instruments provides one of the best checks on the care and accuracy of an observer.

A convenient means of interpolating between corrections made at regular hours, if such interpolation is thought necessary, is described in *Circular A* of the United States Weather Bureau. It consists of a stout card as shown in Fig. 4, having notches in each edge, corresponding to the correction of the instrument in any convenient units—tenths of degrees, tenths of millibars, per cent, etc. Positive corrections are found in the upper half of the card, negative ones below. A rubber band is stretched between the notches appropriate to the corrections at 8.00 A.M. and 8.00 P.M.[8] and its intersection with the vertical lines automatically performs the required linear interpolation for each intervening hour. In the example shown, the initial and final corrections are −2 and +5 units, and the intervening ones

−1, −1, 0, 0, +1, +2,
+2, +3, +3, +4, +4.

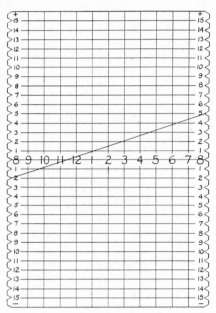

FIGURE 4
Card for interpolating between term-hours.

This is the place to mention a curious psychological fact which can influence the abstracting of records. If a chart is ruled with lines every two units (e.g., every two miles per hour of wind speed), there is a tendency for a frequency diagram made from many readings to show consistently greater frequencies for the even numbers (i.e., those provided with lines) than for the odd. If this is brought to the attention of the computer, it is more than probable that the next few thousand readings will show the opposite effect, because of his desperate attempts to be honest. Only the most complete objectivity will prevent errors of this sort.

An excellent test of the observer's (or computer's) ability to read to tenths of a division is to take about 1000 readings and count the occurrences of 0, 1, 2 . . . up to 9 in the last figure. The results may surprise even the most experienced observer or computer, and may also show him his habitual preferences among the tenths, to the lasting improvement of the observations.

[8]This is probably the only meteorological instrument or procedure in which the 24-hour system of counting time is less convenient.

CHAPTER II

THE MEASUREMENT OF ATMOSPHERIC PRESSURE

1. General Principles and Methods

The atmosphere, by virtue of its weight, exerts a pressure on the surface of the earth and all other surfaces immersed in it. Pressure is defined as force per unit area (dimensions $[L^{-1}MT^{-2}]$), and thus the atmospheric pressure is equal to the weight of a vertical column of the air, of unit area, and extending up to the outer limit of the atmosphere. There are three general methods of measuring atmospheric pressure, which will be dealt with in order of importance.

(a) The mercury barometer

The most accurate and most generally used method of measuring the pressure of the atmosphere involves balancing it against the weight of a column of liquid. For various reasons, the only liquid which can conveniently be used is mercury.

A mercury barometer consists essentially of some form of U-tube with one limb hermetically closed. The other limb is open to the atmosphere, and often takes the form of a *cistern*, a cylindrical vessel into which the closed tube dips. If all air and vapour, except the vapour of the mercury, is exhausted from the closed tube, the mercury will rise in it until it stands a certain distance above the level in the open vessel. This distance is often referred to as the *height of the barometer*, or (more correctly) the height of the mercury column. This height may be determined by various means more or less simple, and when reduced to standard conditions is itself often adopted as a measure of the atmospheric pressure (see section 2 below).

Alternatively, the mercury column may be weighed on a balance, and its weight converted into pressure units.

(b) Elastic barometers

A membrane of an elastic substance, held at the edges, will be deformed if the pressure on one side is greater than on the other. This is the principle of the well-known *aneroid barometer*, in which two such membranes form the walls of a chamber. The changes in the thickness of this chamber are magnified by means of a system of levers and read on a scale. A thin curved tube of elliptical cross-section, which increases its curvature as the pressure outside it increases, forms the essential part of another type of elastic barometer (the Bourdon barometer).

Elastic barometers have the advantage of portability and convenience, since they contain no liquid, and they may readily be made to give a record.

However, they cannot be made as accurate or as stable as mercury barometers, and they cannot be calibrated from first principles.

(c) The hypsometer

The boiling-point of a liquid is a function of the pressure under which it boils. Once this function has been determined, the temperature at which the liquid boils may be used to determine the atmospheric pressure. The liquid generally used is pure water, and the actual quantity measured is the temperature of the vapour immediately over a free surface during ebullition.

This method of pressure measurement is seldom used, except on difficult expeditions where the safe transport of a mercury barometer is impossible. Under such conditions it is probably more free from systematic errors than the aneroid, in particular from secular changes. Taking an observation, of course, consumes a good deal of time.

2. Discussion of Units of Pressure

Three units are used for the measurement of atmospheric pressure, in different countries and for different ends—the inch of mercury, the millimetre of mercury, and the millibar. The first two of these are direct measures of the height of the mercury column, and in order that they may have an exact significance, a standard set of conditions must be specified. The third is an absolute unit and therefore does not depend on the properties of any substance.

The inch and the millimetre of mercury involve the following specifications:

(1) *The density of mercury.* The standard value[1] is 13.5951 grams per cubic centimetre at 0°C., but different specimens may vary by ±0.0001, since mercury is a mixture of several isotopes. Fortunately these differences affect only the most precise barometry.

(2) *The temperature of the mercury column.* The relation between the temperature and the density of mercury is as follows (temperature in °C.) with sufficient accuracy for meteorological purposes:

$$d_\theta = 13.5951 \ (1 - 0.000182\theta) \ \text{gm. cm}^{-3}$$

The standard temperature is 0°C. or 32°F.

(3) *The temperature of the scale* upon which the height of the mercury column is measured. This scale is commonly of brass, but may be of glass, steel, invar, or other material. Whatever is used, if graduated in millimetres it will be standard at 0°C., while if graduated in inches it will be so at 62°F., the reference temperature for the standard yard.

(4) *The acceleration due to gravity.* The standard "gravity"[2] is that found at mean sea-level in latitude 45°, $g_{45} = 980.62$ cm. sec^{-2} At any other latitude or elevation this quantity will be slightly different, and thus the weight of a given volume of mercury will change somewhat.

---

[1]Organization Météorologique Internationale, *O.M.I. No. 45, Comm. Mét. Int. Procès-verbaux de la session de Berlin, 21-25 juin 1939.* Lausanne 1941, p. 75.
    [2]*Ibid.*

The inch of mercury (as a unit of pressure) is therefore the pressure exerted by a column of pure mercury at a temperature of 32°F. and under standard gravity, one inch in height when measured by means of a standard inch scale at a temperature of 62°F.

The millimetre of mercury is the pressure exerted by a column of pure mercury at a temperature of 0°C. and under standard gravity, one mm in height when measured by means of a standard metric scale at a temperature of 0°C.

The c.g.s. unit of pressure is the *bar*, which is equal to 1 dyne cm^{-2}. In meteorology, however, the bar is equal to one million dynes per square centimetre, and the millibar (mb), being $\frac{1}{1000}$ of this, equals 1000 dynes cm^{-2}. This confusion between the physical and the meteorological units can be forgotten if we remember that in meteorology the bar ($=1000$ mb) is approximately the normal pressure at sea-level.

The relation between the millibar and the millimetre of mercury can be derived from the hydrostatic equation

$$10^3 p(\text{mb}) = d \cdot (b/10) \cdot g$$

where b and d are the height of the barometer in mm and the density of mercury under standard conditions. Introducing the appropriate constants we have

$$10^4 p = 13.5951 \times 980.62 b$$

so that, setting $b = 1$, we find

1 mm Hg $= 1.3332$ mb.

760 mm Hg $= 1013.2$ mb (the "normal pressure" of physics and chemistry).

Since one inch equals 25.4 mm (to within about one part in a million[3]), 1 inch Hg $= 33.863$ mb. It is convenient to remember that 3 inches of mercury is about 100 millibars, and that 1 millibar is almost exactly three-quarters of a millimetre of mercury.

3. General Errors of Pressure Measurements

Under this heading we shall discuss only those sources of error which are common to all barometers.[4]

(a) The effect of wind

Air in motion produces in general either a pressure or a suction on all surfaces exposed to it. A barometer exposed to a gusty wind is, therefore, likely to exhibit dynamic fluctuations in its reading, superimposed on the static pressure. Indeed it is not necessary that the barometer itself be exposed to the wind; for the wind may produce changes of pressure in the room in which the instrument is hung. In strong winds the resulting fluctuations of the barometer may reach 0.1" Hg (3 mb) or more.

Unfortunately this "pumping," as it is called, depends not only on the

[3] This is true of the Imperial inch. The U.S. inch $= 25.4001$ mm.

[4] See also GLAZEBROOK, *Dictionary of Applied Physics*. London 1923, Macmillan, vol. III, p. 165.

wind speed but also on the direction of the wind and the arrangement of doors, windows, chimneys, and other openings in the room. It is common experience that a wind from a certain quarter will cause violent pumping, while an equally strong wind from some other direction causes little. Thus the effect cannot be calculated.

(b) Uncertainties in the temperature of the instrument

In nearly all barometers it is necessary either that the mean temperature of the instrument should be known, or that all parts of it should be at the same temperature, or both. It will be obvious that neither of these conditions is likely to be fulfilled if the barometer is hung in a room which has large gradients of temperature in it. Proximity to heating apparatus and badly-fitting windows or doors is to be avoided, and of course the sun should not shine on the instrument (or its box) at any time of day. For an accurate recording barometer the best location would be a windowless, almost airtight, unheated basement room, provided with a small electric fan to prevent a stratification of temperature being set up. The temperature at the ceiling of an ordinary room, especially when it is being heated, is often several degrees higher than at the floor. A fairly stable stratification may be set up in such a room, so that the top of a mercury barometer may be as much as two or three degrees warmer than the cistern. With the rather primitive method which is generally used to measure the temperature of the mercury column, it is doubtful whether this quantity is often known to within 1°F.

4. The Mercury Barometer

(a) Descriptive

The forms of mercury barometers are very numerous, but they can really be classified into a few types. We shall confine ourselves to a description of the types chiefly used in English-speaking countries.

(i) *The Fortin barometer*

The distinguishing feature of the Fortin barometer is the means provided to raise or lower the level of the mercury in the cistern. A cross-section of the cistern of one make[5] of Fortin barometer is shown in Fig. 5. It consists essentially of a short piece of wide glass tube F, three boxwood fittings G, I, and J, and a leather bag N. The top ring of boxwood carries an ivory fiducial point H, the extremity of which is at the zero of the scale of the barometer; and by means of the screw O the leather bag can be raised or lowered until the surface of the mercury just touches the ivory point.[6] This condition is judged by the coincidence of the point and its reflected image.

---

[5] By Wm. Green of Brooklyn, N.Y. The construction is fairly typical.

[6] Stainless steel points have been tried; but for some unexplained reason they appear to collect dirt from the mercury surface.

The lower part of the cistern is made in two pieces (I, J) in order to simplify the operations of filling and cleaning the barometer. These pieces are held together very ingeniously, with a thin leather gasket between, by means of two pairs of half-rings and four screws—an excellent and utterly simple device. Gaskets are also required between the glass tube (which has its ends ground flat) and the fittings I and G. The outer tube S is of brass, and performs the double function of protecting the cistern and supporting the screw O.

The barometer tube proper, T, enters the cistern through the central aperture in G. It is attached to G by means of a piece of soft leather, which is first tied firmly to the tube at its constricted part, and then brought over and tied to the neck of G. This piece of leather, while allowing the passage of air, so that the pressure within the cistern may be equal to that outside, prevents leakage of mercury when the barometer is inverted for transport.

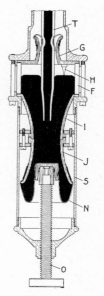

FIGURE 5
Cistern of a Fortin
barometer.

The tube is encased in an outer tube of brass, which performs several functions: (1) it protects the barometer tube, (2) it carries the scale, (3) it forms a bearing in which slide the index and vernier, (4) it carries a thermometer, usually referred to as the "attached thermometer," on which can be read the temperature of the barometer, and (5) since the barometer is generally hung from the top, it carries the entire weight of the instrument. Two long slots, about as wide as the internal diameter of the barometer tube, are cut opposite one another in its upper part, so that the top of the mercury column can be seen. The scale is either engraved on the outer tube beside one of these slots or (as in the barometer we have been describing) on a separate piece of metal. The vernier runs up and down in the slot, being mounted on a short piece of tube which slides inside the outer tube, and can be raised or lowered by a rack and pinion.

There are numerous variations on this fundamental construction. For instance, an eyepiece may be provided for setting to the fiducial point, its optical axis being inclined at an angle of about 20° to the horizontal. In this event, the cistern can be mainly of iron and boxwood, with two small glass windows. Attempts, more or less successful, have been made to replace the leather bag by a solid piston,[7] especially in barometers for use at high level stations.

Barometers of the Fortin type are made with tubes of all (inner) diameters from about 3 mm to 15 mm. The 3 mm to 5 mm sizes are intended for mountain use, and are made as light as possible on that account; on the other

---

[7] See, for example, U.S. Weather Bureau, *Circular F, Instrument Division.* 5th ed., Washington 1930, p. 7.

hand, any tube over 10 mm is intended for a major observatory.   It will appear
below (para. 4 (f) ii) that the larger tubes are capable of greater accuracy.

The advantages of the Fortin barometer are: (1) its ready portability, and
(2) that it permits the inspection of both the free mercury surfaces whose
difference in level is to be measured.   Its disadvantages are: (1) that the
cistern and the mercury in the cistern require frequent cleaning if the fiducial
point is to be set with accuracy; and (2) that an observation of the atmospheric
pressure requires two settings, one of the fiducial point and one of the scale.
This is of no importance at large observatories, but may be of some moment
at outlying stations with untrained personnel, and at airports where many
readings are required.

(ii) *The fixed-cistern barometer ("Kew" pattern barometer)*

To obviate the double setting required by the Fortin barometer, the fixed-
cistern barometer was devised.   The construction of the cistern of a simple
barometer of this type is shown in Fig. 6.   The main
vessel A is of cast iron, or often of stainless steel, and is
provided with an internal flange B, half-way down, which
tends to damp out oscillations of the mercury when the
instrument is being carried about.   The iron cistern is
threaded into the casting C in such a manner that the
two pieces clamp the piece of boxwood D which forms
the roof of the cistern.   Into this the barometer tube E
is cemented.   The leather joint used in the Fortin type
is difficult to apply here, since the barometer tube must
be firmly fixed with respect to the cistern; consequently
the porosity of the boxwood is relied upon to provide
communication with the outside atmosphere.   The upper
parts of the barometer are of the same general construction as in the Fortin, except for the tube itself, which is generally constricted to about 2 mm over the greater part of its
length, and is provided with an air trap as shown at A in
Fig. 7, which serves to prevent air finding its way into the
upper chamber C, even if it should enter the tube.

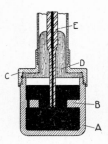

FIGURE 6
Cistern of "Kew"
barometer.

In a barometer of this pattern, since the volume of the
cistern is fixed, a rise of the mercury in the tube will always be
accompanied by a fall of its level in the cistern, and *vice versa.*
A change in pressure of one inch, therefore, will change the
level of the mercury in the tube by some amount less than an
inch, depending on the relative areas of tube and cistern.   If
S be the area of the tube (at the level of the mercury), and A
the area of the cistern (minus that of the tail of the tube), a
rise of x inches in the tube will involve a fall of xS/A inches in
the cistern.   The change of pressure corresponding to a rise of
x inches in the tube is therefore

FIGURE 7
Tube of "Kew"
barometer (sta-
tion pattern).

$$x + xS/A = x \cdot (A+S)/A$$

and a rise of pressure of one inch will produce a rise of $A/(A+S)$ inches in the mercury level. To avoid a computation after each reading, the scale of such a barometer is not graduated in standard inches, but in units of $A/(A+S)$ standard inches. The value of $A/(A+S)$ usually lies between 0.95 and 0.99, the latter value being found only in very large and heavy observatory barometers.

In order that the contraction of the scale may be uniform, it is necessary that the cistern, the tail-piece, and the upper chamber be accurately cylindrical, especially the cistern. Fortunately this presents no problem, being merely a matter of lathe work; and the selection of suitable pieces of glass tube is easy nowadays. However, should a tube be broken, it is essential that it be replaced by one of exactly the same diameter, if the scale is to remain accurate.

It is an interesting point that in such a barometer the zero of the scale lies at the level which the mercury in the cistern would reach, if the whole column in the tube, supposed of uniform cross-section, were emptied into it.[8] Such barometers, however, are always graduated by comparison with a separate standard instrument. It is necessary only that the mercury shall not completely fill the cistern at the lowest pressure which can be read on the scale, nor sink as far as the central flange when the mercury is at the top of its range.

For use on board ship, the tube of the Kew pattern barometer is provided with a fine capillary section in order to damp out the oscillation of the mercury caused by the motion of the ship. Such a barometer is known as a *marine* barometer. The constriction is generally chosen to give a lag-coefficient (see chapter III) of about 240 seconds; this is considered to give a reasonable compromise between the suppression of oscillations and the instantaneous following of changing pressures.

Loss of mercury (which does not immediately affect the readings of the Fortin barometer) leads to lower readings of the fixed-cistern instrument. Accumulation of air in the air-trap (A, Fig. 7) raises the reading, as it is equivalent to an increase in the volume of the mercury. The magnitude of this effect is less, the nearer the bottom of the tube the air-trap is placed.

The convenience of this type of barometer from the standpoint of the observer is unquestionable; and it is probable that many observers will make more consistent readings with it

[8]KLEINSCHMIDT, E., *Handbuch der Meteorologischen Instrumente.* Berlin 1935, Springer, p. 301. This will be referred to as *Handbuch*.

3

FIGURE 8
Patterson barometer, partly in section.

than with the Fortin. Its chief disadvantage lies in the care necessary to transport it.   Various attempts have been made to get over this difficulty, for example the Schneider barometer described in the Circular on barometry of the United States Weather Bureau.[9]   This involves the mercury-tight fitting of a screw into its nut, a matter of critical workmanship.

A very different solution is sought in a new design by J. Patterson,[10] the main features of which will be apparent from Fig. 8.   Strictly speaking, this is not a fixed-cistern barometer; but it operates as one when the leather bag is lowered to its full extent by the complete removal of the screw at the bottom.   This screw is replaced by a short plug when the instrument is in use, to avoid accidental raising of the bag.   The upper part of the cistern has 49 times the area of the tube, so that the barometer is graduated in units of 0.98 inches.

(iii) *The movable-scale barometer*

The movable-scale barometer, like the Fortin, is provided with a glass cistern and a fiducial point; but instead of the volume of the cistern being capable of alteration, the ivory point and the scale can be moved vertically as a unit.   The principle is shown in Fig. 9.

This construction has the very great advantage that with a tube and cistern of large diameter it can be graduated from first principles; that is to say, it constitutes a primary barometer.   However, it is not easily portable and is more suitable for large observatories than for ordinary stations.   A barometer of this type by Newman was in continuous use at Toronto from 1840 to 1939, and is still in good working order.

FIGURE 9
Principle of the movable-scale barometer.

(iv) *Siphon barometers[11]—the Dines float-barograph*

The distinguishing feature of the siphon barometer is that the upper and lower mercury surfaces have the same area; hence the movement of either surface is only half that of the upper surface in a cistern barometer.   Such instruments are not widely used in English-speaking countries.   We shall, however, describe a recording siphon barometer of great excellence, devised in 1904 by W. H. Dines.[12]

The working parts of the instrument are shown in Fig. 10. AB is the barometer tube proper, with large upper and lower chambers equal in size, of which the upper one can be exhausted by a pump and sealed by the U-tube shown at the left. In the lower chamber floats a glass bell C, surrounded by a ring of steel balls to keep it central and reduce friction.   The glass stem of C fits loosely

[9]*Circular F*, p. 8.
[10]Unpublished.   A large number of these barometers are in use in the Canadian Service.
[11]See KLEINSCHMIDT, *Handbuch*, p. 293, for further details.
[12]DINES, L. H. G., *Q.J. Roy. Met. Soc.*, **55**:37-53, 1929.

into a steel tube which supports a balance weight D and a length of steel rod E.

The motion of the assembly C D E is transmitted by a pair of platinum wires F to the smaller of two pulleys G and H, fixed to a common axis.   From the right-hand side of the larger pulley is hung a glass rod J by means of the platinum wires K.   The pen L, fixed to this rod, records on the drum M the motion of the float, magnified by the ratio of the diameters of the two pulleys, about 4 to 1.   Two fixed pens provide base lines which afford a check on the expansion or contraction of the paper due to changes in relative humidity.

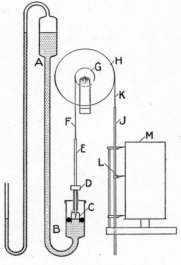

For the very interesting details of construction the original paper must be consulted. It has been found that the instrument can be completely compensated for temperature at some one pressure, and very nearly so at neighbouring pressures, by leaving a certain volume of air beneath the glass float C.   This volume is subject to calculation.

FIGURE 10

Diagram of the Dines
float-barograph.

(v) *Weight barometers and barographs*

It was mentioned on page 11 that instead of measuring the height of the barometric column, the column itself might be weighed on a balance in order to determine the atmospheric pressure.   Such a process has no advantages for the purpose of making individual readings, but lends itself well to automatic recording.

For the sake of logical precision it should be stated that the weight of the mercury column does not actually hang from the balance.   Much ink has been expended to show that it is really the pressure of the air on the top of the tube which acts on the beam of the balance,[13] and indeed it would seem difficult for some to accept this very simple paradox;[14] but to the writer it seems clear that the function of the mercury column is simply to provide a Torrecellian vacuum, in order that the top of the tube may be a surface which has the pressure of the air on its upper side, and no pressure on its lower side, after the manner of those rubber cups which are used to attach small fixtures to plate-glass windows.   In addition, the weight of the glass tube (less the buoyancy of the part dipping into the cistern) will act on the balance.

A weight barometer was constructed by Moreland about the year 1675,[15]

[13]KLEINSCHMIDT, E., *Met. Zeits.*, **49**:398-399, 1932.

PFEIFFER, A., *Met. Zeits.*, **49**:399-400, 1932.

[14]SKREB, S., *Met. Zeits.*, **49**:275-276, 1932.

[15]ABBE, CLEVELAND, *Ann. Rep. Secy. of War for 1887*, vol. IV, part 2, Washington 1888.

but it remained for Sprung[16] to investigate the instrument in detail.   To him we are indebted for the following improvements: (1) he showed that by making the *outside* diameter of the tail-piece equal to the *inside* diameter of the remainder of the tube, the weight on the balance is rendered independent of the distance the tailpiece dips into the mercury in the cistern.   (2) He devised an elegant method of temperature compensation, consisting merely of a cylindrical enlargement of appropriate volume at any part of the tube between the two mercury surfaces.

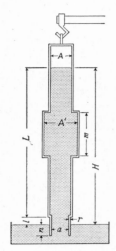

FIGURE 11
The Sprung weight-barometer—diagram of tube.

Fig. 11 shows the form of tube developed by Sprung, exaggerated in its horizontal dimensions, and with the rounded ends and joints essential to glassware compressed into planes perpendicular to its axis.   Since all the forces which interest us act axially (i.e., along the vertical), this schematization involves no loss of generality.   The area of the main part of the tube is A, that of the enlarged portion is A' and its length m. $H = L + l$ is the height of the mercury column. r is the cross-sectional area of the *walls* of the tailpiece, n its depth of immersion.

On the assumption that p, the atmospheric pressure, is constant throughout the height of the tube, the forces acting on the balance arm can be derived immediately.   Let G be the weight of the tube, and let s be the density of mercury; then the force on the balance arm is

$$X = G + pA - p(A - a) - nsr + Ls(A - a) + ms(A' - A)   \quad \dots \dots \dots (2.1).$$

But $p = (L + l)s$

$$\therefore X = G + pA - ls(A - a) - nsr + ms(A' - A)   \quad \dots \dots \dots (2.2).$$

Since l is of the order of 1 cm, this is not very different from

$$X = G + pA + ms(A' - A).$$

Sprung's first proposition may now be proved.   Suppose the tube is raised 1 cm.   The loss of buoyancy will be sr grams, and the loss of downward force due to the decrease in L will be $s(A - a)$ grams.   For the two to be equal

$$r = A - a, \text{ or } r + a = A$$

which was to be proved.

Koschmieder[17] has given an interesting treatment of the theory of this barograph.

The conditions for temperature compensation can be derived very easily from equation (2.2).   We wish to find the extra volume $m(A' - A)$ which must be provided as an enlargement in the tube.   Let a be the linear expansion coefficient of glass per °C., and β the volume coefficient of expansion of mer-

[16]SPRUNG, A., *Zeits. f. Inst.*, **6**:189-198, 232-237, 1886; **25**:37-45, 73-82, 1905.
[17]KOSCHMIEDER, H., *Geophys. Mag.* (Tokyo), **9**:23-28, 1935.

cury. Then at a temperature $t°C.$, from (2.2), introducing Sprung's first proposition,

$$X_t = G + pA_t - (l_t + n_t)s_t(A_t - a_t) + m_t s_t(A'_t - A_t) \qquad \dots \dots (2.3),$$

or

$$X_t = G + pA_0(1 + 2at) - (l_0 + n_0)s_0(A_0 - a_0)(1 + 3at)(1 - \beta t)$$
$$+ m_0 s_0(A_0' - A_0)(1 + 3at)(1 - \beta t) \qquad \dots \dots (2.4).$$

Differentiating, and putting $p = s_0 H_0$,

$$\frac{dX}{dt} = 2as_0 A_0 H_0 - (l_0 + n_0)s_0(A_0 - a_0)(3a - \beta) + m_0 s_0(A'_0 - A_0)(3a - \beta) \dots (2.5).$$

For this to vanish,

$$2aA_0 H_0 - [(l_0 + n_0)(A_0 - a_0) - m_0(A'_0 - A_0)](3a - \beta) = 0 \quad \dots \dots (2.6).$$

Now $m_0 (A'_0 - A_0) = V'$, the extra volume required, and therefore

$$V' = \frac{2aA_0 H_0}{\beta - 3a} + (l_0 + n_0)(A_0 - a_0) \qquad \dots \dots (2.7).$$

It will be noted that the second term is the actual volume of the tailpiece.

The mechanical arrangements of the instrument may be described by reference to Fig. 12, which is a drawing of an improved instrument constructed at the Meteorological Office, Toronto, in 1939.[18] The principle of this barograph is exactly the same as in earlier instruments; it differs mainly in being completely operated from the alternating current supply, and in having a balance with equal arms.

The duralumin beam A (Fig. 12) is supported by a bracket B through a steel knife-edge at C on an agate plane (actually part of a cylinder, since the positioning arrangements of an analytical balance are absent). Similar knife-edges and "planes" (D) support the barometer tube H and the counterweight G. The tube hangs freely in a wide cistern. The counterweight has an extension carrying a damping vane which dips into a bath of oil; this damps the oscillation of the beam somewhat, but is chiefly necessary to prevent pendulum oscillations of the counterweight. The beam is provided with a pointer carrying a platinum-iridium contact on each side, which make contact with either of the platinum-tipped screws at F.

Along the top of the beam a weight M rolls on two rollers with jewelled bearings. It is driven by the screw K and the nut L, through a fork and ball arrangement in the plane of the knife-edges. This provides a constraint in one degree of freedom only, a condition necessary to the proper functioning of the rolling weight.

A glass pen N is attached to the nut and moves with it. This makes a record on a chart which is driven by sprockets over a roller. In Fig. 12 the chart drive assembly is drawn swung out (as to replace the chart); the supply roll and drive roll are both attached to the frame X, which swings out on hinges and can be locked in place by the lever Y.

[18]PATTERSON, J., and W. E. K. MIDDLETON, Q. J. Roy. Met. Soc., 67:19-31, 1941.

An important feature of the instrument is the printing mechanism Q. Each hour, within a few seconds of the exact hour, this prints the pressure (to the nearest tenth of a millibar) on the right-hand edge of the chart.[19]   Not only does this establish a time scale, but it also provides a means of correcting for the changes produced by variations of humidity in the width of the chart paper, since the printing mechanism is quite unaffected by changes in humidity.   A reading counter R is also attached to the mechanism.

The barometer tube is of Sprung's form and compensated for temperature as described above.   The main part of the tube is 20 mm internal diameter.

The action of the barograph is as follows: suppose that the barometric pressure rises, causing the beam to turn in a counter-clockwise sense, and closing the right-hand contact.   This closure connects the grid and cathode of a vacuum tube (through a high resistance).   The resulting increase in plate current closes a relay which causes a small reversing motor to turn the screw K in the proper direction to move the rolling weight to the right.   This restores the balance, the pointer is centred between the contact screws, the motor stops.   The pen has moved with the nut to indicate the rise in pressure, and the printing and reading counters have turned to the same effect.   A fall of pressure causes the motor to move in the opposite direction.

The design of the tube compensates the instrument for temperature except

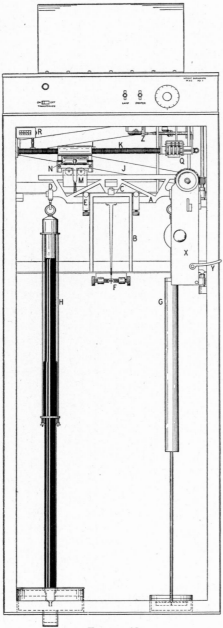

FIGURE 12
The weight barograph.

---

[19]Such a mechanism was first attached to a barograph by Hough about 1862 (*Annals of the Dudley Obs., Albany*, **2**:xxv, 1871).

for the effect of the expansion of the mechanical parts, particularly the beam and the lead screw.　It can be shown that these errors are entirely negligible. The probable error of a single reading of this barograph is apparently a little less than 0.1 mb.

An entirely different type of weight barograph was described by Fergusson.[20] In this the cistern of a large barometer was suspended by long springs, the deflection of these being magnified by a linkage to give magnifications of from 3:1 to 10:1.　Nothing is said about the temperature errors of such an instrument, but it would seem that they might be of importance.

(vi) *Photographic barographs*

One of the simplest and most reliable of all barographs is the photographic barograph designed by Balfour Stewart for the Meteorological Committee of the Royal Society in 1867,[21] which has been in use at many of the British observatories for more than sixty years.　Its greatest defect lies in the amount of time necessary to interpret the photographic trace.

The general principle of this instrument is simple.　A narrow vertical slit, of which the lower extremity is the top of the mercury column, is illuminated by a lamp and condenser.　A photographic objective forms an image of this slit on a drum covered with photographic paper, the record, when developed, appearing as a dark band of variable width.　The temperature compensation is effected by a pair of zinc rods running beside the barometer tube; these, by means of a long lever, move a screen up and down in front of the sensitive paper in such a way as to form the other limit of the dark band.　The arms of the lever are adjusted until the motion of the screen is equal to the *thermal* change in the image.　It is obvious that such a compensation is strictly correct for one pressure only.

The time scale is obtained by cutting off the light for four minutes every two hours.

(vii) *Normal barometers*

The forms of barometer which we have been considering are in general sufficiently accurate for use at meteorological stations, especially as a great deal of uncertainty is attached to the reduction of observed pressures to a datum level.　But for national and international standards of atmospheric pressure, much more complicated and specialized instruments are required. It will serve our purpose to describe only the latest, the normal barometer at the National Physical Laboratory, Teddington, England.[22]

As shown diagrammatically in Fig. 13, the "tube" of this barometer consists of two chambers, B, C, connected by a tube A, the whole being machined out of a solid piece of stainless steel.　The lower chamber communicates with the atmosphere through the tube D and the port E.　The upper one can be evacuated by means of a diffusion pump.　The bottom of the barometer is

[20]FERGUSSON, S. P., *Bull. Amer. Met. Soc.*, **20**:135-141, 1939.

[21]Royal Society of London, *Rep. Met. Comm. for 1867*, H.M. Stationery Office, pp. 40-46.

[22]SEARS, J. E., Jr., and J. S. CLARK, *Proc. Roy. Soc. Lond.*, A.**139**:130-146, 1933.

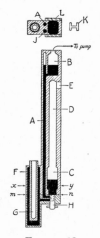

FIGURE 13

Diagram of the N.P.L. normal barometer.

another piece of stainless steel, joined to the upper part along the line *mn*.

A plunger G, working in a cylinder F, can be raised or lowered in order to change the level of the mercury in B and C. A four-way valve, H, permits the connection or isolation of the various parts of the barometer. The temperature of the column is measured by a special thermometer with a bulb 30 inches long, immersed in mercury in the hole J.

The upper figure shows a cross-section in the plane *xy*, and also indicates the relative position of the barometer tube and its scale K, a secondary line-standard made of invar. The plane-parallel glass windows L, 11 mm thick, form the sides of the chambers, and permit reading the mercury levels by optical means.

The double cathetometer with which the vertical separation of the mercury surfaces is measured, consists of a vertical column carrying two micrometer microscopes and two collimators. The entire column may be moved sideways so that the microscopes may be directed either at the scale K or at the chambers B and C.

The purpose of the collimators is to form a real image of a cross-wire just above each mercury surface. This image and its reflection in the surface are both visible in the microscope, the surface being taken to be half way between them. This method of reading has been exhaustively investigated and found to meet all requirements.

The mean residual error of a single reading of this instrument is about 5 microns. The greater part of this is probably to be ascribed to the small fluctuations of pressure which take place at almost all times. There is a further uncertainty of about 5μ in the absolute pressure, because of the possible variation of 7 parts per million in the density of mercury.

(b) *Filling barometer tubes*

It is necessary that the mercury used in a barometer should be pure (in the sense that it is not contaminated by other metals), clean (free from grease, etc.), and dry. It must also be introduced into the tube in such a manner that no air or water-vapour remains in the vacuum chamber above the mercury column.

Mercury may be purchased in a fairly pure state, but should be agitated for a day or two with strong caustic soda, distilled water, sulphuric or nitric acid, and distilled water again, then boiled in order to dry it thoroughly. In this state it is often used to fill barometers by the "boiling" method. A small quantity of mercury is placed in the closed end of the tube, which is set in an inclined position with a small bent tube attached. The latter dips into a reservoir of mercury. The lower end of the barometer tube is then heated; the ebullition of the mercury drives out some of the air, and when the heat is removed, additional mercury comes over from the reservoir. The tube is then heated a little higher up, and the process repeated until it is full. This operation requires some skill and involves the risk of breaking the tube.

A somewhat elaborate but entirely satisfactory apparatus (Fig. 14) for filling barometer tubes has been developed by J. Patterson at Toronto. By the use of this apparatus, any number of tubes up to eight can be filled at once without the slightest risk of accident.

The right-hand portion of the apparatus consists of three mercury stills, S_1, S_2, S_3, operated in series, the last of which delivers mercury directly into the header H connected with the barometer tubes. The whole apparatus is kept exhausted by a diffusion pump backed by a mechanical pump; and once the apparatus is set in operation, the distillation and filling proceeds automatically as long as heat is supplied to the stills and the container C is kept replenished with mercury.

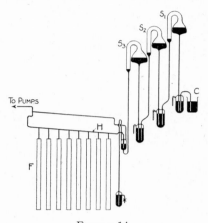

FIGURE 14

Apparatus for filling barometer tubes.

Before the filling is begun, the tubes are outgassed by heating for several days, first under the vacuum produced by a mechanical pump, and finally for several hours under the diffusion pump. A tubular electric heater F surrounds each tube for this purpose. By this means, barometers are produced with the vacuum-space as nearly free from air and water vapour as possible; the very moderate amount of labour involved is repaid with interest in the resulting freedom from troubles due to a defective vacuum.

(c) Transportation of barometers

It is the experience of the writer that it is unsafe to send mercury barometers by railway express or by steamer, unless one can arrange to hang them oneself in the express car or steamer, and to have someone familiar with barometers remove them at their destination. This is especially true of Kew pattern barometers, which may get air in the tube if suddenly inverted. The usual practice is to carry them as hand-baggage.

To prepare a barometer for transport, it is removed from its mounting on the wall and *slowly* turned upside down. The adjusting screw of a Fortin barometer will previously have been screwed up until the cistern is full and the tube nearly so. The barometer may then be wrapped in several thicknesses of corrugated board and finally in strong wrapping paper fastened with gummed tape, and provided with a sling of very heavy cord which will permit its being carried over the shoulder with the cistern upwards. The labour of carrying three or four station barometers in this way is well known to seasoned meteorological inspectors.

A very light and strong case made of cardboard cylinders and wood has recently been devised in the Canadian Service (Fig. 15), and found excellent for this purpose. The bottom is nailed and glued in; the top held by adhesive tape. Strong cords are provided for carrying over the shoulder.

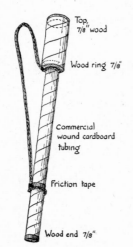

Top, 7/8" wood

Wood ring 7/8"

Commercial wound cardboard tubing

Friction tape

Wood end 7/8"

FIGURE 15
Barometer carrying-case of wood and cardboard.

A standard portable barometer for comparison purposes is usually carried in a tubular leather case provided with a sling. Since the case is made to fit the diameter of the cistern, it is a good idea to have an inner case of light wood in the form of two half-cylinders, hinged together, and hollowed out to take the tube. This is made to fit snugly in the leather case, and protects the tube against damage from accidental knocks.

(d) Installation of barometers

When a barometer is being installed at a meteorological station, it is of the greatest importance to select its location with care. The guiding principle is that the instrument should not be subjected to sudden changes of temperature. Hence it must not be installed where the sun can shine upon it at any time, or near any heating apparatus, or in a place subject to draughts. In a private residence it is often necessary to compromise in this regard, but in a building erected for meteorological purposes some attention should be given to the provision of a suitable location.

The barometer may be hung on a board fixed to the wall, but it is better to provide a box with a hinged door to protect the instrument from damage, from dust, and from air-currents. A substantial hook is fitted in this box near the top, and near the bottom a ring somewhat larger in diameter than the frame, and provided with three screws to maintain the instrument in the vertical. Pieces of milk glass, white celluloid, or even cardboard, are fastened to the back of the box in such a way as to provide a white background for the mercury meniscus and the fiducial point. To the same end, the inside of the box may be painted white.

A barometer of the "Kew" pattern may generally be trusted to take up a vertical position when hanging freely. The Fortin barometer should be tested for verticality by setting the fiducial point and then rotating the instrument as a whole. If it is vertical, the setting of the point will be maintained. Any barometer of notably unsymmetrical build should, of course, be set with a plumb-line or a builder's level—never "by eye."

Adequate artificial illumination should be provided for reading the barometer; and it is seldom that the ordinary lighting of a room is enough for this purpose. A flashlight has the advantage of providing adequate light with little heat; but a portable lamp run from the mains is perhaps more convenient.

(e) Corrections to the readings of the mercury barometer

In order that the pressure of the atmosphere may be expressed in recognized units, it is necessary to correct the readings of the barometer for errors peculiar to the individual instrument, and for the departure of the prevailing values of gravity and of temperature from standard conditions.

(i) Correction for index error

A barometer is graduated on the assumption that a given reading on the scale represents the actual difference of level between the upper and lower mercury surfaces. Only in primary ("normal") barometers, however, is it possible to determine whether this is actually so; all other barometers must be calibrated by comparison with existing standards. Since it is frequently impracticable to adjust a barometer so that the zero of the scale is exactly at the level of the lower mercury surface, in general there will remain a small difference between its readings and those of the instrument which is regarded as standard. Errors due to capillarity (see below, page 34) will be included in this. Unless the scale lacks uniformity this difference should be sensibly constant over the range of pressures which the barometer is designed to measure. This constant error is known as the *index error*, and a corresponding correction, *the index correction*, must be applied to the barometer reading before it is corrected for gravity and temperature. In a well-constructed barometer it will not generally exceed one- or two-tenths of a millibar.

(ii) Correction to standard gravity

As mentioned on page 12 above, the definitions of the units of pressure involve the acceleration of gravity. Since the height of the barometer at a given pressure and temperature varies inversely as the value of gravity, we may write

$$h_{45,\,0} = h_{\phi,\,z} \cdot \frac{g_{\phi,\,z}}{g_{45,\,0}}.$$

Where $g_{45,\,0}$ is the standard value, 980.62 cm sec^{-2}, which prevails[23] at sea-level in latitude 45°,

$g_{\phi,\,z}$ is the value of gravity at the barometer in latitude ϕ and height Z above sea-level,

$h_{\phi,\,z}$ is the height of the barometer as read, corrected for index error, and

$h_{45,\,0}$ is the height of the barometer corrected to standard gravity.

For the most precise work it is necessary to measure accurately the local value of gravity. For ordinary work at meteorological stations, it is sufficient to calculate it from one of the following formulae:

$$g_{\phi,\,z} = g_{45,\,0}(1 - 0.00259 \cos 2\phi)(1 - 0.000,000,2Z)$$

if Z is in metres;

$$g_{\phi,\,z} = g_{45,\,0}(1 - 0.00259 \cos 2\phi)(1 - 0.000,000,06Z)$$

if Z is in feet.

[23] In the absence of local disturbances.

The correction for gravity varies directly with the barometric pressure; but its value is not large in temperate latitudes, and a constant correction, corresponding to the mean pressure at the station, is usually applied.   For use on shipboard a table of corrections, corresponding to different latitudes, is necessary.[24]   The correction for gravity and the index correction are in practice usually combined into a single correction.

(iii) *Correction for temperature*

The correction for temperature involves the expansion of the mercury and of the scale, and in the case of the fixed cistern barometer, of the cistern also. It will be convenient to treat the fixed cistern barometer separately, especially on account of the contracted scale.   For reasons which will become apparent, the correction of the barometer graduated in millibars will also be treated later.

(a) The Fortin, movable-scale, and siphon barometers

Let h_t be the height of the barometer at temperature t, corrected for index error and gravity;

Let h_0 be the corresponding height corrected to standard temperature;

Let a be the expansion coefficient[25] of the scale, and β the cubical expansion coefficient[25] of mercury.

In the metric barometer the scale and the mercury are both standard at 0°C., and it may easily be shown that the correction is

$$h_0 - h_t = -t(\beta - a)h_t/(1 + \beta t) \qquad \ldots\ldots\ldots (2.9),$$

which is subtractive for positive values of t.

In the *inch* barometer the mercury is standard at 32°F., the scale at 62°F. Thus if t, a, and β refer to Fahrenheit degrees,

$$h_0 - h_t = -\frac{(t-32)(\beta-a)+30a}{1+(t-32)\beta} \cdot h_t \qquad \ldots\ldots\ldots (2.10)$$

which is subtractive when t is greater than about 29°F.

The value of a generally adopted is about 18×10^{-6} per degree centigrade for brass scales.   In barometry of high precision it is, of course, measured for the scale actually used.

(β) The fixed cistern (Kew) barometer

The temperature correction to the Kew barometer is not the same as that of the Fortin, for two reasons:

(1) The expansion of the cistern affects the level of the mercury in it.

(2) The change in the height of the column is measured on a contracted scale.   The effect of this has been treated by several authors.[26]   Here we shall follow in its main lines the argument of Irgens.

---

[24]*Meteorological Observer's Handbook.* 1939 ed., London 1939, H.M. Stationery Office, p. 148.

[25]In reality the mean coefficient between t and the standard temperature.

[26]GLAZEBROOK, *Dictionary of Applied Physics.*   London 1923, Macmillan, vol. III, article "Barometers and Manometers."   IRGENS, K., *Met. Zeits.*, **45**:441-444, 1928; and **50**:507-508, 1933.   KLEINSCHMIDT, E., *Met. Zeits.* **51**:194-195, 1934.

The notation (see Fig. 16) is:

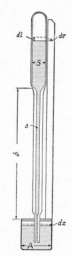

A = effective area of cistern $\left.\begin{array}{l}\end{array}\right\}$ $S/A = K.$
S = inner area of upper chamber
s = inner area of constricted portion of tube.
V = total volume of mercury in the barometer.
v_t = volume of mercury in tube above lower mercury level.
v_c = volume of mercury in cistern.
v_g = volume of tailpiece below the lower mercury level.
a = linear expansion coefficient of the (brass) scale.
β = cubical expansion coefficient of mercury.
γ = linear expansion coefficient of glass.
η = linear expansion coefficient of the (iron) cistern.
b = length of constricted portion of tube above top of cistern.

We first assume that the scale is so calibrated that it gives the correct barometric pressure h_0 at the standard temperature. If now we raise the temperature of the instrument by t degrees, the pressure remaining constant, we shall obtain a new reading $h_{\sigma, t}$ on the scale. The change is in part due to the change of position of the upper mercury surface in the chamber, dl, and in part to the change in the scale, $d\sigma$. We must also recall that the level of the mercury in the cistern has changed by a quantity dz.

FIGURE 16
Illustrating the temperature correction of the fixed-cistern barometer.

The correction we wish to find is

$$h_0 - h_{\sigma, t} = -(dl - d\sigma)(1 + K) \qquad \ldots\ldots\ldots(2.11).$$

We have

$$V = v_t + v_c$$

and

$$dV = dv_t + dv_c + (Adz + Sdl) \qquad \ldots\ldots\ldots(2.12),$$

where

$$dV = V\beta dt$$
$$dv_t = v_t \cdot 2\gamma dt - b(S-s)\gamma dt$$
$$dv_c = (v_c + v_g)3\eta dt - v_g \cdot 2\gamma dt$$
$$= v_c \cdot 3\eta dt + v_g(3\eta - 2\gamma)dt.$$

As we suppose the pressure constant, we have

$$h_0\beta dt = dl - dz$$

or

$$dz = dl - h_0\beta dt$$

and therefore

$$Adz + Sdl = A[(dl - h_0\beta dt) + Kdl]$$
$$= A(1+K)dl - Ah_0\beta dt \qquad \ldots\ldots\ldots(2.13).$$

Setting these values in (2.12), we get

$$V\beta dt = v_c \cdot 3\eta dt + v_g(3\eta - 2\gamma)dt + v_t \cdot 2\gamma dt - b(S-s)\gamma dt$$
$$+ A(1+K)dl - Ah_0\beta dt \qquad \ldots\ldots\ldots(2.14).$$

Setting $v_c = V - v_t$ and rearranging,

$$(1+K)dl = h_0\beta dt + \frac{V}{A}(\beta - 3\eta)dt$$

$$+\left[\frac{v_t - v_g}{A}(3\eta - 2\gamma) + \frac{b(S-s)\gamma}{A}\right]dt \qquad \ldots\ldots\ldots(2.15).$$

The term in square brackets is about $\frac{1}{10}$ the magnitude of $\frac{V}{A}(\beta - 3\eta)\ dt$.

Neglecting it, equation (2.15) becomes

$$(1+K)dl = h_0\beta dt + \frac{V}{A}(\beta - 3\eta)dt \qquad \ldots\ldots\ldots(2.16).$$

Now $\qquad\qquad h_0(1+\beta dt) = h_{\sigma,t}/(1+\alpha dt) \qquad \ldots\ldots\ldots(2.17),$

so that from (2.16)

$$(1+K)dl = \frac{1-\alpha dt}{1+\beta dt}h_{\sigma,t}\,\beta dt + \frac{V}{A}(\beta - 3\eta)dt \quad \ldots\ldots\ldots(2.18).$$

Furthermore $\qquad\qquad d\sigma = h_{\sigma,t}\,\alpha dt$

and $\qquad\qquad (1+K)d\sigma = (1+K)h_{\sigma,t}\,\alpha dt \qquad \ldots\ldots\ldots(2.19),$

so that finally, putting (2.18) and (2.19) in (2.11) and adding, to the first order in small quantities,

$$h_0 - h_{\sigma,t} = -\left[\frac{\beta - \alpha}{1+\beta t}h_{\sigma,t} + \frac{V}{A}(\beta - 3\eta)\right]dt \quad \ldots\ldots\ldots(2.20).$$

This is not linear in temperature, but a mean value of $(\beta - \alpha)/(1+\beta t)$ can be used without measurable error. In Centigrade units

$$(\beta - \alpha)/(1+\beta t) = 163 \times 10^{-6} \text{ for room temperatures,}$$
$$\beta - 3\eta = 152 \times 10^{-6},$$

so that

$$h_0 - h_{\sigma,t} = -\left[0.000163 h_{\sigma,t} + 0.000152\frac{V}{A}\right]t \quad \ldots\ldots\ldots(2.21),$$

the standard temperature being 0°C. The first term is the same as the whole correction of the Fortin barometer; but the second term is independent of the pressure and characteristic of the particular instrument. The correction may be put in the form

$$h_0 - h_{\sigma,t} = -0.000163\left(h_{\sigma,t} + \frac{152}{163}\frac{V}{A}\right)t \quad \ldots\ldots\ldots(2.22).$$

The ordinary tables of correction may thus be used for the Kew barometer if they are entered at a pressure $\frac{152}{163}\frac{V}{A}$ mm higher than the barometer reading; in a station barometer of the usual design this may be about 25-35 mm (35-50 mb).

For the *inch* Kew barometer we may go back to equation (2.16) remembering that the scale is standard at 62°, and finally obtain

$$h_0 - h_{\sigma,\,t} = -\frac{[(\beta-a)(t-32)+30a]}{1+(t-32)\beta}\,h_{\sigma,\,t} + \frac{V}{A}(\beta-3\eta)(t-32) \quad \ldots\ldots (2.23),$$

where a, β, and η will of course be referred to Fahrenheit degrees.

A fixed cistern barometer with a tube of uniform bore (except for the tail-piece) will differ slightly in its corrections from the above. Considering again the square bracket of equation (2.15), we see that in this case the second term is very small. In general v_t is about $\frac{1}{2}V$ in such a barometer, so that we might take the bracket into consideration by writing (2.20)

$$h_0 - h_{\sigma,\,t} = -\left\{\frac{\beta-a}{1+\beta t}\,h_{\sigma,\,t} + \frac{V}{A}\left[(\beta-3\eta) + \tfrac{1}{2}(3\eta-2\gamma)\right]\right\} dt \quad \ldots\ldots (2.24)$$

or if $\gamma = 8\times10^{-6}/°C.$,

$$h_0 - h_{\sigma,\,t} = -\left[0.000163 h_{\sigma,\,t} + 0.000159\,\frac{V}{A}\right]t \quad \ldots\ldots (2.25).$$

The smallness of the difference from (2.21) demonstrates that the shape of the tube is relatively unimportant.

(γ) The correction of barometers graduated in millibars[27]

Barometers which are graduated in millibars are, in England, generally adjusted to read true millibars at a temperature of 285°A. (12°C.) when used under conditions of standard gravity. Small errors (index errors) often cause such barometers to read correctly at some other temperature near 285°A. Whatever this temperature may be, it is known as the *standard* temperature for the instrument, and is found by comparison with a calibrated barometer. The following table, taken from the *Observer's Handbook*, shows the relation between index error and standard temperature, for the Kew barometer.

RELATION BETWEEN STANDARD TEMPERATURE AND INDEX CORRECTION OF A KEW PATTERN
BAROMETER (N.P.L. STANDARD)

Standard temperature	Barometer reading (mb)					Standard temperature
	880	920	960	1000	1040	
282.0°A.	0.45	0.47	0.49	0.51	0.53	288.0°A.
282.5	0.37	0.39	0.41	0.43	0.45	287.5
283.0	0.30	0.32	0.33	0.34	0.36	287.0
283.5	0.23	0.24	0.25	0.26	0.27	286.5
284.0	0.15	0.16	0.17	0.17	0.18	286.0
284.5	0.07	0.08	0.08	0.09	0.09	285.5
285.0°A.	0	0	0	0	0	285.0°A.

The correction is negative for all standard temperatures in the left-hand margin, and positive for all the standard temperatures in the right-hand margin.

[27]*Observer's Handbook.* London 1939, H.M. Stationery Office, p. 16.

For example, a barometer which had an index correction of $+0.26$ mb at 1000 mb would have a standard temperature of $286.5°$. Call the standard temperature T_s. To take into account the variations of gravity we find another temperature, the *fiducial* temperature, at which the instrument will read correctly under the prevailing gravity $g_{\phi, z}$. Call this T_F. Then the temperature correction to the barometer will be

$$p - p_t = 0.000163 p_t (T_F - T) \qquad \ldots\ldots\ldots (2.26)$$

for a Fortin barometer, or

$$p - p_t = 0.000171 p_t (T_F - T) \qquad \ldots\ldots\ldots (2.27)$$

for a Kew barometer $(V/A = \frac{3}{2}'')$, where p_t is the reading in mb at $T°A$. It will immediately be seen that the fiducial temperature T_F is given by

$$0.000163 p (T_s - T_F) = p (0.00259 \cos 2\phi + 0.00000006Z)$$

for a Fortin barometer or

$$0.000171 p (T_s - T_F) = p (0.00259 \cos 2\phi + 0.00000006Z)$$

for a Kew. It should be noted that the temperature correction will be a linear function of pressure, and also depend on V/A.

In practice a standard card is provided, having a table of temperature corrections for various pressures and for various temperatures of the attached thermometer, usually at intervals of one degree. To suit the actual barometer and its location, the column showing temperature is written (or pasted up from printed figures) in the correct relation to the rest of the table. In this way, one reference to the table suffices to correct for index error, gravity, and temperature.

In many British ships, barometer corrections are obtained by means of the Gold Slide, so called after its inventor. This is a special slide rule attached to the barometer and incorporating the attached thermometer, and having scales of temperature, index correction, latitude, and height above sea-level. It gives the complete correction and reduction to sea-level with sufficient accuracy.[28]

(δ) Comparison of barometers

When a station is being inspected, it is usual to make a comparison between the station barometer and a portable standard, usually a Fortin, carried by the inspector. The portable standard should be hung up near the station barometer and left for at least half an hour—much longer if it has just been brought indoors from winter temperatures—before readings are begun.

When it is reasonably certain that both instruments are in equilibrium with their surroundings, careful readings will be taken at intervals of fifteen minutes or more. The attached thermometers should be read first and recorded, then both barometers should be set before either is read.

The inspector will be provided with correction cards for both Fortin and

---

[28]For further details, see *Admiralty Weather Manual, 1938*. London, H.M. Stationery Office, p. 12.

fixed-cistern barometers, calculated on the assumption that the index corrections and gravity correction are zero. Each instrument will be corrected
separately by means of these tables, and the corrected pressure compared, as
in the following scheme:

Date	Hour	Standard no. (1234) (1)			Station no. (5678) (2)			Correction to Standard (1) — (2)
		as read	A.T.*	Corrected	as read	A.T.	Corrected	
6/5	1330	1003.2	68.0	1001.9	1003.0	66.2	1001.8	+0.1

*Degrees Fahrenheit. This scale is used in Canada and the United States for the correction
of barometers; the M.O. (London) uses degrees absolute [°C.+273°].

At least six independent readings should be taken, preferably ten or more,
over as long a time as possible. If there is plenty of time, as when a new
observer is being coached, readings should be made during periods of falling,
rising, and steady pressure. Very windy days should be excluded; an extra
day spent at a station is better than barometer comparisons in a gale.

Even if the barometers are of the same pattern and the two thermometers
read almost alike, the uncorrected readings should on no account be compared.
The comparison of the corrected readings will also look after small errors in the
attached thermometers; and such errors are of frequent occurrence.

(f) The errors of mercury barometers

The general errors of pressure measurement were discussed above (p. 13);
it remains to consider the sources of error which are special to mercury barometers. In this discussion we must distinguish carefully between constant
errors which are determinable by calibration, and random errors, which are
not. It must be remembered that all mercury barometers except a very few
"normal" barometers are *relative* instruments, calibrated by comparison with
an instrument having known errors.

(i) The vacuum space

When we read a barometer we tacitly assume that there is a perfect vacuum
above the mercury column, except for the vapour pressure of mercury corresponding to the temperature. This assumption, while only approximately true,
leads to no trouble as long as the amount of air or other gases in the space is
very small. The residual pressure must be less than the accuracy desired from
the instrument.

The presence or comparative absence of permanent gases in a barometer
tube can usually be estimated by inclining the tube and listening to the "click"
as the mercury reaches the end. The sound should be sharp and metallic.
If it recalls the sound of a leather mallet, there is probably a good deal of air
in the tube; if it is inaudible, there is certainly too much. This test will not
be available with a marine barometer because of the constricted bore.

The test will not, however, reveal the presence of water vapour, since this

4

condenses to liquid water as the volume of the space is reduced. Water vapour is a worse offender than air if there is enough of it to saturate the space within the working range of the barometer, for under these conditions, the error due to the water vapour varies rapidly with the temperature. Filling barometer tubes by the method described above (page 25) is a certain preventative of this sort of trouble.

Air or unsaturated vapour produces an error which increases inversely as the volume enclosed above the mercury, according to Boyle's law. This can be allowed for by a calibration over the entire scale. Nevertheless, if the error is of any magnitude it is highly inconvenient, especially if the process of correcting for index error, gravity, and temperature by a single table is employed. In a modern meteorological service there is little excuse for issuing a barometer with a defective vacuum.

(ii) *The capillary depression of the mercury surfaces*

Glass is normally not wetted by mercury. The meniscus in a barometer tube is therefore convex upwards, which leads to a depression of the surface. The shape of the mercury meniscus is in fact a fortunate circumstance, for if the surface were flat, it would be almost impossible to set an ordinary vernier slide.[29] Since all the barometers used in meteorology are secondary instruments, calibrated by comparison with other barometers, it is not primarily the *amount* of the capillary depression which interests us, but its *constancy*.

The capillary depression is usually given in tables as a function of the diameter of the tube and the height of the meniscus.[30] This latter quantity is the vertical distance between the extreme crest of the meniscus and the plane containing its line of contact with the tube, and is itself a function of the angle of contact between the mercury and the wall of the tube.

The height of the meniscus, and hence the capillary depression, may vary in one and the same tube from time to time, and according to the position of the mercury in the tube. In a tube 5 mm in diameter, the range of variation has been given[31] as about ±.008 inch; in a 10 mm tube, ±.002 inch. It is evident that 5 mm tubes are too small for accurate work; but a tube more than 8 or 9 mm in diameter is unhandy for a portable instrument, and scarcely necessary in view of the other errors of barometry.

When the pressure is rising or falling, the meniscus tends to change its shape, owing to the tendency of the line of contact to maintain its position. A barometer should always be tapped before setting the vernier, in order to

[29]On two occasions, barometers which were filled by the method described on page 25 have had almost exactly flat menisci. The cause of this is not known, and attempts to reproduce the phenomenon failed; but it is possible that the barometers in question were outgassed even more drastically than usual. The tubes had to be discarded, it being much too difficult to set the verniers. See also BATE, A. E., *Phil. Mag.*, **28**:252-255, 1939.

[30]Tables in GLAZEBROOK, *Dictionary of Applied Physics*. London 1923, Macmillan, vol. III, p. 159.

KAYE and LABY, *Tables of Physical and Chemical Constants*. 6th ed., London 1928, Longmans, Green, p. 19.

[31]GLAZEBROOK, *op. cit.*, p. 160.

assist the formation of a stable meniscus.   This advice is generally given concerning Kew barometers, but in the opinion of the writer it should be followed
with Fortin instruments also, since with these the mercury in the cistern has
usually been brought *up* to the fiducial point just previously.   Probably the
barometer will have been shaken a little in this operation, but perhaps not
enough to stabilize the meniscus.

In this connection H. Christoff[32] has made interesting observations on the
effect of the ship's vibration on marine barometers.   During a voyage in the
Red Sea, he found that when the ship's vibration was damped out by taking
hold of the metal arm which supported the barometer, the level of the mercury
dropped about a millimetre.   The suggested explanation is that (1) the surface
tension may be effectively altered by the vibration, and (2) the lower surface
of the mercury may be otherwise defined.   It is also possible, according to
Christoff, that there may be some transfer of kinetic energy into potential, as
in the hydraulic ram; but this does not carry conviction.

There is a further source of variable error in the cistern of the Kew barometer, due to a variation of the angle of contact of the mercury and the cistern
walls.   Exposure to a moist atmosphere and to the products of combustion
may make the meniscus almost or entirely flat.   This reduces or eliminates
the downward pressure on the mercury surface, due to surface tension, and
causes the barometer to read lower by as much as 0.5 mb in a cistern one inch
in diameter, or 0.1 mb in a cistern 4 inches in diameter.   A barometer with a
large cistern is therefore to be preferred.

(iii) *Non-uniformity of temperature*

Since an uncertainty of 1°F. in the temperature of a mercury barometer
produces an uncertainty of about 0.1 mb in the corrected reading, it is desirable
for meteorological purposes that the mean temperature of the barometric
column should be known to 1°F. or better.   In the practical use of a barometer,
there are two main sources of uncertainty in the temperature:

(1) The temperature of the room is changing.   Since the barometer tube
and its contained mercury have a much greater heat capacity than the bulb of
the attached thermometer, in proportion to their surfaces, the temperature of
the barometer tube will lag behind that of the thermometer.   This error begins
to be appreciable if the change of air temperature is at the rate of about 3°F.
per hour, a value often greatly exceeded at isolated stations where the fire in
the office stove is lighted every morning and allowed to go out at night.

(2) The temperature of the room has a large vertical gradient.   In a room
otherwise very well suited to barometry, having almost no diurnal variation
of temperature, it was found (by means of differential thermocouples) that
the temperature at the top of a barometer was 2°F. higher than that at the
bottom.   The installation of a small electric fan in the room reduced this
difference to less than 0.05°F.   This stratification of temperature is probably
more common than is generally supposed.

[32]CHRISTOFF, H., *Ann. d. Hydr.*, **66**:473-474, 1938.

(iv) *The scale contraction of Kew barometers*

The scale of a Kew barometer, as explained on page 16, is contracted to suit the relative diameters of the tube, the cistern, and the tailpiece. An error in the measured diameter of the tube will make this contraction incorrect. However, this is a matter for the manufacturer. In filling the cistern of a Kew barometer, care must be taken that the mercury level is not so high that at low readings the cistern will become full. (This is more likely to happen in those barometers which have a screwed joint between the frame and the cistern for zero adjustments.) The absence of this defect, and the accuracy of the scale contraction, should be verified by reading the barometer at several pressures distributed over its scale. A suitable chamber for this is shown in Fig. 17. It will be noted that the vernier can be set from the outside by means of a shaft passing through a stuffing-box.

If a Kew barometer is repaired, one of two precautions must be taken. Either a new tube with a chamber of the same diameter as the old one must be found, or a slightly larger one obtained, and the cylinder bored out to give the proper contraction. The size of the tailpiece, if of usual proportions, does not enter greatly into the results.

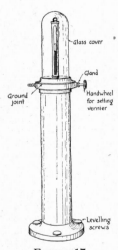

FIGURE 17
Barometer
test-chamber.

(v) *Verticality*

If a completely symmetrical barometer is installed at an angle θ with the vertical, its indications must obviously be multiplied by cos θ to obtain the true barometer reading. Suppose an accuracy of 0.1 mb is desired. Then this error should certainly not exceed 0.02 mb, or 2×10^{-5} of 1000 mb; this corresponds to an angle of $0°21'$. If the barometer be 36 inches long, the lower extremity may thus be moved about 7/32 of an inch without exceeding the above error. A well-constructed Kew barometer will certainly hang more nearly vertical than this.

A Fortin barometer, however, cannot be considered a symmetrical instrument. The fiducial point is commonly about $\frac{1}{2}''$ from the centre line of the tube, and in one recent instrument much more than this. If this displacement is denoted by R, then a maximum error of R sin θ may arise from lack of verticality, to be added to, or subtracted from, the other error according to whether the barometer is inclined away from, or towards, the fiducial point. An error of 0.02 mb may arise if R is $\frac{1}{2}''$ and θ is only about $0°04'$; this corresponds to the bottom of the barometer being about 3/64$''$ out of plumb. The Fortin barometer should therefore be arranged so that it may be revolved around its axis, and should be adjusted so that a setting of the fiducial point to the mercury remains good in all positions during a rotation.

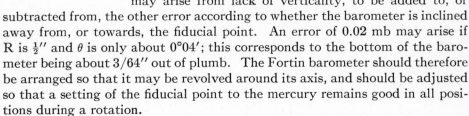

(g) *General accuracy and permanence of calibration*

Experience has shown that the Fortin type of barometer is capable of giving more consistent results than the Kew, over a long period of time, in spite of the two settings which have to be made in order to read the former instrument. This circumstance is chiefly due to changes in the condition of the mercury surface in the cistern, discussed above. As a matter of fact, the setting of the fiducial point can be performed with ample accuracy even if the surface of the mercury is not quite clean. The fixed-cistern barometer is, however, coming more and more into favour for use at meteorological stations, because of the saving in time required to read it.

Apart from precision barometry, a final accuracy of 0.1 mb is all that can be asked for in meteorological work. Anything beyond this is certainly useless at stations more than a few hundred feet above sea-level, because of the uncertainties of the reduction to that datum. The attainment of this accuracy is just possible with fixed-cistern barometers if inspections and re-calibrations are carried out not less frequently than once a year. In the opinion of the writer, however, the actual precision of one of a series of readings, such as are made at an ordinary station, is probably not much better than 0.2 or even 0.3 mb, on account of pumping and errors in the temperature of the barometer. The desideratum is to reduce the *systematic* errors to 0.1 mb, in order that monthly mean pressures shall be reliable to that degree. It is altogether likely that the Fortin barometer is somewhat better in this regard.

5. Elastic Barometers

(a) *Definition. Types*

An elastic barometer is one in which the elastic deformation of some solid system is used as an indicator of atmospheric pressure. There are two types, the Bourdon barometer and the Vidie barometer. The latter is almost always called the *aneroid* barometer in English-speaking countries, but strictly the Bourdon barometer is also "aneroid"—without liquid.

The Bourdon barometer is so little used in meteorological practice nowadays that it will be dismissed with a short note. It consists simply of a closed, curved tube of elliptical cross-section. Changes in the atmospheric pressure result in changes in the radius of curvature of the tube. One end being fixed, the motion of the other is magnified by a system of levers and indicates the pressure. The principle is largely used in pressure gauges for steam boilers, refrigeration apparatus, and every kind of engineering pressure measurements.

(b) *The aneroid barometer—general description*

Fundamentally the aneroid barometer consists of two parts—a closed box of thin metal, partly or fully evacuated, and a strong spring. The spring operates to keep the box from collapsing under the external pressure of the atmosphere, and at a given pressure there will be an equilibrium between the force due to the air and that due to the spring. In practice the metal box is usually made thin and flexible, so that the elastic properties of the spring determine those of the whole instrument.

The basic aneroid is shown in Fig. 18. It consists of a single flat chamber C made of flexible sheet metal, and an external steel spring S. The connection between the aneroid chamber and the spring is made by means of knife-edges KK′ which pass through posts PP′ attached to the two sides of the chamber. These posts pass through rectangular slots in the spring. The lever L is the first element of a mechanical magnifying system.

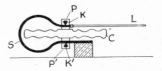

FIGURE 18
Basic aneroid.

This simple aneroid is used in several meteorographs (see chapter X) practically in its basic form. For use as a station or ship's barometer it is commonly modified as shown in Fig. 19(a), in which it should be noted that the aneroid chamber is entirely behind the spring, not within it.

The bottom of the aneroid chamber C is fastened firmly to a base-plate A, which also carries a bridge B, over the top of the chamber. The spring D is held by a slot in this bridge, the entire bridge being adjustable in height by means of two screws EE′. A further screw F tilts the bridge about an axis through EE′, providing a means of adjusting the zero of the instrument.

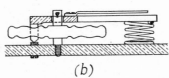

(a)

(b)

FIGURE 19
(a) Lever system of aneroid, usual form.
(b) Aneroid with external helical spring.

The chamber is prevented from collapsing by the spring, acting through a knife-edge G. The movement of the upper surface of the chamber is transmitted by the linkage H J K L M N to the staff P, which is controlled by the hairspring Q, to eliminate backlash. The axis K is known as the "regulator," and revolves in jewelled bearings. The element N is a fine steel chain.

In this instrument temperature compensation (see para. 5 (c)) is effected by a strip of metal let into the arm H, forming a bimetal. The angular relationship of the links J and L is a matter of importance.

Most non-recording aneroid barometers are of this general pattern. In some French instruments the flat spring is replaced by a helical spring under an extension of the bridge, as shown diagrammatically in Fig. 19(b), but the remainder of the mechanism is little changed.

An alternative construction, much used in altimeters, substitutes a gear-sector and pinion for the chain and pulley. This requires the staff K to be parallel to the hand-staff P.

An entirely different arrangement is employed in the Paulin aneroid (Fig. 20), which is unique in that there are no pivots whatever. In Fig. 20, A is the aneroid chamber, on which is mounted a lug B. To this lug is attached a strong tension spring C, which balances the force due to the atmospheric pressure on the aneroid chamber. The upper end of the spring can be moved vertically, without twisting, by the screw D and the knob E, to which is attached the pointer F. This pointer moves over a dial graduated in pressure or altitude units.

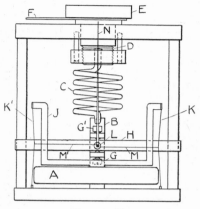

FIGURE 20

The Paulin aneroid (schematic).

The motion of the lug B, and consequently of the upper face of A, is restricted to about 0.001'' by the stops G, G', which are attached to B and work against a cross beam H. To B is also attached a cradle J; and to the ends of this are fastened slightly bowed phosphor-bronze strips K, K', having their lower ends attached to the base plate of the instrument.

A shaft L, really a wire held in tension by two helical springs (not shown), passes through holes in the beam H and the lug B. The horizontal wires M, M' from the middle of K, K' are attached, one to the bottom of L, one to the top. An upward movement of J moves M to the left, M' to the right, causing L to revolve in a counter-clockwise direction. A pointer N, passing through a slot in the dial of the instrument, indicates the angular position of L and consequently shows the position of B relative to H, minute movements being very greatly magnified. To read the aneroid, the knob E is turned until the pointer N comes to a fixed mark, and the pressure then read from the position of the pointer F.

It is claimed that a height difference of 6 inches will be indicated by this instrument; this corresponds to 0.02 mb, approximately, near sea-level.

To make the aneroid a recording instrument it is necessary only to substitute a pen on the end of a long arm for the parts L, M, N of Fig. 19(a), and to arrange a moving sheet of paper to receive the record. Aneroids

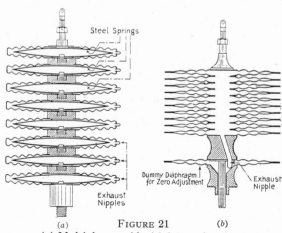

(a)   FIGURE 21   (b)

(a) Multiple aneroid with internal springs.
(b) Steel aneroid.

(Courtesy of Negretti and Zambra)

with external springs are little used in barographs, however. In order to make the deflection adequate, it is necessary to mount several chambers in series, and the external spring becomes difficult to apply.

An early type of multiple aneroid with inner springs, still met with in many barographs, is shown in Fig. 21(a). It has the disadvantage that each chamber must be exhausted separately, usually through a tube set in the edge. Furthermore, there is an uncertain amount of friction between the ends of the springs, which sometimes causes sticking.

An obvious improvement is the patented steel aneroid of Negretti and Zambra (Fig. 21(b)). In this the chambers, which are of tempered steel, act also as the spring, completely eliminating frictional errors. The flat edges of the corrugated diaphragms which form the chambers are welded together, and the entire system is exhausted at once through one tube. There is no doubt whatever that this aneroid is of excellent quality; it seems to the writer a pity that it is made so small in diameter (see 5e below), since the excellent properties of the chamber are thereby partly wasted, at least in recording instruments.

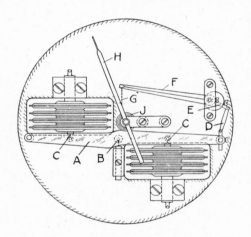

FIGURE 22
Precision aneroid movement.
(Courtesy of Negretti and Zambra)

These steel chambers have been utilized by their makers in a remarkable precision aneroid (Fig. 22). The general principle of this instrument is obvious from the figure, but it should be particularly remarked that the main lever A rotates by the flexing of a strip of stainless steel B. Similar strips C, C connect the lever with the two sets of chambers. The magnifying levers D, E, and F drive the pointer H through a chain G, and a hairspring J keeps the chain under tension. All the parts except the very light link D are balanced, so that the instrument is particularly insensitive to changes of attitude, accelerations, or vibration. It is claimed that this instrument is compensated for temperature at all pressures within its range (see below, page 44).

A barograph on similar principles is also obtainable, having four chambers, opposed in groups of two.

The modern tendency is to use the flexible metal bellows which are made in such large quantities for various engineering purposes. Probably the first barograph with a metal bellows as an element was made by Friez of Baltimore about twenty years ago; other manufacturers followed, until at the present time (the Negretti and Zambra instrument excepted) nearly all new barographs are made in this way. This construction involves an internal helical spring. Now when a helical spring is compressed, one end tends to rotate with respect to the other, and so the possibility of friction is present. In designing a new barograph to be manufactured for the Canadian Service (Fig. 23), ball bearings were therefore provided; a thrust bearing T to take the axial load (about 75 lbs.) of the spring S, and a small radial bearing R to allow for the dissymmetry which is always present in such an assembly. This aneroid chamber is a good deal larger in diameter than most others; the result is that the control of the pen is excellent, and even minor fluctuations in pressure are recorded. The complete barograph is shown in Fig. 24, which illustrates the main features of nearly all such instruments, others differing chiefly in the means of adjusting the zero. In this instrument the entire aneroid chamber can be moved vertically by means of a lever under the base, operated by the screw A.

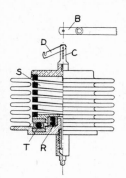

FIGURE 23

Canadian barograph chamber, showing ball bearings.

The motion of the upper end of the aneroid is transmitted to the lever B by a compound link consisting of a slotted bar C and a hook D (Fig. 23). The bar has an array of tapered holes, in one of which a pin is placed; this pin holds the hook. The reason for this is as follows: at times it is necessary to ship the instrument to a mountain station, or to a station beyond the mountains, or by air. If the connection were solid, the deflection during shipment would be much beyond the range of the instrument. With this construction, the pin is simply located in the hole which is appropriate to the mean pressure of the station, and the hook tied back out of

FIGURE 24

Canadian barograph.

the way. On receipt of the barograph, the observer has only to engage the hook with the pin, and adjust the zero of the instrument by means of the screw A (Fig. 25). Other means of achieving the same result are possible; the main thing to be desired is that the observer will not have to perform any operation which can put any strain on the pivots of the lever B or the pen arm.

The lever B is fastened to an axis which rotates in miniature ball bearings,[33] and has a link E at its far end, transmitting its motion through the arm F to the pen-arm axis G, similarly supported in ball bearings. The arm F is ad-

[33]See page 7, footnote.

justable in length by a micrometer screw, and determines the scale value of the instrument.

The pen arm H can swing freely in a "gate" J, the axis of which is inclined inwards at an angle of 10° to the vertical. Thus the pen rests on the chart by gravity and with a constant pressure, independent of irregularities or eccentricity in the drum. This principle is generally adopted in English recording instruments, and is becoming common everywhere.

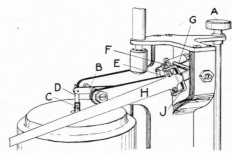

FIGURE 25
Lever system of barograph.

Barographs have been made, especially by Richard of Paris, in which the spring is replaced by a heavy weight. These have excellent elastic properties, but unfortunately act as seismographs to some extent, and are excessively sensitive to vibration.

(c) Compensation of the aneroid for temperature

The assembly of spring and chamber, or spring and bellows, may be thought of as a compound spring. In most instruments the spring is very much stiffer than the chamber, so that to a first approximation the elastic properties of the system will be those of the spring.

Nearly all metals and alloys have negative temperature coefficients of rigidity[34] and of Young's modulus. The following table, from various sources, shows the approximate magnitude of these coefficients for well-known materials:

Material	$\beta=$ Temp. coeff. of Young's modulus per °C.	$\eta=$ Temp. coeff. of modulus of rigidity per °C.
Steel (carbon)...............	-0.0002 to -0.0005	-0.0002 to -0.0003
Phosphor-bronze............	-0.0004	-0.00048
Brass......................	-0.0004	-0.0005
Nickel-silver................	-0.00035	-0.00035
Copper.....................	-0.0002 to -0.0004	

Thus the deflection of a spring subjected to a constant force will increase as the temperature increases. In a barometer chamber an increase in temperature will therefore lead to an apparent increase in pressure, because of the weakening of the spring.

There are two general methods of compensating for this: (i) by means of a bimetallic link, usually formed by letting a piece of a different metal into

[34]See BROMBACHER, W. G., and E. R. MELTON, Report no. 358, National Adv. Comm. for Aeronautics, Washington 1930.

one side of the first lever (H, Fig. 19a) and (ii) by leaving a certain amount of gas inside the chamber. The first of these methods is more frequently employed in indicating instruments, and the second in aneroid barographs.

In its simple form the bimetallic compensator compensates only for one particular pressure. This can be shown as follows: the spring exerts a total force approximately equal to the force exerted by the air on one end of the chamber, that is, to Ap, where A is the effective area of the chamber and p the pressure. The change in the force exerted by the spring per degree centigrade is therefore βAp (or ηAp if a helical spring is involved). This produces a change $(1/K)\beta Ap$ in the deflection of the spring, where K is the spring rate. Now the bimetallic link is not at all affected by the pressure of the atmosphere. It operates merely to shift the zero of the instrument by an amount K' per °C. The instrument will therefore be compensated for a pressure $p_0 = KK'/\beta A$, but only approximately for neighbouring pressures, the compensation being less accurate the further the pressure departs from p_0. The design of the bimetallic link may be approximated theoretically (see below, page 68), but in view of the variability of springs a good range of individual adjustment should be allowed for.

A very ingenious bimetallic compensation is used in some types of aircraft altimeters, operating with a mechanical linkage which changes the lever-arm of the compensating member as the pressure varies. It would be going beyond the limits of this book to describe this in detail; but it is claimed for the best of these instruments that they are almost completely compensated for temperature at all pressures between about 1000 and 300 mb.

The second method of compensation is also complete only at some one *compensation pressure*. Suppose a chamber of effective area A as before, sustained by a spring having a temperature coefficient of modulus of rigidity η. Let a certain amount of gas, sufficient to produce a pressure π_0 at a temperature t_0, be left inside the chamber. Then the force exerted by the spring is $A(p-\pi_0)$, and the force due to the internal gas is $A\pi_0$. The sum of these two forces balances the force Ap exerted by the outside air. Now let the temperature rise 1°C. The change in the force exerted by the spring is $A\eta(p-\pi_0)$; the change in the force due to the internal gas is $Aa\pi_0$, where a is the cubical coefficient of expansion of air. If the sum of these changes is zero, there will be no change in the deflection of the spring. Thus at the compensation pressure p_0

$$A\eta(p_0-\pi_0)+Aa\pi_0=0 \qquad \ldots\ldots\ldots(2.30);$$
$$(p_0-\pi_0)/\pi_0 = -a/\eta \qquad \ldots\ldots\ldots(2.31).$$

Since η is negative, π_0 is positive and compensation is possible. As an example, if $\eta = -0.00025$ (steel), and since $a = 1/273$,

$$p_0/\pi_0 = \left(\frac{1}{273}\Big/.00025\right)+1 = 15.7.$$

A compensation pressure of 1000 mb would be obtained by leaving about 64 mb of gas inside the chamber. Actually it is preferable to introduce pure dry nitrogen after outgassing the chamber for several hours.

The above simple derivation makes two approximations:

(i) It neglects the changes in dimensions of the various components.   (ii) It neglects the fact that the chamber walls may be of a different material to the spring, as in fact they nearly always are,[35] and may contribute to the stiffness of the chamber.

The first approximation involves an error of not more than about 5 per cent in π_0. The second would be more serious if we were obliged to make the compensation without trial. Actually the value of β (or η) depends a good deal on the heat-treatment and other previous history of the spring, so that in practice each aneroid must be compensated individually by experiment. The elementary theory is useful (and sufficiently accurate) as a point of departure.

In most aneroids, especially those of the bellows type, the change in the total volume of the chamber with changing pressure is a small fraction of the total volume for the entire range of the instrument. In some aerological aneroids, however, this is not so. Over a limited range of pressures it should be possible to have the internal volume vary approximately inversely as the external pressure; or more accurately, to have the product p_1v_1 of the pressure and volume at one end of the range equal to a similar product p_2v_2 at the other. Such an aneroid could have two compensation pressures, since p/π could be of the correct value at both p_1 and p_2; and if the range were moderate, the temperature error would not be great at any point. This property is claimed for the aneroid illustrated in Fig. 22, p. 40.

(d) Elastic errors of aneroids

Suppose an aneroid to be taken through a cycle of pressure variations from about 1000 mb to some low pressure (e.g., 300 mb) and back, in the course of an hour or so, as would occur to an instrument carried up and down on an aircraft. As the pressure decreases, a certain relation between pressure and deflection will be observed, leading to a calibration curve such as OP in Fig. 26. As the pressure again increases, it will be found that the relation no longer follows the original curve, but instead the curve PO'; and when the original pressure is again reached, a residual deflection OO' will remain. The phenomenon is known as *hysteresis*, prob-

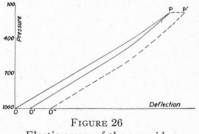

FIGURE 26
Elastic errors of the aneroid.

ably by analogy with the magnetic properties of materials as expressed by a B-H curve; and while there are no established standards, the amount of hysteresis may well be indicated by the area of the closed curve traced out as the instrument undergoes a given cycle.

If the pressure be now maintained at its maximum value, the deflection will gradually return from O' in the direction of O.   If, on the other hand, the

---

[35]In the Negretti and Zambra instrument the chamber acts as its own spring.

cycle be repeated within a few hours, a somewhat narrower closed curve will result. Each repetition produces a narrower figure until after four or five cycles a stationary state is attained. In the conduct of aeroplane ascents for meteorological purposes, the same aneroid is used day after day, so that this state is at least approximated.[36] In the case of radiosondes, on the contrary, it is best to calibrate them on the decreasing pressure part of their first cycle, and then to lay them away for some days or weeks before use, so that they may recover, as far as possible, their original state. The readings on the other part of the cycle are not generally used.

If the pressure is held at a low point for some time, the deflection will slowly increase from P to P′ (see Fig. 26). This process, which is known as *creep*, proceeds rapidly at first, reaching a maximum value asymptotically after many hours.

All the elastic errors of aneroids vary (1) directly with the temperature, (2) directly with the range of pressure, (3) directly with the rate of change of pressure, or for a given pressure range, inversely as the time taken for the cycle; and differ greatly according to the materials of which the system is made. For the steel spring it is probable that the elastic errors are very small, the spring being stressed far below its elastic limit. Therefore a means of reducing these errors is plainly to be sought in making the steel spring responsible for as much of the stiffness of the system as possible, by having the walls of the chamber thin and flexible.

Elastic errors are usually unimportant in station aneroid barometers and barographs, because of the limited range of pressure involved, and the small rate of change of pressure at a fixed level. Faulty temperature compensation is a much more important defect of such instruments.

(e) General accuracy of aneroids

The aneroid affords a beautiful illustration of the difference between *sensitivity* and *accuracy*, discussed in chapter I. Some aneroids, such as the Paulin, are undoubtedly more sensitive than most mercury barometers; but who will claim for them a comparable accuracy? It is not unfair to say that an aneroid should not be depended on for *absolute* values of pressure. Nevertheless these instruments are of great value for giving *relative* indications, and for measuring pressure changes over a few hours; and it is for this purpose that they are most frequently used at meteorological stations.

A first-class modern indicating aneroid will give self-consistent readings over a period of weeks within ±0.15 mb or better, provided the temperature range be not too large. A barograph of equally good construction should not change its correction by more than ±0.2 mb in, say, a fortnight, though the scatter of individual errors may be greater than in the indicating instrument because of pen friction. In an indicating aneroid, the scatter of the readings is a function chiefly of the accuracy of the mechanical workmanship, especially

---

[36]The final breadth of the curve is called *Hysteresis* by German authors (see Kleinschmidt, *Handbuch*, p. 318); the portion which vanishes on repeating the cycle *elastische Nachwirkung*.

where pivots are used; in the barograph, on the other hand, it depends principally on the control of the pen. A few remarks on this quantity are in order.

The *control* may be defined as the working stiffness of the entire instrument considered as a single spring with a load applied at the pen. Numerically, it may be expressed as the number of grams weight, applied at this point, required to deflect the pen over 1 millibar of the scale. (Other similar units may be used.) This is equal to the force required to keep the pen from moving if the pressure changes by 1 millibar.

If we assume no friction in the pivots this is easily calculated.

Let A be the effective cross-sectional area of the aneroid (cm²)

" K be its spring constant (grams weight per cm)

" M be the magnification

" g be the acceleration due to gravity (cm. sec^{-2})

and neglect all bending of the magnifying levers.

Then the change of spring force *at the aneroid* for 1 mb change in pressure is $(1000/g)A$, and the force required to keep the pen from moving is $(1000/g) . A/M$. So the force at the aneroid varies as A,

∴ the deflection of the aneroid spring and chamber varies as A/K

∴ for a given scale value the magnification M varies as K/A

and the force required to keep the pen from moving varies as A/M or as A^2/K.

Thus for a given scale value the best control would be provided by a large aneroid with a very weak spring. Unfortunately it is necessary to get most of the air out of the aneroid, and a comparatively strong spring is necessary to prevent its complete collapse. (If air at approximately atmospheric pressure were left in, there would, of course, be an enormous temperature error.) In practice the value of K, for a given design of chamber, will have to be approximately proportional to A. Therefore the control of a barograph pen varies roughly as the effective cross-section of the aneroid.

There will be friction at all the pivots and bearings of the instrument, as well as at the contact between pen and paper. In a well-made instrument, the friction of the pen is by far the greatest of these resistances. The necessary and sufficient condition for the proper functioning of the barograph is that the sum of the frictional resistances should be at all times less than the control multiplied by the least change in millibars which it is desired to record. If this is not so the pen will have a perceptible "lost motion" which will produce different errors for rising and for falling pressures.

Many barographs, otherwise excellent, have aneroids which are too small. No one who has not seen them can have any idea how much clearer are the records from an instrument with an aneroid 7.5 cm in diameter than from a 4 cm one. The same effect can of course be obtained by a number of smaller chambers in parallel.

6. The Hypsometer

The hypsometer (Fig. 27) consists of a boiler with a long double tube above it, and a thermometer hanging in the steam. The steam passes up the centre tube and back down the outer tube, minimizing radiation from the thermometer to the walls of the centre tube, which are in this manner kept nearly at the temperature of the steam. A small U-tube manometer serves to measure any excess of pressure over that of the outside air, due to the finite, though small, resistance of the tubes to the escape of the vapour.

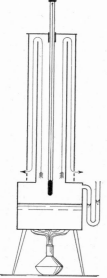

The measurement of pressure by this instrument depends on the one-to-one relation which exists between the vapour-pressure of water and its temperature. The vapour of distilled water boiling freely will have a temperature appropriate to the surrounding pressure, and thus its temperature (not that of the water itself) is a measure of the pressure.

The change of temperature per mb change in pressure is about 0.027°C. in the neighbourhood of 1000 mb. If, therefore, we wish to determine the pressure to 0.2 mb we must be prepared to measure the temperature to about 0.005°C.; a difficult though not impossible task. A very necessary precaution is to make sure that the shortest possible length of the mercury column projects above the steam chamber, to reduce stem corrections (see below, page 63).

FIGURE 27
Hypsometer.

7. Pressure Variographs

For some purposes it is desirable to study the very small fluctuations of pressure which escape record on ordinary barographs. There is thus a need for special barographs with great magnification and correspondingly large time-scales. Such instruments are of two types, classified according to whether they furnish a record of p or of dp/dt.

(a) Variographs for p (statoscopes)

The simplest type of variograph for p is an aneroid with great magnification, usually by an optical lever. The useful magnification of such an instrument would be limited by the internal friction of the aneroid-and-spring system. An optical lever can also be fitted to the cistern of a siphon barometer, or better, in the vacuum chamber of a large instrument; the useful sensitivity is then limited by any sticking of the mercury.

A third method employs an aneroid diaphragm which is part of the wall of a closed chamber, carefully insulated against temperature changes. Magnification may again be by optical means, or by a lever system as in the Richard statoscope.

In all these instruments it is necessary to bring the record back on to the scale at frequent intervals when large pressure changes are taking place. In the first two, this is done mechanically; in the third, by placing the closed chamber temporarily in communication with the outside air. It is obvious that this could be done automatically by electrical means.

There seems to be no reason why the principles of modern recording potentiometers could not be applied to this problem, as they have been to the weight barograph.

(b) Variographs for dp/dt

To get over the difficulty of having to readjust the zero of the instrument at frequent intervals, numerous variographs have been devised which record, not the value of p, but the value of dp/dt. Of these the best-known in English-speaking countries is the *microbarograph* of Shaw and Dines.[37]

The essentials of this instrument are a large closed vessel with a small leak, and a means of measuring the difference between the pressures inside and outside the vessel. The measuring element is a small bell-jar floating in mercury, with a system of magnifying levers. The leak is a piece of capillary (thermometer) tubing.

The amount of the leak can be characterized by a value τ (seconds), where τ is the time for an artificially produced pressure difference to fall to 1/2.718 of its original value. Then if p is the pressure outside the chamber, p' that inside, assuming no change of temperature,

$$\frac{dp'}{dt} = \frac{1}{\tau}(p-p') \qquad \ldots\ldots(2.32).$$

The deflection of the instrument is proportional to $(p-p')$. If in this equation p is constant, p' approaches p asymptotically, and when equilibrium is established the deflection is zero. If $p = p_0 + at$, so that $dp/dt = a$, then after a time $t >> \tau$, $p - p' = a\tau = \text{const}$.

The response of such an instrument to periodic oscillations of pressure depends on their period. If we write

$$p = p_0 + A \sin 2\pi t/T$$

(where T is the period of the oscillation, considered a sine wave) the solution of the above equation (2.32) is

$$p - p' = c_1 e^{-t/\tau} + \frac{A}{\sqrt{1 + \dfrac{T^2}{4\pi^2\tau^2}}} \sin\left[2\pi t/T + \cot^{-1}(2\pi\tau/T)\right] \ldots\ldots(2.33).$$

The first term on the right-hand side becomes negligible if t is large,[38] leaving a periodic term of amplitude less than that of the pressure change, and out of phase by an angle $\cot^{-1}(2\pi\tau/T)$.

---

[37] SHAW, W. N., and W. H. DINES, *Q. J. Roy. Met. Soc.*, **31**:39-52, 1905.

[38] If $p' = p_0$ at $t=0$, $c_1 = (1 + T^2/4\pi^2\tau^2)^{\frac{1}{2}}$. This corresponds to the sudden commencement of oscillations.

The value of τ may well be about 100 sec. The following table shows how the response varies with the period T of the oscillations:

RESPONSE OF THE SHAW-DINES MICROBAROGRAPH IF $T = 100$ SEC

T (sec)...............	10	20	50	100	200	500	1000	2000
Relative amplitude...	1.00	1.00	0.99	0.96	0.87	0.58	0.33	0.055
Phase angle (degrees) .	1	2	5	9	18	38	58	73

Note that short period waves will be recorded not only fully but promptly, while long ones are scarcely recorded at all. In other words, the system is highly selective. This severely limits its usefulness for the quantitative study of pressure oscillations.

A variograph on completely different principles has been described by Benndorf and Zimmermann.[39] A large vessel, of which the top portion is shown at B (Fig. 28) is fitted with a chimney Z about 5 cm in diameter, supported separately from the vessel but joined to it by a water seal at R. In the chimney hangs a very light aluminum fan wheel, supported by a fine wire and carrying a mirror. The deflection of this wheel is proportional to the air speed in the chimney, which in turn is proportional to dp/dt. A wind speed of 10 microns per second is detectible with a vessel 50 litres in volume. To calibrate the instrument, the cylinder G is provided, hung from the top of B by three wires t. This can be filled with water, or emptied, through the tube R; and after the water-level is raised enough to seal the bottom of the chimney, further addition

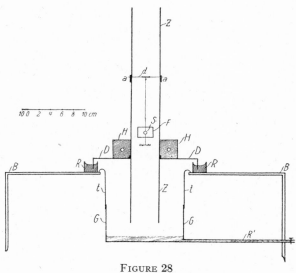

FIGURE 28

The Variograph of Benndorf and Zimmermann (from the *Meteorologische Zeitschrift*, 1938).

of water produces an artificial wind which can easily be calculated from the rate of water-flow and the dimensions of the apparatus.

The response of this apparatus to simple harmonic variations of pressure is complicated by the resonant system formed by the fan wheel and its support; this system has a period of the order of 25 sec. If the system were undamped it would resonate with, and enormously exaggerate, dp/dt variations of about this period. With suitable damping, however, it can be made to have almost

[39]BENNDORF, H., and W. ZIMMERMANN, *Met. Zeits.*, **55**:273-283, 1938.

constant sensitivity to dp/dt variations of period greater than about 1.4 times the natural period of the instrument. In contrast to the Shaw-Dines instrument, its response to variations of short period is very small.

Numerous other variographs have been constructed. We shall content ourselves with a reference to the electromagnetic barograph of Benioff and Gutenberg.[40] This instrument consists essentially of a permanent-magnet loud speaker mounted in the wall of a large (200 litre) vessel. The e.m.f. induced in the coil of such an instrument is proportional to dp/dt, and is recorded photographically. The natural frequency of the system is stated to be about 150 cycles per second, while that of the galvanometer may be about one cycle per second; thus oscillations of period greater than about 3 sec should be fully recorded. The method of calibration is not stated.

[40]BENIOFF, H., and B. GUTENBERG, *Bull. Amer. Met. Soc.*, **20**:421-426, 1939.

CHAPTER III

THE MEASUREMENT OF TEMPERATURE IN METEOROLOGY

1. Scope of the Chapter.　Definition of Temperature.　Units.

The meteorologist wishes to measure, and often to record, the temperature of

> (i) the air near the surface,
> (ii) the upper air,
> (iii) the soil, at various depths,
> (iv) the surface water of rivers, lakes, and the sea,

and it has been the task of the instrument-maker to devise instruments for these purposes.　In this chapter we shall deal with thermometers, indicating and recording, for the measurement of temperatures not far above or below the surface of the earth or the water, reserving until chapter x the discussion of the measurement of temperatures in the upper air.

The idea of temperature scarcely has a meaning apart from its association with material bodies.　If we think of the temperature of empty space we are probably constrained to visualize the indications of a thermometer brought into the void; and thus we are led to define temperature as the condition of a body which determines its ability to communicate heat to other bodies or receive heat from them.[1]　In a system of two bodies, that which loses heat to the other is said to be at the higher temperature.

Although a scale of temperatures can be referred to the fundamental laws of thermodynamics,[2] actual thermometers are calibrated with reference to *fixed points*, relating to certain easily reproducible changes of state, the temperatures of which have been determined once and for all from first principles. The four which interest meteorologists are the following:

(1) Equilibrium between solid and gaseous CO_2

$$-78.5°C. +0.01595(p-760) -0.0000111(p-760)^2 \quad [p=\text{atmos-}$$
pheric pressure in mm of mercury].

(2) Temperature of melting ice, 0.00°C.

(3) Transition temperature of $Na_2SO_4 . 10 H_2O, +32.38°C.$

(4) Equilibrium between water and its vapour

$$+100.00°C. +0.0367(p-760) -0.000023(p-760)^2.$$

---

[1]In the absence of chemical reactions, adsorption, etc.　For example, a piece of platinum sponge can be strongly heated by being placed in cold hydrogen.

[2]See *Temperature, Its Measurement and Control in Science and Industry*, ed. Amer. Inst. of Phys., New York 1941, Reinhold Publ. Co., for many physical considerations.

Of these (2) and (4) are primary fixed points recognized by international agreement; (1) and (3) are convenient secondary points reproducible with ample accuracy for meteorological purposes.

The degree *centigrade* (°C.), in terms of which the above temperatures are given, is defined as the variation in temperature which produces 1/100 of the increase in pressure suffered by a mass of a perfect gas at constant volume, when the temperature passes from 0° (temperature of melting ice, as officially defined) to 100° (temperature of the vapour of boiling water at 760 mm pressure). On this *centigrade* scale the pressure of a perfect gas will be zero at a temperature of −273.16°, the "absolute zero" of temperature. We may therefore form another scale, the *absolute* scale, by adding 273.16 (in meteorological practice, 273) to all centigrade temperatures.

Starting with the same fixed points, the *Fahrenheit* scale, used in English-speaking countries, has its ice-point at 32° and its boiling point at 212°. The Reaumur scale has 0° and 80° for the same points. It is no longer used officially but is to be met with in old records from the continent of Europe. The following table summarizes the properties of all these scales from the meteorological standpoint. English-speaking meteorologists nearly always use the

Scale	Ice-point	Boiling-point	Use
Centigrade (°C.).......	0°	100°	All records in other than English-speaking countries; international upper air records since 1935; measurements in physics and chemistry.
Absolute (°A.)........	273°	373°	Thermodynamical calculations; upper air records for some years before 1935; temperature of attached thermometer on English barometers since 1915.
Fahrenheit (°F.).......	32°	212°	All records, other than upper-air temperatures, in English-speaking countries.
Reaumur (°R.)........	0°	80°	Old records from parts of Europe.

Note that 9 degrees F. = 5 degrees C. = 4 degrees R.

Fahrenheit scale for surface observations, but must be familiar with the centigrade scale for upper-air work and the absolute scale for thermodynamical calculations.

2. Exposure of Thermometers

(a) Temperature equilibrium with the air

In a steady state, any thermometer will attain thermal equilibrium with its entire neighbourhood, by the processes of conduction, convection, and

radiation. In measuring the temperature of the air it is necessary to take
into account its great transparency to radiation and its poor conductivity; for
a thermometer placed in the open will come to a temperature which is a compromise between that of the air and those of the surfaces of surrounding objects,
including the sun when it is visible. In order that a thermometer may indicate
the temperature of the air, it is necessary that the transfer of heat by radiation
should be minimized.

There are two ways of doing this: (1) by means of a louvred box; (2) by
means of polished metal screens. Either may be supplemented by artificial
ventilation of the thermometer, not to alter the heat transfer
by radiation but to increase that by conduction and convection.

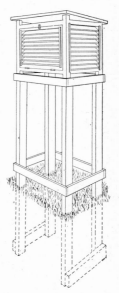

The louvred thermometer box, or *Stevenson screen*, is
shown in Fig. 29. Many variations are used in different
countries, but the important feature is that there is no
possibility of radiation proceeding in a straight line from
outside to inside without encountering solid matter. In the
Canadian pattern, the ceiling is louvred, and is separated
by an air space of about $1\frac{1}{2}$ inches from the solid roof. The
floor is of staggered boards.

The screen is usually made of pine or a similar wood,
and painted white. It is important that the paint be kept
in good condition to minimize the absorption of radiation
by the screen.[3]

In calm, sunshiny weather the material of the screen gets
warmed through by the sun, forming an enclosure having
a temperature greater than that of the air. At night the
entire screen can radiate to the sky, cooling the walls a little
below air temperature. Artificial ventilation of the thermometers is the only remedy for this source of error, which
can produce readings more than 1°F. too high in the after-
noons, and a little too low on clear, calm nights. As con-

FIGURE 29

Stevenson screen,
smaller Canadian
pattern.

tinuous artificial ventilation is not usually practicable, the screen should be
designed to offer as little resistance as possible to the natural movement of air,
while excluding radiation from all directions.

The screen is usually supported on an open wooden support, firmly anchored,
over short grass, the floor of the screen being about 4 feet above ground in
English-speaking countries, and from 1.7 to 2.0 m in central Europe. Uniformity of practice is greatly to be desired, because of the very large temperature gradients which can occur near the ground. The installation of important
stations on the roofs of tall buildings (a practice which is happily on the decline)
renders the resulting temperatures of doubtful validity either for synoptic

---

[3]Aluminum paint has the advantage of greater durability but its other properties are less
suitable. Comparisons between the temperatures observed in screens painted with white
and with aluminum paint would be of interest.

purposes or as an indication of the thermal climate of a city. It is true that many people work *inside* the tall buildings; but their exposure to the *natural* climate takes place near street level.

In tropical countries the Stevenson screen has been felt to be inadequate, and thermometers are exposed under an extensive (15×20 feet) thatched roof mounted on posts, and having a hole at the summit for the escape of warmed air. This does not, of course, cut off radiation from terrestrial surroundings.

Special small screens are designed for use on shipboard, but are not nearly as satisfactory as the provision of a sling or Assmann psychrometer (see chapter IV). A very thorough discussion of temperature measurements at sea will be found in the *Admiralty Weather Manual*.[4]

The second method of protecting thermometers from radiation is more frequently used with artificial ventilation, as in the Assman psychrometer (see Fig. 55, page 92), which will be discussed in the next chapter. It generally involves two concentric metal shields, often tubular, with the air moving in the space between them as well as in the space immediately surrounding the thermometer. When this design is employed, the inner tube is likely to be very nearly at air temperature, being bathed with air on both sides, even if the outer tube is somewhat heated by the sun or cooled by nocturnal radiation. Both tubes should, of course, be highly polished, to reduce to a minimum their absorption of radiant energy.

With thermocouples of fine wire it is often possible to use metal shields without artificial ventilation (see Fig. 48, page 80).

When a thermometer is used in an air stream of high speed the heat developed at the expense of the kinetic energy of the moving air may lead to a large rise in the temperature of the thermometer. The amount of this rise is Cv^2, where v is the air speed, and C an instrumental constant. The error is not usually important in meteorological observations, but may reach several degrees at the speeds of present-day aircraft. Peterson and Womack[5] quote an error of 3.2°C. (5.8°F.) for a resistance thermometer at 200 miles per hour. It should be kept in mind that the error at 20 m.p.h. is only 1 per cent of this.

(b) The necessary and sufficient accuracy of meteorological thermometers

   (i) Thermometers for air temperature

Where it is a question of determining only the temperature, it is a great mistake to insist on extreme accuracy in meteorological work. Laymen (and indeed many meteorologists) have no idea of the rapidity with which air temperature can vary both in space[6] and in time.[7]

---

[4]*Admiralty Weather Manual.* London 1938, H.M. Stationery Office.

[5]PETERSON, J. B., and S. H. J. WOMACK, *N.A.C.A. Report* no. 606, Washington 1937, p. 11.

[6]See for example KRATZER, P. A., *Das Stadtklima*, Braunschweig 1937, Vieweg; or MIDDLETON, W. E. K., and F. G. MILLAR, *J. Roy. Astr. Soc. Canada*, **30**:265-272, 1936. Kratzer's book deserves a place in the library of every city meteorological station, at least in cities where the public asks micro-climatological questions.

[7]See HOLTZMANN, M. J., *Met. Zeits.*, **53**:327-336, 1936. This paper contains a very interesting discussion of these matters.

To deal first with variation in space, we may consider Fig. 30a, which presents two kinds of profile in a north-south direction across the city of Toronto. The stippled line is a profile in the engineering sense, showing the elevations as a function of the distance from the shore of Lake Ontario. The solid line is a graph of air temperatures about 2.3 feet above the street, and was obtained by attaching a sensitive electrical thermometer to an automobile and driving as rapidly as traffic and traffic rules permitted from the lake-shore inland and back again. Particular attention is drawn to the fact that a temperature difference of about 26°F. was encountered within half a mile at about mile 7.

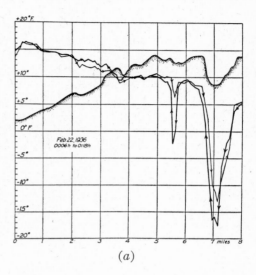

(a)

This is admittedly a spectacular example. The interesting thing is that even under cloudy skies, variations of large fractions of a degree occur in short distances (Fig. 30b).

Short-period variations in time are exemplified in Fig. 31, in which the irregular line shows the result of exposing a fine-wire thermocouple, shielded from radiation, for fifteen minutes on a sunny afternoon in late autumn. Fluctuations of about 2°F. will be observed.

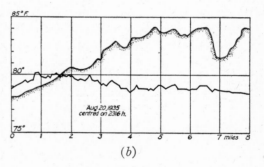

(b)

FIGURE 30

Temperature profiles in Toronto,
(a) on a clear, calm winter night,
(b) on a cloudy summer night.

The reader is asked to study these figures and to consider the proposition that *where only the temperature of the air is in question* (as in reading maximum and minimum thermometers) *it is misleading to state air temperatures more precisely than in whole degrees Fahrenheit.* It is also unnecessary to read such thermometers more closely, except at periodic check readings, after setting (see page 64). Where humidity measurements depend on the readings, the thermometers should, however, be read to tenths (see chapter IV).

In this connection there emerges a real superiority of the Fahrenheit scale over the centigrade for meteorological purposes. The degree F. is a unit of

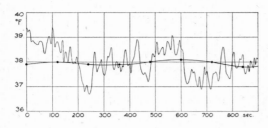

FIGURE 31

Fluctuations in temperature,
afternoon in late autumn.

precisely the right magnitude for use without division in climatological summaries and for stating individual temperatures. The degree C. is a little too coarse a unit, needing decimals, hence nearly twice the space in printed tables;[8] and *with* the decimal division it gives a false impression of accuracy. The writer hopes that no doctrinaire admiration for the metric system (with which, incidentally, the centigrade scale has no real connection) will ever cause the Fahrenheit scale to be supplanted in the British Empire or the United States for climatological purposes or for the daily weather reports.

(ii) *Thermometers for water temperature*

We must anticipate the discussion on page 65, and point out here that while the temperature of the sea is much less subject to local variations than that of the air, there is here an uncertainty as to the depth from which samples are being taken. The variation of temperature with depth, especially in smooth water, probably limits the desirable precision to about 1°F.

(iii) *Thermometers for the temperature of the soil*

Since the temperature changes in the soil take place comparatively slowly, it is legitimate to require a higher degree of accuracy and sensitivity for soil thermometers, especially those to be used at great depths. Such thermometers should certainly be read to 0.1°F., and their corrections should be known to that degree of precision. At depths greater than, say, 4 feet, it would be desirable, though difficult, to be sure of the temperature to 0.02°F. or thereabouts.

3. The Lag Coefficients of Meteorological Thermometers[9]

(a) *Elementary theory*

When a thermometer of any sort at a temperature θ_0 is placed in a medium at temperature θ_e, it does not immediately take up the temperature of the medium, but approaches it asymptotically at a rate which depends on the materials and dimensions of the thermometer and on the properties of the medium itself. The change in the indication of the thermometer with time is given by the equation

$$\frac{d\theta}{dt} = -\frac{1}{\lambda}(\theta - \theta_e) \qquad \ldots\ldots\ldots(3.1),$$

[8] This is apart from the absence of negative signs in degrees F. for all really temperate climates.

[9] See HARPER, D. R. 3rd, *Bull. Bur. Stds.*, **8**:659-714, 1913. MIDDLETON, W. E. K., H. W. EDWARDS, and H. JOHNSON, *Bull. Amer. Met. Soc.*, **19**: 321-326, 1938.

where θ is the instantaneous indication of the thermometer at time t, and λ is a quantity known as the *lag coefficient*[10] of the thermometer. Its dimensions are those of time.[11]

If we integrate this equation on the assumption that θ_e does not change, we obtain

$$\theta - \theta_e = (\theta_0 - \theta_e)e^{-\frac{1}{\lambda}t} \qquad \dots\dots(3.2),$$

as the law according to which the temperature of the thermometer approaches that of its surroundings.

Taking logarithms of each side of equation (3.2) we obtain

$$ln(\theta - \theta_e) = ln(\theta_0 - \theta_e) - \frac{1}{\lambda}t \qquad \dots\dots(3.3).$$

This is the equation of a straight line of slope $\left(-\frac{1}{\lambda}\right)$ on semi-logarithmic paper, the intercept on the axis of θ being the initial temperature difference $(\theta_0 - \theta_e)$. An obvious method of measuring λ is to plot a series of readings in this form and measure the slope of the line; this assumes that the actual temperature θ_e is known, and it can be measured by another thermometer.

If we substitute $t = \lambda$ in (3.2), we see immediately that the lag coefficient is the number of seconds required for the difference of temperature to be reduced to $1/e$ [$= 1/2.718$] of its initial value. It also follows that it will be reduced to $\frac{1}{10}$ of its initial value in 2.3λ seconds, and to $1/100$ in 4.6λ seconds.

In still air the lag coefficient is slightly larger for rising than for falling temperatures, but with even a little ventilation the difference becomes small. The dependence of lag coefficient on ventilation, however, is important and has been investigated by many authors.

VARIATION OF λ WITH v: $\lambda = Kv^n$

Thermometer	Bulb dimensions		λ at $v=4.6$	K (sec.)	n
Mercury-in-glass.......	Spherical,	1.12 cm diam.	56	117	−0.48
ditto as wet bulb*......	"	1.12 " "	52	89	−0.36
Mercury-in-glass.......	"	1.065 " "	50	98	−0.43
Spirit-in-glass.........	"	1.44 " "	85	158	−0.41
Mercury-in-steel........	Cylindrical, 1.90 cm diam.				
	×14.5 cm long		280	630	−0.54
ditto as wet bulb*......			120	280	−0.56
Bimetallic............	Helical (station thermograph)		21	57	−0.64

*See chapter IV for further discussion of the lag of wet-bulb thermometers.

[10]Sometimes called the *transient constant* (SPILHAUS, A. F., *Trans. Roy. Soc. S. Africa*, **24**: 185-202, 1936), or the *time-lag constant* (PETERSON, J. B., and S. H. J. WOMACK, *N.A.C.A. Report* no. 606, Washington 1937, p. 10).

[11]Some authors write $d\theta/dt = -\lambda(\theta - \theta_e)$, in which event λ will be measured in seconds^{-1}; it is more convenient and physically expressive, however, as given above.

The general result is that in a wind of speed v the lag coefficient is given by

$$\lambda = Kv^n \qquad \dots\dots\dots (3.4).$$

For dry thermometers n is in the neighbourhood of $-\frac{1}{2}$, rather less for thermometers of simple form, and greater for thermometers which themselves set up a good deal of turbulence. The foregoing table gives values of K and n for several thermometers, the units of v being metres per second. These figures are intended only as a general indication of what may be expected. The exponent n may be expected to increase in its absolute value at very high wind speeds; according to Peterson and Womack[12] it approaches -1.

The lag coefficient obviously must contain the heat capacity of the thermometer element as a factor, and will also be a function of the conductivities of its various materials. It will be less, the greater the exposed surface in proportion to the heat capacity, but the exact laws will be a function of the shape of the instrument, its roughness, etc. In spirit thermometers, where the conductivity of the spirit is poor, the lag coefficient has been shown[13] to increase much more slowly than the quotient of the heat capacity by the surface area; presumably internal convection is important in transferring heat to the interior of the bulb. The lag coefficient of such instruments is therefore a function of the temperature.

(b) Lag with the temperature changing at a constant rate

If in equation (3.1), θ_e is no longer constant but is a linear function of the time such as
$$\theta_e = \theta_1 + \beta t$$
we have
$$\frac{d\theta}{dt} = -\frac{1}{\lambda}[\theta - (\theta_1 + \beta t)] \qquad \dots\dots\dots (3.5).$$

If this is integrated on the assumption that the thermometer was originally in equilibrium with its surroundings, we shall find that
$$\theta - \theta_e = -\beta\lambda(1 - e^{-t/\lambda}) \qquad \dots\dots\dots (3.6),$$
and after a time $t \gg \lambda$
$$\theta - \theta_e = -\beta\lambda \qquad \dots\dots\dots (3.7).$$

That is to say, the thermometer lags behind the actual temperature by an amount equal to the product of λ (seconds) and β (degrees per second). This result is useful in correcting upper-air records.

(c) Response of a thermometer to periodic temperature fluctuations[14]

Suppose the temperature of the medium undergoes periodic variations, so that its value at time t can be represented by
$$\theta_e = \theta_1 + A \sin 2\pi t/T$$

---

[12]PETERSON, J. B. and S. H. J. WOMACK, l.c.
[13]MIDDLETON, EDWARDS, and JOHNSON, l.c.
[14]See, for example, BILHAM, E. G., Q. J. Roy. Met. Soc., **61**:159-166, 1935.

where T is the period. The differential equation may now be written

$$\lambda \frac{d\theta}{dt} = \theta_1 + A \sin 2\pi t/T - \theta \qquad \ldots \ldots (3.8),$$

and a solution is

$$\theta = \theta_1 + c_1 e^{-t/\lambda} + \frac{A}{\sqrt{1 + \frac{4\pi^2\lambda^2}{T^2}}} \sin [2\pi t/T - \tan^{-1} 2\pi\lambda/T] \ldots \ldots (3.9).$$

The value of C_1 can be determined from the initial conditions, but the term containing it becomes negligible when t is much greater than λ. We are left with a temperature indication of reduced amplitude and lagging behind the temperature fluctuations of the medium. The following table shows the response of a thermometer having a lag coefficient $\lambda = 50$ sec. to simple harmonic temperature waves of various periods:

Period T	10	20	30	40	50	60	90	120	240	sec.
Relative response...	0.038	0.063	0.095	0.126	0.157	0.187	0.276	0.357	0.607	
Phase angle..	88.2	86.3	84.5	82.7	80.9	79.2	74.0	69.1	52.5	degrees

Note that fluctuations of short period are scarcely indicated at all, while those of period equal to λ are reduced to one-sixth their true amplitude.[15] The reader is invited to refer to Fig. 31, page 56, in which the heavy line shows the response of a thermometer for which $\lambda = 240$ seconds, the lighter, irregular line that of a fine thermocouple ($\lambda < 10$ sec). The phase relations are well shown.

It is probable that the fluctuations which actually occur consist of sudden excursions at irregular intervals, rather than simple harmonic waves. Such irregular periods allow no simple analysis, but we may consider sudden changes from $\theta_1 + A$ to $\theta_1 - A$ and back, with a period T. This has been done (using a Fourier series) by Bilham.[16] The response to shorter periods is somewhat increased; for example, 0.23 with $T = \lambda$; but the general conclusion remains.

Now the sort of fluctuations which appear in Fig. 31 are prevalent at the time of maximum temperature and through the warmer hours of the day. It is therefore felt that thermometers for ordinary meteorological purposes should not have a lag coefficient less than 30 seconds. It is probably fortunate that most maximum thermometers have lag coefficients in excess of this. These considerations apply with less force to the minimum thermometer, since the time of minimum temperature is usually a time of great stability when rapid fluctuations of temperature are not so likely to occur. In order to obtain representative temperatures, we must arrange our installation to take either a spatial mean

$$\theta_s = \frac{1}{V} \int_0^V \theta(V) dV$$

---

[15]Compare this with the discussion of the pressure variometer on page 48.
[16]BILHAM, *l.c.*

or a temporal mean

$$\theta_t = \frac{1}{t} \int_0^t \theta(t)\,dt.$$

In any random distribution these are identical provided t is large enough. The thermometer, by virtue of its finite thermal capacity, acts as an integrating device.

4. Classification of Meteorological Thermometers

Meteorological thermometers make use of the thermal properties of many different substances, and indicate in many different ways; but they all make use of one of four properties, namely

    (1) Thermal expansion

    (2) Dependence of vapour-pressure on temperature

    (3) Dependence of electrical resistance on temperature

    (4) The thermoelectric effect,

and it would be possible to classify them in this way. It seems preferable, however, to group them on the basis of construction into certain obvious classes as follows:

    (1) Liquid-in-glass thermometers

        (a) Mercury thermometers

            (i) Indicating

            (ii) Maximum

        (b) Spirit thermometers

            (i) Indicating

            (ii) Minimum

    (2) Deformation thermometers

        (i) Bourdon thermometers

        (ii) Bimetallic thermometers

    (3) Liquid-in-metal thermometers

        (i) Mercury-in-steel

        (ii) Other combinations

    (4) Electrical thermometers

        (i) Resistance thermometers

        (ii) Thermoelectric thermometers.

It will be understood that thermographs, as well as thermometers, operate on these principles, and will be discussed with the indicating thermometers of the same type. The order given above will be followed in the next four sections of this chapter.

5. Liquid-in-Glass Thermometers

(a) General

The great majority of thermometers used in meteorology are of the type which depends on the expansion of a liquid in a glass envelope. The excess of the expansion of the liquid over that of the glass is measured by the changes in length of the liquid column in a narrow tube which forms part of the container.

In Fig. 32 are shown cross-sections of four types of tube used in thermometry: (a) the plain, round tube of fine bore, used in many chemical and meteorological thermometers; (b) the tube of a mercury thermometer with a "lens front"—this produces a magnified image of the mercury thread when looked at from the direction S; (c) the tube of a spirit thermometer; (d) the tube of a "red-reading mercury" thermometer.[17] The bore of this last is approximately semicircular, the flat surface of mercury reflecting an image of the red enamel strip when looked at from the proper direction. These new thermometers do not yet seem to have found much application in meteorology, probably for reasons not at all connected with their physical properties.

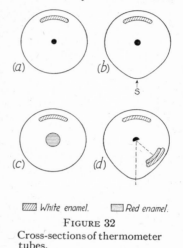

White enamel.   Red enamel.

FIGURE 32

Cross-sections of thermometer tubes.

Before differentiating mercury thermometers from those filled with other liquids, we shall describe the types of mounting used in meteorological work. Fundamentally there are three:

(i) The sheathed type, used in the British Empire.[18]

(ii) The type with enclosed scale separate from the tube, used in most parts of continental Europe (*Einschlussthermometer*).

(iii) The type with the scale engraved on the tube but unprotected, and used with or without a metal back. This type is used for taking air temperatures in the United States, and for many other purposes elsewhere.

The three types are shown in Fig. 33.

There is a real difference between types (i) and (ii), which is not always understood, and has caused confusion in certain quarters. In the *Einschlussthermometer* the scale, usually etched on a piece of opal glass, is *attached* to the thermometer tube and the whole enclosed in a glass sheath; in the sheathed thermometer the scale is engraved directly on the thermometer tube, just as in the third type. The scale is completely protected from wear and sealed away from the atmosphere; it does not need re-blacking during the life of the instrument. In the opinion of the writer, this is a great advantage, especially for small, voluntary stations.

[17]Manufactured by the Palmer Thermometer Co.

[18]British Standards Institution, Specification no. 692/1936 [and associated specifications for Canada].

The metal backs of the third type are usually of stainless steel, and have the main intervals of temperature figured on them. They are made thick enough to be very strong, affording real protection to the tube.

(b) Mercury-in-glass thermometers

(i) General remarks

The mercury-in-glass thermometer, usually called the mercury thermometer, indicates the temperature by virtue of the *differential* expansion of mercury and glass. The volume coefficient of expansion of mercury is 182×10^{-6} per °C., and that of most glasses is from 18×10^{-6} to 27×10^{-6}, an important fraction of that of mercury. Thus the properties of the glass used for the bulb are of importance in determining the scale value of the instrument.

Neither the expansion coefficient of mercury nor that of glass is constant for all temperatures. Thus it is necessary to calibrate mercury thermometers at intervals not greater than about 20°C., if good accuracy is desired. Thermometers for high temperatures, not used in meteorology, are specially liable to errors from this (and other) sources.

Mercury freezes at -38.87°C. (-38°F.). Below this point mercury thermometers cannot be used, but must be replaced by spirit thermometers, etc. (see below).

The metal used to fill thermometers must be chemically clean and free from gases, preferably freshly distilled. After it is introduced into the thermometer, either (1) a good vacuum must be produced in the tube, or (2) the capillary must be filled with a dry, inert gas, such as nitrogen.

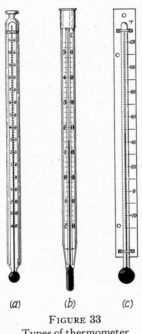

(a)   (b)   (c)

FIGURE 33

Types of thermometer mounting.

European and some American meteorological thermometers are of the vacuum type, as are all maximum thermometers, but there is a growing tendency to use gas-filled thermometers for ordinary purposes.

(ii) Sources of error in mercury thermometers

There was a time, now happily past, when it would have been thought desirable to devote many pages to this section.[19] At the present day it is recognized that no great accuracy can be obtained in most meteorological measurements of temperature, and for most purposes the majority of the sources of error can safely be left to the manufacturer to deal with, or to the

---

[19] ABBE, in his great treatise (Report of Chief Signal Officer, 1887, part 2, Washington 1888) employs 36 pages for the discussion of no less than ten separate sources of error.

standardizing laboratory to discover. We shall deal briefly with the following matters, all of which bear on the practical use of thermometers: (*a*) Elastic errors, (*β*) correction for emergence of stem, (*γ*) Parallax.

(*a*) *Elastic errors.* The elastic errors of thermometers are of two kinds: *reversible* and *irreversible*.

The reversible elastic errors are of importance to the meteorologist only in certain calibration procedures. If a thermometer which has been kept at a high temperature is returned to a known low temperature (for example, that of melting ice), it will at first read too low by a small amount, recovering its original calibration in time. This *temporary zero depression*, as it is called, may reach anything up to 1°C. for poor glass, but may be only 0.03°C. for the best normal glass, after heating to 100°C. It is proportionately less after warming to temperatures less than this, and is of no account in actual meteorological measurements.

The irreversible alteration of the volume of a thermometer is much more serious. In the course of years the glass of a thermometer bulb contracts slightly, *raising* the zero. This alteration can be reduced by heat-treatment of the bulb before filling; but even a heat-treated bulb of the best glass may change by about 0.01°C. per year at first, the amount decreasing after some years. The only remedy is to redetermine the zero of the thermometer and apply a correction.

A great deal of research has been performed with a view to obtaining glasses which show the least possible elastic errors. These efforts have resulted in a great improvement in thermometers. Nowadays all thermometers made to official specifications must have bulbs of one of the "normal thermometer glasses" made, for example, by Chance Bros. in England, Corning in the United States, and Schott in Germany.

(*β*) *Correction for emergence of stem.* A thermometer used to measure air temperature is normally completely immersed in air of approximately uniform temperature. Such thermometers are calibrated by immersion up to the top of the mercury column, or as near it as practicable; this is called *calibration by total immersion.* If such a thermometer is used to measure the temperature of a medium warmer or colder than the surrounding air, the stem will be at a temperature different from that of the bulb, and a correction of the reading will be necessary.

If *n* degrees of the mercury column are out of the medium, and if the temperature of the medium is θ, the *mean* temperature of the emergent stem θ_s, then the necessary *correction* to the reading is

$$\Delta\theta = n(\gamma_h - \gamma_g)(\theta - \theta_s) \qquad \dots\dots\dots (3.10),$$

where γ_h and γ_g are the cubical expansion coefficient of mercury and of glass. For most glasses, $\gamma_h - \gamma_g = 1/6200$ to a sufficient degree of accuracy, if *n* is in °C.; 1/11000 if in °F. The difficulty is to approximate the mean temperature θ_s of the stem, and it is better to operate with total immersion if at all possible. The subject will be discussed further under soil thermometers.

(γ) *Parallax.* A serious error in *reading* a thermometer may occur unless the eye is placed in the plane through the end of the mercury and perpendicular to the stem. For very accurate readings a microscope is fitted up with its axis of collimation perpendicular to the axis of the thermometer; but for ordinary purposes the care and attention of the observer must be depended on.

(iii) *Special forms of mercury thermometers*[20]

(a) *Maximum thermometers.* The mercury thermometer can be made to register the maximum temperature attained during an interval, by providing a constriction in the capillary (Fig. 34). If this is of suitable dimensions, the mercury will be forced past it when the temperature is rising, but the column will break at the constriction as soon as the temperature begins to fall, leaving the thread of mercury in the tube indicating its highest reading. If a good maximum thermometer is examined with a microscope when its temperature is rising, the mercury will be seen to move past the constriction in *very small*

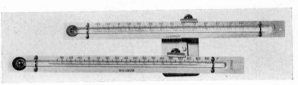

FIGURE 34
The constriction
of a maximum
thermometer.

FIGURE 35
Townsend support with maximum and minimum thermometers.
(Courtesy of Julien P. Friez and Sons)

droplets, not continuously. Each droplet should represent only a small part of a degree, perhaps one-fiftieth.[21] Poorer thermometers show motion in large drops, or else continuous motion. The thermometer is set (1) by removing it from its support and, holding it firmly in the hand by the end remote from the bulb, swinging it briskly downwards, or (2) by whirling it. For this purpose a special mounting, known as the Townsend support, is used in the United States Weather Bureau (Fig. 35). An acceleration of about 4g is sufficient to set most maximum thermometers.

Whichever method is used, it is important to *start* the motion with the mercury thread resting against the constriction. If it is allowed to strike violently against the constriction, the tube may crack at this point. Such a crack may not extend to the surface, but may be visible as a tiny iridescent flake near the capillary. The result will be that the thermometer will act like an ordinary thermometer if mounted in the usual way, that is to say with the bulb slightly lower than the other end. A thermometer having this defect is known as a *retreater.*

Sometimes a maximum thermometer may appear to be in good condition, but may actually be retreating for a degree or more before the mercury thread

---

[20]See also under psychrometers in chapter IV.
[21]This can be demonstrated to a large audience by means of a projection microscope.

breaks. Such a condition may escape detection for some time; and in order to guard against it the United States Weather Bureau issues instructions to instal maximum thermometers with the bulb slightly *higher* than the other end. When the temperature begins to go down, the thread breaks and allows the mercury to run to the end of the tube. Before reading the instrument, the outer end is raised very carefully until the mercury runs *very slowly* down to the constriction. This method of mounting has been carefully compared with the other, and in good hands gives identical results. It makes the specification of maximum thermometers much less exacting.

(β) *Sea-surface thermometers.*[22] The usual method of taking sea-surface temperatures is to lower a canvas bucket overside, haul it aboard, and read the temperature of the water with an ordinary thermometer. Thermometers in a perforated metal case, known as armoured thermometers, are convenient for such work. Another form has a well surrounding the bulb, in which some of the water may be lifted; but it should be read with some celerity when the air temperature is much different from that of the sea, or when the sun is shining on the deck.[23] Better results may be obtained by means of a sea-water thermograph (see page 73).

(γ) *Soil thermometers.* Mercury thermometers are widely used to measure the temperature of the soil at various depths. For measurements at depths less than one foot, thermometers with bent stems are used (Fig. 36*a*); the scale lies on the surface of the ground. At greater depths a specially constructed thermometer (Fig. 36*b*) is hung in a pipe and pulled out for reading; and in order that its temperature shall not change appreciably during the process, the bulb is surrounded by a mass of paraffin wax to give it a high lag coefficient. This is permissible, because the temperature at depths of more than a few inches changes very slowly. At depths of one or two feet there may be some possibility of the temperature being altered by the conductivity of the pipe, but the effect is probably small. A mild steel pipe, heavily painted, is usually supplied, terminated by a sharp cone so that it can be driven in with as little disturbance of the soil as possible.

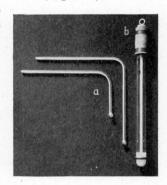

FIGURE 36

Two types of soil thermometer.

Appreciable errors in the readings of the angle type of soil thermometer may arise if the stem is in bright sunshine. Under such conditions the stem may attain a temperature of, say, 120°F., perhaps 80° above that of the bulb. The amount of tube exposed being equivalent to about 40°, we have from (3.10), $\Delta\theta = 40 \times (-80)/11000 = -0.3°F.$ Tenths of a degree are significant in this work.

---

[22]Deep-sea thermometers are considered as oceanographic, not meteorological instruments, and are not treated here.

[23]See BROOKS, C. F., *U.S. Mon. Wea. Rev.*, **54**:241-254, 1926.

Soil temperatures under snow demand the permanent installation of some form of distant-reading thermometer (see below). It will not do to disturb the surface of the snow by walking to the thermometers.

(c) Spirit-in-glass thermometers[24]

(i) General

Spirit thermometers are precisely like mercury thermometers except that the thermometric liquid is some organic substance, in meteorological thermometers usually ethyl alcohol C_2H_5OH, sometimes Pentane C_5H_{12}, Toluol $C_6H_5CH_3$, or other substances. In general these substances have expansion coefficients about six times as great as that of mercury, and very low freezing points (below $-100°C$.). It is for this latter reason that they are chiefly used, except as minimum thermometers, since they are not as accurate, and cannot be made as accurate, as mercury thermometers of equal cost and quality. The greatest attainable accuracy is far inferior to that of mercury thermometers.

The reason for this is that besides having the errors of mercury thermometers, these instruments have troubles of their own, the most important of which will now be rehearsed.

(ii) Sources of error in spirit thermometers

(α) *Breaking of the column.* By a process of slow distillation, drops of spirit often form and grow in the outer part of the thermometer tube. If these are noticed, steps can be taken to reunite them, but the beginning of the process may cause an error. The whole column of spirit is often broken into short sections during transport.

To reunite the column, hold the thermometer bulb downwards and tap it *lightly and rapidly* against the fingers or against something elastic and not too hard, such as a piece of rubber. Continue this process for some time (5 minutes) if necessary; nothing may seem to happen at first, but patience will be rewarded. Some thermometers respond better if held at a low angle rather than vertically. Afterwards the thermometer should be hung with the bulb downwards for at least an hour, before being put into service.

If this fails, a more drastic cure is to immerse the bulb in crushed solid CO_2 (obtainable commercially as "dry ice"), keeping the stem warm, and waiting for the spirit to distil back again. This never fails. A freezing mixture of ice and salt will serve, but will take longer.

(β) *Adhesion of the spirit to the glass.* In contradistinction to mercury, the spirit wets the glass. If therefore the temperature falls very rapidly (as in a calibrating bath), a certain amount of the liquid may remain on the walls, causing the thermometer to read low.

(γ) *The correction for the emergent stem* (see page 63) will be several times as great as in mercury thermometers, because of the greater value of the

---

[24]See GRUNDMANN, W., *Flussigkeitsthermometrie*, Weimar 1938, R. Wagner Sohn, for a detailed study.

expansion coefficient. This is a rather serious matter in low-temperature calibrations using liquid baths.

(δ) *Secular changes in the liquid.* The organic liquids in question have a
slight tendency to polymerize with exposure to light and after the passage of
time. This is particularly evident if they are impure.[25] (B.S.I. Specification
692/1936, for example, insists on the alcohol used in minimum thermometers
being completely free from acetone.) For the same reason, thermometers filled
with coloured liquids are not admitted for official use, although some manufacturers claim to have developed satisfactory dyes.

The gradual polymerization leads to a diminution of the volume of the
liquid, *lowering* the zero of the instrument. This is in the opposite direction
to the secular change in the glass, but cannot be depended upon to cancel it.
A change in the viscosity of the liquid may also occur, leading to a corresponding change in the lag coefficient of the thermometer.

(iii) *Special types of spirit thermometer*

(a) *The minimum thermometer* is a spirit thermometer with a small dark
glass index in the bore, of the shape indicated in Fig. 37. This index is kept
inside the spirit column by the surface tension of the meniscus. The thermometer is always installed in a horizontal position,
and as the temperature falls the index is pulled
towards the bulb, remaining stationary as the temperature rises. The position of the *outer* end of the index is
therefore an indication of the minimum temperature
which has occurred since the last setting. The setting
merely involves raising the bulb, when the index will run
slowly down the tube as far as the meniscus.

FIGURE 37
Index of minimum
thermometer.

The minimum thermometer is also used to obtain the minimum temperature
of the surface of the ground at night, being known as a *grass minimum thermometer* when used for this purpose. It is supported about 2 inches above
short grass, and the measurement involves the tacit assumption that the grass
and the thermometer have the same emissive properties for temperature
radiation. It has been found that any obstructions, even a very open network,
in the immediate vicinity of the thermometer, alter its minimum reading.[26] To
obtain comparable results it should be exposed near the middle of a large lawn.

(β) *The strut thermometer* is a large spirit thermometer fitted with a bold
scale which can be read from a distance, and having a polished metal shield
for the bulb. Coloured spirit is generally used to increase the legibility. Such
a thermometer is intended for mounting on a strut of an aeroplane in such a
position that it can be read from the cockpit or cabin; but there is no suitable
place for it on modern aircraft and other types of thermometer are finding
favour (see page 189).

---

[25]See HIGGINS, W. F., and E. G. BILHAM, *M.O. Prof. Notes*, no. 51, London 1929.
[26]STAGG, J. M., *M.O. Prof. Notes*, no. 43, London 1925.

(γ) *Six's combined maximum and minimum thermometer* is really a spirit (creosote) thermometer with a mercury indicator. As it is not accepted as a suitable instrument for official meteorological stations, and can develop serious errors, a description will be omitted.[27]

(d) Liquid-in-glass thermographs

Liquid-in-glass thermometers can be made to record by photography, either by photographing the thermometer at intervals, or by projecting the image of an air-bubble in the tube on to a sheet of bromide paper carried on a revolving drum, as in the Kew photographic thermograph.[28] Such instruments are inconvenient, besides having to be installed on the wall of the building containing the photographic apparatus.

6. Deformation Thermometers

(a) The bi-metal thermometer

The bi-metal consists of a compound strip of metal, formed by *welding* together two bars of different metals and rolling the resulting compound bar.

The metals most generally used are invar and brass, or invar and steel. The resulting strip bends as its temperature changes, because of the difference in expansion of the two metals.

Let us suppose that we have such a strip of unit width, composed of thickness h_1 and h_2 of metals I and II (Fig. 38).[29] Let E_1, E_2 be the values of Young's modulus for the two metals.

Let a_1, a_2 be their coefficients of expansion (linear), I_1, I_2 be the moments of inertia of the two cross-sections, given by

$$I_1 = h_1^3/12 \qquad I_2 = h_2^3/12.$$

FIGURE 38

Illustrating the theory of the bi-metal.

Suppose that at a temperature θ_0 the curvature of the strips is $1/\rho_0$, and let the temperature rise from θ_0 to θ, causing the curvature to change from $1/\rho_0$ to $1/\rho$. We shall calculate $\left(\dfrac{1}{\rho} - \dfrac{1}{\rho_0} \right)$ on the assumption that ρ and ρ_0 are both large compared to (h_1+h_2), and on the further assumption that the curvature across the width of the strip can be neglected.

Consider a segment of unit length (Fig. 38). The forces on this are two axial tensions P_1, P_2, and two bending moments M_1, M_2. Since there are no external forces acting on the strip we have

$$P_1 + P_2 = 0, \text{ or } P_1 = P, \ P_2 = -P \qquad \ldots\ldots\ldots (3.11)$$

and

$$M_1 + M_2 + P \cdot \tfrac{1}{2} (h_1 + h_2) = 0 \qquad \ldots\ldots\ldots (3.12).$$

---

[27]A very full account in GRUNDMANN, *l.c.*, pp. 47-61.
[28]Report of the meteorological committee of the Royal Society for 1867.
[29]For a full treatment see TIMOSHENKO, S., *J.O.S.A. and R.S.I.*, **11**:233-255, 1925.

From elementary elastic theory

$$M_1 = E_1 I_1 \left(\frac{1}{\rho} - \frac{1}{\rho_0}\right), \quad M_2 = E_2 I_2 \left(\frac{1}{\rho} - \frac{1}{\rho_0}\right),$$

so that

$$(E_1 I_1 + E_2 I_2)\left(\frac{1}{\rho} - \frac{1}{\rho_0}\right) = -\frac{P}{2}(h_1 + h_2) \quad \ldots\ldots\ldots(3.13).$$

Another equation containing the curvatures is obtained by noting that the strains at the common surface are equal. These strains are due to (1) thermal expansion, (2) the axial force P, (3) bending. Then

$$a_1(\theta - \theta_0) + \frac{P}{h_1 E_1} - \frac{h_1}{2}\left(\frac{1}{\rho} - \frac{1}{\rho_0}\right)$$
$$= a_2(\theta - \theta_0) - \frac{P}{h_2 E_2} + \frac{h_2}{2}\left(\frac{1}{\rho} - \frac{1}{\rho_0}\right) \quad \ldots\ldots\ldots(3.14).$$

Eliminating P between (3.13) and (3.14) and reducing, we obtain

$$\frac{1}{\rho} - \frac{1}{\rho_0} = \frac{(a_2 - a_1)(\theta - \theta_0)}{\dfrac{h_1 + h_2}{2} + \dfrac{2(E_1 I_1 + E_2 I_2)}{h_1 + h_2}\left(\dfrac{1}{E_1 h_1} + \dfrac{1}{E_2 h_2}\right)} \quad \ldots\ldots\ldots(3.15).$$

This apparently unwieldy expression can be simplified by substituting

$$\delta = h_1 + h_2, \quad m = h_1/h_2, \quad n = E_1/E_2, \quad h_1^3/12 = I_1, \quad h_2^3/12 = I_2.$$

It now becomes

$$\frac{1}{\rho} - \frac{1}{\rho_0} = \frac{6(a_2 - a_1)(\theta - \theta_0)(1+m)^2}{\delta[3(1+m)^2 + (1+mn)(m^2 + 1/mn)]} \quad \ldots\ldots\ldots(3.16),$$

which may be written

$$\frac{1}{\rho} - \frac{1}{\rho_0} = (A/\delta)(a_2 - a_1)(\theta - \theta_0) \quad \ldots\ldots\ldots(3.17).$$

The value of A is not very sensitive to the ratio of the Young's moduli if the ratio of the thicknesses is near unity, but varies a good deal if the latter differs much from 1, as is shown in the following table:

m......	$\frac{1}{2}$	$\frac{1}{2}$	$\frac{1}{2}$	1	1	1	2	2	2
n.......	$\frac{1}{2}$	1	2	$\frac{1}{2}$	1	2	$\frac{1}{2}$	1	2
A......	1.12	1.33	1.46	1.45	1.50	1.45	1.46	1.33	1.12

Now suppose we have a bi-metal AC of length L, clamped at one end A, and initially having a radius of curvature ρ_0 at a temperature θ_0 (Fig. 39). Let AB be a tangent to the bi-metal at the clamped end, O the centre of curvature at θ_0, and O' that at a temperature θ, when the end of the bi-metal has moved to C' and the radius has become ρ. Let the chord $AC = r_0$, and the chord $AC' = r$. Let ϕ_0 and ϕ be the central angles in the two conditions, and let $\angle CAB = \psi_0$, $\angle C'AB = \psi$.

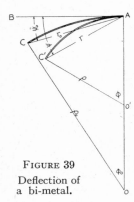

FIGURE 39

Deflection of a bi-metal.

Then $\quad \phi\rho = L = \phi_0\rho_0$

and since $\quad \phi = 2\psi, \quad \phi_0 = 2\psi_0$

$$\frac{1}{\rho} - \frac{1}{\rho_0} = \frac{2}{L}(\psi - \psi_0),$$

and, differentiating,

$$\frac{d}{d\psi}\left(\frac{1}{\rho}\right) = \frac{2}{L} \qquad \dots\dots\dots (3.18).$$

Now let the movement of the end C for a small change of temperature (from θ to $\theta + d\theta$) be dS. Consider the movement of C in polar co-ordinates with A as origin:

$$dS = [dr^2 + (rd\psi)^2]^{\frac{1}{2}}.$$

But $\qquad r = 2\rho \sin \psi = L \sin \psi/\psi$

$\therefore dr = (L/\psi^2)(\psi \cos \psi - \sin \psi)d\psi$

$rd\psi = (L/\psi^2)\psi \sin \psi d\psi,$

whence, after a little simplification

$$dS = \frac{L}{\psi}\left[\frac{\psi^2 + \sin^2\psi - 2\psi \cos \psi \sin \psi}{\psi^2}\right]^{\frac{1}{2}} d\psi \qquad \dots\dots\dots (3.19).$$

The fraction within the brackets is a function of ψ alone; write it $B(\psi)$:

$$dS = \frac{L}{\psi} \cdot B(\psi)d\psi \qquad \dots\dots\dots (3.20).$$

Now from (3.17),

$$\frac{d}{d\theta}\left(\frac{1}{\rho}\right) = (A/\delta)(a_2 - a_1),$$

and from (3.18)

$$\frac{d}{d\psi}\left(\frac{1}{\rho}\right) = 2/L.$$

Eliminating ρ,

$$d\psi = (LA/2\delta)(a_2 - a_1)d\theta$$

whence, from (3.20)

$$dS = L^2 \cdot \frac{B(\psi)}{\psi} \cdot \frac{A}{2\delta}(a_2 - a_1)d\theta \qquad \dots\dots\dots (3.21).$$

The values of $B(\psi)/\psi$ have been tabulated as follows by Robitzsch.[30]

[30]ROBITZSCH, M., *Die Beobachtungsmethoden des modernen Meteorologen.* Berlin 1925, Borntraeger, p. 33. The formula for the bi-metal derived on page 48 of his book is not correct; it takes no account of the elastic properties of the material.

ψ	0°	10°	20°	30°	40°	50°	60°	70°	80°	90°
$B(\psi)/\psi$	1.000	0.996	0.987	0.970	0.945	0.916	0.885	0.844	0.800	0.753
ψ	100°	110°	120°	130°	140°	150°	160°	170°	180°	
$B(\psi)/\psi$	0.706	0.653	0.601	0.549	0.497	0.447	0.400	0.356	0.318	

It will be seen that the movement is greatest for a straight bi-metal, and varies inversely as the total thickness of the strip. It is greatest if the two components are of equal thickness and their Young's moduli about the same.

The question of stiffness is important in design. Timoshenko[31] has shown that in the calculation of the stiffness of a bi-metal it can be treated as a homogeneous bar of modulus $E=\frac{1}{2}(E_1+E_2)$ without serious error. Then the change of curvature produced by a bending moment M per unit width is

$$\frac{1}{\rho} - \frac{1}{\rho_0} = 12M/E(h_1+h_2)^3 \qquad \ldots\ldots\ldots(3.22),$$

and from (3.18) and (3.20) the motion of the end of the coil is

$$S = \frac{L^2}{\psi} \cdot B(\psi) \cdot \frac{6M}{E(h_1+h_2)^3} \qquad \ldots\ldots\ldots(3.23).$$

It should be noted that the stiffness increases as the cube of the thickness of the bi-metal; the deflection with temperature changes inversely as its first power. The lag coefficient also increases directly as the thickness; and any design is usually a compromise between lag coefficient and stiffness.

In meteorology the bi-metal is not much used as an ordinary indicating thermometer, but chiefly for two purposes—either as a station thermograph or to record temperatures in the upper air. (The latter use will be dealt with in chapter x.) In industry and in the home, however, indicating thermometers on this principle are finding an ever-increasing application, and bi-metallic thermostats are a common feature of numerous heating devices.

The bi-metallic thermograph (Fig. 40) has an element in the form of a helical coil of several turns (Fig. 41). One end of this is attached to an adjustable arm; the relation of this arm to the frame can be altered by a tangent screw A. At a point near the other end, the bi-metal is clamped to an arm B which is fastened to the pen axis C. This axis runs in plain bear-

FIGURE 40
Bi-metallic thermograph.
(*Courtesy of Short and Mason*)

[31]TIMOSHENKO, *l.c.*, p. 239

ings and carries the pen-arm through the medium of an inclined hinge or "gate" such as was described on page 42.

The zero of the instrument is adjusted by means of the screw A; the scale value by altering the position of the clamp B along the bi-metal. The angular

motion of the axis in such an apparatus is proportional to the total effective length of the coil; is in fact equal to $L\left(\dfrac{1}{\rho} - \dfrac{1}{\rho_0}\right)$. The scale value of the instrument can thus be adjusted fairly closely on the first or second try by simple proportion.

The lag coefficient of one of these instruments is about half that of an ordinary mercury thermometer. The bi-metal is about 1/32 inch thick, and in the opinion of the author it would be a great improvement to make it about twice as thick, thus greatly increasing the stiffness of the control.

FIGURE 41
Bi-metal of thermograph.

(b) The Bourdon thermometer

The Bourdon thermometer consists of a curved tube of elliptical cross-section, *completely* filled with some organic liquid (Fig. 42). It is therefore really a liquid-in-metal thermometer, but is discussed in this section because it is the deformation of the element itself which indicates the changes in temperature.

The theory of the Bourdon thermometer is much like that of the bi-metal, and leads to somewhat similar expressions for the deflection. Grundmann[32] gives the formula

$$dS \sim L \cdot B(\psi)(\gamma_e - \gamma_m)d\theta \qquad \ldots\ldots\ldots(3.24)$$

FIGURE 42
Bourdon thermometer element.

where γ_e and γ_m are the cubical expansion coefficients of the liquid and of the metal, and the remainder of the notation is as in the discussion of the bi-metallic thermometer. Note that $B(\psi)$ is zero when ψ is zero; i.e. a straight Bourdon tube gives no deflection.

(c) Relative merits of the bi-metal and the Bourdon thermometers

There is no doubt that bi-metallic thermometers are more commonly used than heretofore, and Bourdon thermometers less so. Seeking the reasons for this, we shall present a tabular condensation of the discussion given by a European authority[33] on thermometry.

---

[32]*l.c.*, p. 68.

[33]GRUNDMANN, *l.c.*, pp. 72-75.

BI-METAL	BOURDON TUBE[34]
1. *Secular Alteration* is likely to take place, but can be got over by "thermal massage"—cyclic warming and cooling.	1. *Secular Alteration* can occur in both the metal and in the filling liquid (polymerization). It can be reduced by very great care in manufacture.
2. *Lag coefficient* can be made small or large.	2. *Lag coefficient* greater than that of bi-metal for the same stiffness.
3. *Ability to exceed normal range*: Very *low* temperatures may cause a sudden change of the zero, which will happen only once, after which there is no further change. This does not happen if the temperature is taken down slowly. Moderately *high* temperatures have no bad effect.	3. *Ability to exceed normal range*: Not damaged by *low* temperature, but may not respond properly to changes. Easily spoilt by moderately high temperatures, because of excess internal pressure.
4. *Resistance to corrosion*: If steel is a component, protection against rust is needed.	4. *Resistance to corrosion*: Non-ferrous metals generally employed.
5. *Mechanical resistance*: very insensitive to rough handling. Generally stiffer.	5. *Mechanical resistance*: easily damaged by only slight bending. Less stiff.

Taking into account the further fact that the Bourdon tube is more expensive, the balance seems to be in favour of the bi-metal. Regarding the fourth item, there seems to be no reason why both the bi-metal and the Bourdon tube should not be gold-plated (the latter often is). In city climates, many non-ferrous metals corrode fairly rapidly.

7. Liquid-in-Metal Thermometers

(a) *Mercury-in-steel thermometers*

The mercury-in-steel thermometer is really a special form of Bourdon thermometer, in which the expansion of the liquid takes place in another container, the change of pressure being transmitted to the Bourdon tube by a steel capillary tube of narrow bore.

Fig. 43 shows such an instrument of the type employed for recording sea temperatures, the steel bulb being installed in a well in the condenser intake of a steamer. The entire system, including the Bourdon tube, is made of steel and filled with gasfree mercury; but the capillary and the bulb are always coated with lead or copper. Similar thermographs are widely employed for recording earth temperatures and also air temperatures.

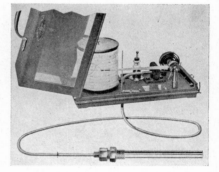

FIGURE 43
Mercury-in-steel sea thermograph.
(Courtesy of Negretti and Zambra)

An instrument with two bulbs, two elements, and two pens makes a very good recording psychrometer (see chapter IV), if the bulbs are adequately ventilated. Special bulbs of small cross-section are available for measuring air temperatures, reducing the lag coefficient to a reasonable amount.

[34]Note that this discussion does not apply to the Bourdon tube used as a barometer (p. 37).

The length of capillary tubing may be as much as 150 feet. When such a length is used, the total volume of the capillary becomes an important fraction of the volume of the bulb, and if the temperature of the capillary varies, errors will occur. An ingenious method of compensation is available, however. A certain volume of invar, a nickel steel with a very low coefficient of expansion, is enclosed in the capillary (Fig. 44). This may take the form of a wire along the whole length, or of a number of slugs of invar in local enlargements. If we let γ_t, γ_i, γ_h be the cubical expansion coefficients of the steel tube, the invar, and the mercury, respectively, and V_t be the internal volume of the tube, V_i the volume of the invar, it can easily be shown that if the ratio of V_i to V_t is

FIGURE 44

Compensation for temperature of capillary.

$$V_i/V_t = (\gamma_h - \gamma_t)/(\gamma_h - \gamma_i)$$

the expansion of the mercury will be exactly taken care of by the increase in volume of the tube. Using ordinary values of the constants, it results that a wire nine-tenths the diameter of the capillary would be required, if the compensation were distributed uniformly along the tube.

The mercury-in-steel thermograph is probably the most accurate and durable *recording* thermometer available for meteorological purposes, if we except the resistance thermometer (see below) used with a self-balancing bridge. (This is possibly slightly more accurate, certainly not more durable, and much more expensive.) The chief disadvantages of the mercury-in-steel thermograph are two in number: (1) It is limited to temperatures above the freezing point of mercury ($-38°F$.); (2) the practical limit to the length of the capillary is about 150 feet. One of its principal merits is the very great control on the pen; this results in a very clear, detailed record.

(b) Other liquid-in-metal thermometers

Under this heading could more or less legitimately be included an astonishing number of instruments, mostly found in industrial surroundings; even vapour-pressure thermometers are strictly in this class, since they contain free liquid.

These thermometers have found a limited employment as distant-indicating instruments for use at airport offices, etc. They consist of a bulb, usually fairly large, a connection of fine capillary tube, and a pressure gauge. This may be a Bourdon tube, a diaphragm gauge, or a flexible metal bellows. The advantage of such systems lies in the very large amount of power they make available for moving a pointer or a pen. Their disadvantages are the possibility of changes in the filling liquid and their generally large lag coefficients, greater than that of the mercury-in-steel thermometer because of the lower conductivity of the organic liquid.

8. Electrical Thermometers

(a) General

Electrical thermometers are of two kinds: resistance thermometers and thermoelectric thermometers. Each of these has a place in meteorological work, though neither is very common in climatological or synoptic routine. It is chiefly as a research tool that the electrical thermometer comes into its own.

Such thermometers can be made to have a lag coefficient negligible for practically all purposes; to indicate and record temperatures, or to measure differences of temperature between two points, at any reasonable distance; to measure temperatures in minute spaces; and to be almost insensitive to radiation. In principle they are simplicity itself; and it is only when we come to establish and maintain such devices that we discover the need of some experience, if reliable results are to be obtained.

(b) Electrical resistance thermometers

(i) Construction

The electrical resistance of all metals varies to a greater or less extent with their temperature, but not all metals are suitable for resistance thermometers. Without going into the reasons for the choice, we shall simply state that the overwhelming majority of such thermometers are made of platinum, nickel, or copper.[35]

For fundamental standards, and indeed for all resistance thermometers which are expected to maintain a calibration over a long period, platinum should be chosen. For secondary instruments, nickel is satisfactory. Copper is used for special applications (e.g., differential thermometry) when a close approach to a linear relation between resistance and temperature is desirable.

Whatever the metal chosen, the actual sensitive element consists of some sort of coil, either supported in the air or other medium, or protected by a sheath of suitable shape. For meteorological thermometers, the nature of this protection is often a critical matter, and the weather-proofing of the whole assembly one of the chief difficulties of the installation.

For accurate work, a platinum coil of the form shown in Fig. 45 is generally used. The wire, which should be of diameter not less than 0.05 mm, and preferably 0.1, is wound bifilar on a cross-shaped mica frame, after having been heated electrically to about 1000°C. for half an hour. Four

FIGURE 45

Platinum coil on mica frame for precision thermometry.

---

[35]For a much fuller treatment than is possible here, see the book *Temperature, Its Measurement and Control in Science and Industry*, ed. Amer. Inst. of Phys., New York 1941, Reinhold Publ. Co. This will be referred to as *Temp.*

leads, of rather larger wire, go to the terminals, the platinum-to-platinum junctions being welded and the others silver-soldered. These leads are kept apart by mica discs. After the instrument is complete, except for its protective cover, it should be heated electrically to 700°C. several times in order to relieve all strains caused by winding and to ensure the constancy of the zero of the instrument. The precision of such a thermometer is limited by that of the measuring circuits; its accuracy by that of its calibration.

The attainable order of accuracy is not necessary for meteorological work. Nevertheless a platinum thermometer on these principles is an asset to the headquarters of any meteorological service, and some dimensions may be indicated.

A metre of platinum wire 0.1 mm in diameter has a resistance of about 15 ohms at 0°C. Five metres could be put conveniently on a mica cross 1 cm in diameter and 10 cm long. For obtaining the temperature of liquid baths, this assembly could be put into a pyrex tube of about 12 mm inside diameter; or for use in an air chamber, it could be protected by a wire cage.

For outdoor measurements, a coil of nickel wire is wound on a nickel tube or strip,[36] insulated with mica or one of the newer plastics. Further insulation is placed over the wire, and the whole assembly enclosed in a metal tube. The attachment of the leads is variously performed; one of the most successful ways is to swage the end of the tube on to a piece of "cab-tire" cable, as at A in Fig. 46.

Such a "bulb" has a rather large lag coefficient. For measurements over a short period of time, where this is a disadvantage, a thin wire stretched

FIGURE 46

Resistance thermometer bulb for outdoor use.

through the air on (say) a glass frame, can be used. This type of thermometer has the advantage that it is very nearly insensitive to radiation, and can be used in full sunlight with sufficient accuracy for many purposes. It must, however, be kept from contact with anything solid; and a very small measuring current must be used, or the thermometer will also act as a wind-speed meter (see below, page 142).[37]

(ii) *Principles of calibration*

The international scale of temperature is defined by certain fixed points, as explained above. In the region between absolute zero and 660°C., the official instrument for interpolation between these points is the platinum resistance thermometer. The relation between resistance and temperature is

$$R = R_0(1 + A\theta + B\theta^2) \qquad \dots\dots\dots(3.25),$$

where the three constants R_0 (the resistance at 0°C.), A, and B are determined by measurements at the temperatures 0°, 100°, and 444.60° (the boiling-point

---

[36]To avoid temperature strains; but manufacturers adopt other measures. The ordinary instrument-maker should be encouraged to purchase such outdoor thermometers from makers who specialize in such things, at an eventual economy of money and assuredly of effort.

[37]An entirely different type of resistance thermometer is described in chapter x (p. 198).

of sulphur). For temperatures below 0°C. and above −190°C., the relation is

$$R = R_0[1 + A\theta + B\theta^2 + C(\theta - 100)\theta^3] \qquad \ldots\ldots\ldots(3.26),$$

where the additional constant C is determined by measuring R at −182.97°C. (the boiling point of oxygen). The determination of all these constants is a matter requiring much time and fairly elaborate apparatus.

Fortunately, for meteorological purposes (with the possible exception of the calibration of very accurate soil thermometers) it is quite adequate to calibrate at 100°, 0°, and −78.51°C. (sublimation of CO_2),[38] and apply equation (3.25). In the range −80° to +40°C. the maximum error of about 0.05° will occur at about −50° and +40°. Much better results in the upper part of the range will be obtained by substituting the Na_2SO_4 point (+32.38°C.) for the boiling-point of water.

(iii) *Measurement of resistance*

For precision resistance measurements in thermometry, some form of potentiometer circuit is always used, the accuracy being limited only by the degree to which thermal e.m.f.'s can be got rid of. But for meteorological purposes, the Wheatstone bridge circuit is more usual, and generally accurate enough.

The common form of circuit is shown in Fig. 47, which embodies a compensation for the resistance of the leads. These take the form of a cable of three equal wires; and it will be seen that changes in the temperature of this cable alter the resistance in the arms A and X equally. X is the thermometer coil. If then the bridge is constructed with $C = D$, the balance will not be changed by such changes in the resistance of the leads.

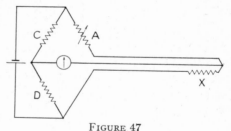

FIGURE 47

Compensated Wheatstone bridge circuit.

There are two ways of using a Wheatstone bridge for temperature measurement—the balance, or null, method, and the out-of-balance, or deflection method. In the former, the galvanometer is employed merely as a null indicator, and the resistance A is altered, by hand or automatically, until there is no current in the galvanometer; then

$$X = AD/C \qquad \ldots\ldots\ldots(3.27),$$

a relation which is independent of the battery voltage and of the galvanometer sensitivity.

The deflection method makes use of the galvanometer as a measuring instrument, and is therefore dependent on both battery voltage and on the sensitivity of the meter (which will be affected by its temperature). This

---

[38]*Temp.*, p. 212.

method should not be used, except for rough work, if there is time to use the
null method; but it sometimes comes in handy for recording small ranges or
differences of temperature when the cost of a self-balancing potentiometer or
bridge is out of the question.   Rather better accuracy can be obtained by a
crossed-coil galvanometer, but this is not a normal laboratory instrument, and
a recording potentiometer is greatly to be preferred if money is available for
new apparatus.

This latter instrument is now produced in quantity by several firms, and
can be recommended if temperature records of good and permanent accuracy
(say 0.2°F.) are required at a distance.   It would be invidious to describe any
particular instrument in this highly competitive field; but the general principle
of them all is as follows: The movements of a galvanometer coil are used to
direct the motion of a sliding or rolling contact along a resistance wire, in a
direction which tends to reduce the current through the galvanometer to zero.
The position of the recording pen bears a unitary relation to that of the moving
contact.   Fundamentally the operation of these instruments resembles that of
the weight barograph described above (page 21), but for further details the
manufacturers' publications should be consulted.

The current through the resistance coil will cause the production of a
certain amount of heat; and care must be taken to find out whether this heat
produces a significant rise in temperature.   A simple test is given by Ribaud[39]
as follows:

Let the resistance of the thermometer with zero current be X.   Holding
the medium (e.g., air) at a constant temperature, measure the resistance with
a current I flowing (for example, with one dry cell across the bridge).   Let this
resistance be $X+\epsilon$.   Next use a current $2I$ (e.g., two dry cells) and measure
the new resistance, which should be approximately $X+4\epsilon$, since the heating
effect of the current is I^2X.   Then the required resistance X is given by

$$X = \frac{4(X+\epsilon) - (X+4\epsilon)}{3} \qquad \dots\dots\dots(3.28),$$

and the change in resistance ϵ produced by the current I is

$$\epsilon = \frac{(X+4\epsilon) - (X+\epsilon)}{3} \qquad \dots\dots\dots(3.29).$$

This change ϵ may now be translated into terms of temperature, and if not
negligible, must be allowed for.

Peterson and Womack[40] have shown that the temperature rise of a given
resistance thermometer in a given medium is

$$\theta - \theta_0 = (\lambda/M)I^2R \qquad \dots\dots\dots(3.30),$$

where λ is the lag coefficient for the thermometer in seconds under the conditions (air-speed, air density, etc.) of use, M the heat capacity of the thermometer in watt-seconds per degree, I the current through the thermometer

[39]RIBAUD, G., *Mesure des températures*.   Paris 1936, Colin, p. 67.
[40]PETERSON, J. B., and S. H. J. WOMACK, *N.A.C.A. Report*, no. 606, Washington 1937, p. 10.

and R its resistance.   The quantity M can either be measured, or calculated from the dimensions, densities, and specific heats of the parts.

(c) Thermoelectric thermometers

When an electric circuit is made of two or more dissimilar metals, and the various junctions between these metals are not all at the same temperature, a current will flow in the circuit.   If we have two metals only, the total electromotive force in the circuit is proportional to the difference in temperature of the two junctions, of which one is called the *measuring junction*, the other the *reference junction*.   For the measurement of temperatures, the reference junction is kept at a constant temperature, for example in melting ice.

For precision measurements of high temperatures the approved thermoelectric metals are platinum, and an alloy of 90 parts platinum to 10 parts rhodium.   For meteorological measurements these metals are seldom used, copper and constantan (a copper-nickel alloy) affording a much larger E.M.F. per degree difference of temperature.   Iron and constantan, manganin and constantan, and chromel and alumel are also used.   The E.M.F. per degree at meteorological temperatures is about as follows:

Copper-constantan	40	microvolts
Iron-constantan	50	"
Manganin-constantan	40	"
Chromel-alumel	40	"

but varies a good deal according to the mechanical and thermal history of the samples.

The relation between E.M.F. and temperature-difference is not strictly linear, but of the form

$$E = a\theta + b\theta^2.$$

Over the range of temperatures generally involved in meteorological measurements with thermocouples, however, the departure from linearity is seldom of importance.

One of the great advantages of thermocouples is that they can be made very small.   For example, a needle may be made of a fine constantan tube enclosing an insulated copper wire, for the measurement of the temperature in the interior of a leaf or fruit.   Or by welding together two wires each about $0.003''$ in diameter, a couple of negligible lag coefficient can be constructed. The irregular curve of Fig. 31 (page 56) was obtained with such a couple.

Over a fair range of temperatures, a couple of copper and constantan will indicate a temperature-*difference* without much error.   This property is of use in measuring the vertical gradient of temperature, especially as fine couples are not very sensitive to radiation and can be used without artificial ventilation.   Fig. 48 shows a type of couple and shield used with success in such work.   The direct rays of the sun, except when it is very near the horizon, are intercepted by the two upper plates, which also prevent the couple radiating to most of the sky at night, while permitting free ventilation by the wind. To prevent leakage currents between the wires in wet weather, the stout copper and constantan wires forming the supports emerge from a surface of cast sulphur in the inverted cup.

Other methods of installation will occur to the researcher as they are required.[41]

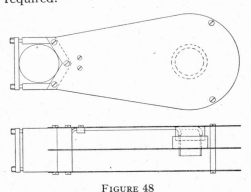

FIGURE 48

Thermocouple and shield for gradient measurements.

The E.M.F. in the circuit is measured (1) directly by means of a potentiometer, or (2) by means of a millivoltmeter. The circuits are shown in Figs. 49(a) and 49(b), in which T_1 and T_2 are the two junctions at different temperatures. (If neither metal is copper, care must be taken to have the terminals A and B at the same temperature.)

(1) In Fig. 49(a), E_m is a storage cell or a dry cell, and E_s a standard cell. When a measurement is to be made, the switch S_1 is first thrown to connect E_m in the circuit. Then S_2 is operated to connect E_s and the galvanometer across the resistance ce. R is then adjusted until zero current appears on G. The switch S_2 is then thrown over, to connect the thermoelectric circuit in series with G and the portion cd of ce. The position of d having been adjusted for no current, the E.M.F. given by the couples is found by the relation

$$E = \frac{cd}{ce} E_s.$$

The advantage of this method is that no current flows in the thermoelectric circuit; thus the calibration will be independent of the resistance of the leads and of the sensitivity of the galvanometer.

(2) Fig. 49(b) is self-explanatory. The deflection of the millivoltmeter or galvanometer obviously depends on the resistance of all parts of the circuit, and on the sensitivity of the instrument. It will not do to assume that the relation between deflection and current is linear, but the entire circuit should be calibrated at several temperatures over its range.

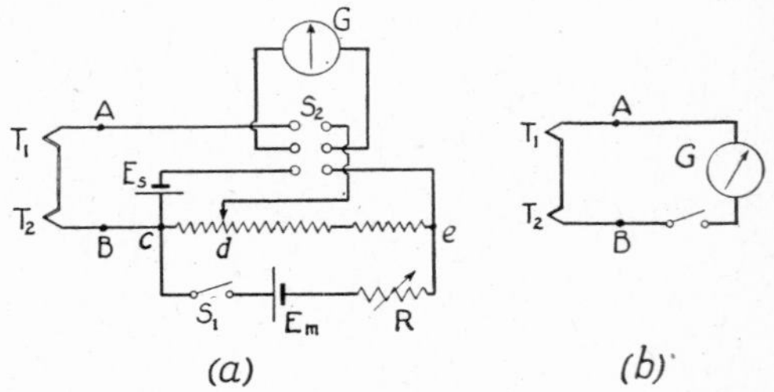

This simple circuit is, however,

FIGURE 49

(a) Potentiometer circuit for thermocouple measurements. (b) direct deflection circuit.

the one generally used in meteorological research, especially for the indication

[41] *Temp.*, p. 180.

of differences of temperature. For indicating *equality* of temperature between two points it is of course excellent, being then a null method. With a good suspended-coil galvanometer there is no difficulty in making visible a temperature difference of 0.01°C.

A useful tool for making spot measurements of air temperature is the "bottle thermometer" (Fig. 50). In this instrument the measuring junction at E is made of copper and constantan wires 0.0025″ in diameter, carried on posts of similar materials F(copper) and G(constantan). The reference junction is at H in the Dewar flask A. The junction E is surrounded by a double metal shield D, supported on a fibre block C.

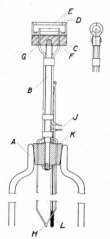

A portable galvanometer of fair sensitivity (0.2μA per division, resistance 15 ohms, for example) is connected by flexible copper leads to the terminals J. A thermometer L serves to measure the temperature of the reference junction, which may be varied by filling the Dewar flask with water at the desired temperature. Owing to the small lag of this apparatus, a large number of spot temperatures can be read in a short time.

More trouble than might be supposed can be caused by leakage currents in thermocouple measurements.[42] The source of energy is not usually to be found in the thermoelectric circuit, but in neighbouring power circuits, especially if direct-current mains are present. Care must also be taken to avoid galvanic currents, especially

FIGURE 50
The "bottle thermometer."

in wet weather, and to design all circuits so that unwanted thermo-junctions do not vitiate the measurements.

9. The Testing of Thermometers and Thermographs

The large-scale testing of thermometers and thermographs (particularly the former) is usually undertaken at institutions like the National Physical Laboratory and the Bureau of Standards. Such standardizing laboratories test thermometers in large batches on their way from the manufacturer to the consumer, and have developed routine methods of testing to the accuracy required by standard specifications. The certificate of the N.P.L. or the Bureau has the confidence of manufacturer and consumer alike, and thermometers for official purposes are best ordered complete with such certificates.

Nevertheless at any meteorological office or research institution a certain amount of calibration is necessary from time to time, the range of temperatures involved being from about 130° to −50°F., or lower if upper-air apparatus is being used (see chapter x).

As stated above, it is highly desirable to construct or acquire a platinum resistance thermometer for this work. In default of this, two liquid-in-glass

---

[42] See *Temp.*, p. 279.

7

thermometers of the highest quality should be obtained; a mercury ther-mometer with a range of about −40° to +140°F., and a spirit thermometer for lower temperatures. They should be graduated in half-degrees Fahrenheit. Certificates will of course be obtained with them, and their ice-points should be checked at least once a year and a history kept.

To check the ice-point of a thermometer, a Dewar flask should be nearly filled with ice made from distilled water, and further distilled water added to moisten it. An ordinary "thermos bottle" will deal with total-immersion ther-mometers of ordinary length, since the ice-point is seldom more than half way up such instruments. The least possible part of the mercury or spirit column should emerge from the ice bath.

Frequently it will be necessary to check commercial thermometers which have indicated extremes of temperature of public interest.[43] For this purpose a fairly tall Dewar flask can be filled with water (for temperatures above 32°F.) or with alcohol[44] or gasoline.

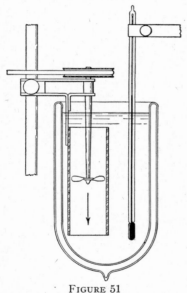

FIGURE 51
Simple bath for testing thermometers.

The water can be heated in any con-venient manner; the cold baths are obtained by means of solid carbon dioxide, available commercially in all larger towns as "dry ice." *Very little* of this should be added at a time, or much of the liquid will be blown out of the flask.

The standard thermometer and the ther-mometer under test should be supported independently of the flask by a laboratory stand, arranging to have as little of their columns as possible out of the bath. As the flask cannot be entirely full, it should be possible to lift both instruments quickly through a short distance for reading.

In using such a bath, the most difficult problem is to ensure uniformity of tempera-ture. If the size of the flask will permit it, by far the best way is to submerge a tube as shown in Fig. 51, and install a motor stirrer.[45] If this is impossible, a stirrer which will not damage the thermometers must be improvised; a goose feather has been suggested.[46] *The stirring action of the dry ice is not adequate.*

[43]Often the exposure is even more doubtful than the instrument; but the calibration should be undertaken nevertheless, in the interest of "public relations."

[44]The vapour of denatured ethyl alcohol is less unpleasant than that of methanol. If the thermometer is decorative, consideration should be given to the nature of the finish in the choice of liquids. Ethylene glycol is another possibility.

[45]A small induction fan motor, with no brushes, is safe near inflammable liquids. A d.c. motor should be made vapour-proof, or a water-motor might well be used.

[46]KLEINSCHMIDT, *Handbuch*, p. 48.

The thermometers will probably have different lag coefficients; and serious errors can occur if the temperature of the bath is not allowed to become steady before a reading.

Maximum thermometers can only be tested on a rising temperature. A heating coil can usefully be wound around the tube which contains the stirrer; this can be run from a storage battery or from the secondary of a transformer, about 50 watts being a suitable power consumption. It would be unwise to connect it directly to the 110- or 220-volt circuit, or to an auto-transformer, because of the danger of a ground.

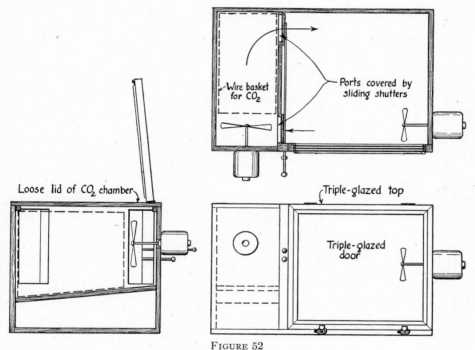

FIGURE 52
Box for calibrating thermographs.

By very careful work, two thermometers can be compared in this way to about 0.1°F., but errors two or three times as great are easy to make.

The calibration of bi-metallic thermographs and such apparatus is best done in air, in a large chamber of the kind referred to in chapter x. Fairly good results can be obtained with a box such as is shown diagrammatically in Fig. 52. Note (1) that the dry ice is in a separate compartment which can be closed off, (2) that the air in the main compartment can be circulated independently. A heater (not shown) may be installed in the main compartment. Temperatures down to −30°F. can be produced fairly quickly in this apparatus, and brought to a reasonably steady state by manipulating the shutters and the fan motors.

10. Note on the Checking of Thermographs against Thermometers in the Screen

The general procedure, detailed on page 9, for the correction of the records of recording instruments, applies to the thermograph. There is some doubt, however, what temperatures should be used for comparison with its readings.

The lag coefficient of a bi-metallic thermograph is usually rather less, that of a resistance, Bourdon, or mercury-in-steel thermograph much greater, than that of the mercury thermometers generally used in meteorology. Comparisons with the air temperature at synoptic hours are therefore likely to give erroneous results because the temperature is changing at these times. It has consequently been the practice at many stations to use the maximum and minimum temperatures for this purpose, especially as these values are easy to read on the thermograph chart.

Experience with the mercury-in-steel thermograph makes it likely that entirely false results can be obtained by using the maximum in this way. Since the most violent fluctuations (see page 59) in the temperature occur at about the time of the maximum, the mercury thermometer will respond far more to short peaks of temperature than the more sluggish thermograph. On the average, therefore, a spurious positive correction will be obtained. With a bi-metal a false negative correction would be expected, though less pronounced.

It is probable, then, that the best results will be obtained by using only the minima, or supplementing them only by those maximum temperatures which were obtained on completely cloudy days with a moderate or strong wind. A resistance or mercury-in-steel thermograph is sufficiently stable that the annual variation of the minimum in temperate or high latitudes can be left to take care of the scale value of the instrument, while the minima afford the best running check on its zero. The ice-point should also be determined every year or so.[47]

---

[47]With the bi-metallic or Bourdon thermograph this is, of course, impracticable.

CHAPTER IV

THE MEASUREMENT OF ATMOSPHERIC HUMIDITY

1. Introduction. Units of Measurement

The moisture in the atmosphere is in the form of water-vapour, cloud droplets, rain, hail, ice-crystals, and snow. In this chapter we shall fix our attention on the water-vapour only, and begin by discussing the units in which its quantity is expressed. But as a preliminary caution we must note an important distinction between the instruments used to measure humidity and those which have been discussed in the preceding chapters. While barometers and thermometers can easily be made far more accurate than is necessary in meteorological practice, instruments for measuring humidity are seldom as precise or as accurate as is to be desired. In consequence of this, the measurement of humidity is one of the least satisfactory of instrumental procedures in meteorology, and in this field there is still a great opportunity for research and invention.

The following units are used to express the quantity of water-vapour in the atmosphere:

(1) Vapour-pressure
(2) Saturation deficit
(3) Relative humidity
(4) Dew point
(5) Specific humidity
(6) Mixing ratio
(7) Absolute humidity.

Each of these, except the third, affords a complete specification of the amount of water-vapour; the relative humidity alone requires that the temperature be also given.

(a) Vapour-pressure

The partial pressure of the water-vapour present in the air is independent of the presence of the other gases, and we can therefore consider the water-vapour as a separate "atmosphere" and employ its pressure as a means of stating the humidity, under the name *vapour-pressure*. Like the pressure of the atmosphere, it can be measured in inches of mercury, millimetres of mercury, or millibars.[1]

---

[1]For definitions see chapter II, p. 13.

If a space is maintained at any given temperature in contact with a free surface of water or ice, the vapour-pressure in the space will come to a value known as the *maximum vapour-pressure* (M.V.P.) or *saturation vapour-pressure* for the temperature in question. This is a function of the temperature only, but below 0°C. its value depends on whether ice or supercooled water is in equilibrium with the space; so that we have two functions

$$\begin{aligned} e_{m,\,w} &= F_w(\theta) \\ e_{m,\,i} &= F_i\,(\theta) \end{aligned}\Bigg\} \qquad \dots\dots\dots(4.1)$$

of which the first refers to water and covers all meteorological temperatures, the second to ice at temperatures below 0°C.

The value of e_m is independent of the presence of other gases or vapours. Hence it is incorrect to speak of "air saturated with vapour," as one might of "a sponge saturated with water." It is really the space which is saturated with water-vapour.

Many tables of e_m are available; the English-speaking reader may be referred to the tables of Kaye and Laby[2] and of the Smithsonian Institution.[3] The functions have been expressed analytically, but such formulae are of use only as a means of interpolation.

The values of e_m given in the tables refer to a flat surface of pure water or ice. Over a curved surface the vapour-pressure will be somewhat higher; this becomes important in the theory of precipitation and cloud. Over a solution of an electrolyte it is lower.

(b) Saturation deficit

The quantity, $e_m - e$

where e is the actual vapour-pressure, is known as the saturation deficit. It is useful in connection with certain evaporation problems, and is measured in any of the usual pressure units.

(c) Relative humidity

The quantity $u = e/e_m$

is known as the *saturation ratio*. It is generally multiplied by 100 per cent and is called the *relative humidity*

$$U = 100e/e_m \qquad \dots\dots(4.2).$$

Above the freezing point this is unambiguous; but below it, we have two values of the relative humidity

$$\begin{aligned} U_w &= 100e/e_{m,\,w} \\ U_i &= 100e/e_{m,\,i} \end{aligned}\Bigg\} \qquad \dots\dots(4.3),$$

[2]KAYE, G. W. C., and T. H. LABY, *Tables of Physical and Chemical Constants*, 7th ed. London 1932, Longmans, Green, p. 42.

[3]*Smithsonian Meteorological Tables*, 5th rev. ed. Washington 1931, Smithsonian Institution, pp. 166-175.

depending on whether the measurements are referred to water or ice. Probably the best practice is that employed by the United States Weather Bureau, namely to refer all relative humidities to water when the temperature of the air is above the freezing point, and to ice when below it; although it is possible in practice to have supersaturation with respect to ice at temperatures slightly below the freezing point. The subject will not here be pursued further, as it is not related to a discussion of instruments. The reader may be referred to the excellent treatment by Robitzsch in the fifth edition of the Hann-Süring *Lehrbuch der Meteorologie*.[4]

(d) Dew point

If the vapour-pressure is e, a temperature θ_d can be found for which the M.V.P. is e. The temperature θ_d is called the *dew point temperature*, or merely the *dew point*. It is the temperature at which the air, if cooled, would reach saturation, and at which dew would therefore begin to condense out on a solid surface. It follows that in saturated air the dew point and the temperature are equal.

(e) Specific humidity

The density of water-vapour is 0.622 that of air at the same temperature and pressure. Thus we may form the ratio

$$s = 0.622e/(P - 0.378e) \qquad \dots\dots\dots(4.4),$$

where P is the atmospheric pressure. The ratio s is called the *specific humidity*, and is the mass of water-vapour per unit mass of air. It is expressed in grams per kilogram for the purposes of meteorological thermodynamics, or in grains per pound for engineering purposes in English-speaking countries.

(f) Mixing ratio

A similar quantity

$$m = 0.622e/(P - e) \qquad \dots\dots\dots(4.5)$$

is called the *mixing ratio*, and is the mass of water-vapour per unit mass of *dry* air. It differs little from the specific humidity at meteorological temperatures; and at low temperatures either can be calculated sufficiently accurately for many purposes by the simpler formula

$$m = s = 622\frac{e}{P} \text{ (grams per kilogram)} \qquad \dots\dots\dots(4.6).$$

(g) Absolute humidity

The *absolute humidity*, which is less used as a unit than formerly, is the weight of water-vapour per unit *volume* of air. Its numerical expression depends on the choice of pressure units; and it is also a function of the temperature. If pressures are expressed in mb and the temperature T in degrees absolute, then the absolute humidity is

$$d = 217e/T \text{(grams } m^{-3}) \qquad \dots\dots\dots(4.7).$$

---

[4]Leipzig 1939, W. Keller, vol. I, p. 307.

2. Classification of Methods of Humidity Measurement

There are four fundamentally distinct methods of measuring humidity, which may be listed as follows:

(1) Thermodynamic method (the psychrometer)

(2) Method using hygroscopic substances (the hair hygrometer, etc.)

(3) Condensation method (the dew-point hygrometer)

(4) Absorption methods

      (a) chemical (gravimetric, volumetric)

      (b) electrical (change of resistance, change of dielectric constant).

Of these methods, the first is the most widely used in meteorological practice. The four methods have in fact been arranged in the order of their present importance to the meteorologist, though not (as will become evident) in the order of their accuracy. The remainder of this chapter will be devoted to a discussion of the various instruments and the theory underlying them, according to this classification.

3. The Psychrometer

(a) General principles and elementary theory

The psychrometer consists of two thermometers placed in the air side by side, one, known as the dry thermometer or *dry bulb*, being an ordinary thermometer, and the other, called the wet thermometer or *wet bulb*, being a similar thermometer covered with thin wet cloth or with a continuous film of water or ice. Any type of thermometer may be used, provided that it is practicable to arrange the covering of the wet bulb; obviously some types are more manageable than others.

From the readings of the wet and dry bulbs, the vapour-pressure is obtained by substituting in a formula of the type

$$e = e'_m - aP(\theta - \theta') \qquad\qquad \dots\dots\dots(4.8),$$

where θ is the temperature of the dry bulb

        θ' is that of the wet bulb

        e'_m is the M.V.P. corresponding to the temperature θ'

        P is the atmospheric pressure

        a is a "psychrometric constant" dependent to some extent on the speed of the air past the wet bulb.

The derivation of this formula is usually undertaken from a meteorological standpoint in books on mathematical meteorology. As our interest here is instrumental, we shall note only the following simple consideration from a paper by Spilhaus:[5] In addition to the notation above, let c_p = the specific heat of air at constant pressure, L the latent heat of vaporization of water (assumed

---

[5]SPILHAUS, A. F., *Trans. Roy. Soc. S. Africa*, **24**:185-202, 1936.

constant) in the neighbourhood of θ', and r the ratio (0.622) of the density of water-vapour to that of air. Now the heat given up by the air to the wet bulb in unit time may be measured by a mass of air m_1, cooled from θ to θ'; and this heat is used to evaporate enough water to saturate a mass of air m_2 at the temperature θ'. This leads to an equality

$$m_1c_p(\theta-\theta') = \frac{e_m-e}{P}rm_2L \qquad \ldots\ldots\ldots(4.9)$$

or

$$e = e'_m - \frac{m_1c_p}{m_2rL} \cdot P(\theta-\theta') \qquad \ldots\ldots\ldots(4.10).$$

Comparing this with (4.8), we see that the "psychrometric constant" is

$$a = \frac{m_1c_p}{m_2rL} \qquad \ldots\ldots\ldots(4.11).$$

For physical reasons it seems probable that this will be a function of the wind speed, as is indeed the case. Now the wind speed multiplied by the pressure (more correctly by the density of the air) is a quantity known as the *ventilation*; it is therefore convenient to assimilate the pressure into the "psychrometric constant," obtaining a new quantity

$$A = \frac{m_1c_p}{m_2rL} \cdot P \qquad \ldots\ldots\ldots(4.12),$$

depending on the ventilation.

Spilhaus also shows that the lag coefficient λ of the wet bulb[6] is given by

$$\frac{1}{\lambda} = \frac{m_2rL}{Pc_1}(A+\beta) \qquad \ldots\ldots\ldots(4.13),$$

where c_1 is the heat capacity of the bulb, including muslin and water, and β is given by the *average* slope $de_m/d\theta$ of the curve relating e_m and θ over the region in which the lag coefficient is measured. From (4.12) and (4.13), the ratio m_1/m_2 can be calculated from measurements of A and λ; and it is found that at wind speeds over about 3 metres per second this ratio is very nearly unity, so that A approaches a value

$$A_\infty = \frac{c_p}{rL}P \qquad \ldots\ldots\ldots(4.14).$$

We have not space to deal at length with this interesting paper, but one important result deserves to be quoted. In an atmosphere with fluctuating temperatures (see Fig. 31)[7] fictitious fluctuations of the dew point will be obtained from a recording psychrometer, or from readings of a psychrometer at short intervals, *unless the lag coefficient of the wet bulb and that of the dry bulb are equal*. Spilhaus proves that if they are equal, simple harmonic variations in air temperature will produce no spurious variations in the vapour-pressure

---

[6]On the definition given on p. 56. Spilhaus uses the other definition.
[7]And see HOLTZMANN, M. J., *Met. Zeits.*, **53**:327-336, 1936.

calculated from the readings. An elementary proof, which may be left as an exercise for the reader, can be developed for sudden discrete changes in θ, on the assumption (made also by Spilhaus) that e_m is linear in θ over the range of temperatures considered.

If the two bulbs are the same size and are placed in the same air stream, the lag coefficient of the wet bulb will be lower than that of the dry bulb. They can be made equal by (1) increasing the ventilation of the dry bulb, or (2) substituting a smaller thermometer.

(b) The practical psychrometric formula

It will be seen from the above discussion that at sea-level pressures a wind-speed of at least 3 m sec^{-1} (actually a little more is desirable) should be maintained, in order that there may be no uncertainty in the value of the psychrometric constant. The tables most generally used for the ventilated psychrometer in English-speaking countries, and for Fahrenheit temperatures, are those due to Marvin and published by the United States Weather Bureau.[8] These are based on the formula

$$e = e'_m - 0.000367 P(\theta - \theta')\left(1 + \frac{\theta' - 32}{1571}\right) \quad \ldots\ldots\ldots(4.15)$$

due to Ferrel.[9] Note that a correction factor, which does not appear in the simple theory, is contained in the formula; this is entirely empirical.

These tables are not based on the latest values of e_m, but differ very little from the Smithsonian Tables[10] (which are) in their tabulated values. They differ markedly in their arrangement, however; in the U.S.W.B. tables the dry-bulb temperature θ is one argument; in the Smithsonian, the wet-bulb temperature θ'. From the standpoint of the observer, there is no doubt whatever that the arrangement of the U.S.W.B. tables is the more convenient.

For centigrade degrees and metric units of vapour-pressure, the best tables are those published by the Prussian Meteorological Service.[11]

It will occasionally happen that when the air is relatively moist at temperatures near the freezing point, the wet bulb will read higher than the dry. The cause of this lies in the fact that the air can be supersaturated in relation to ice while still unsaturated with reference to liquid water; the bulb being covered with ice, condensation will take place on it, the release of latent heat thereby raising its temperature. The tables do not provide for this, and the usual practice, on these infrequent occasions, is to report the air as saturated. The degree of supersaturation is of some interest, and the formula (4.15) might be used to work it out; but the difference of temperature is small, and great care should be taken with corrections, etc.

[8]U.S.W.B., *Psychrometric Tables* (W.B. no. 235), Washington 1915.

[9]FERREL, W., *Ann. Rep. Chief Signal Officer 1886*, Appendix 24, pp. 233-259.

[10]*Smithsonian Meteorological Tables, l.c.*

[11]*Jelineks Psychrometer-Tafeln*, ed. F. M. Exner, 7th ed. Leipzig 1929, *Akad. Verlag*.

(c) Description of various psychrometers

Although the old practice of using wet and dry bulb thermometers in a screen, with no artificial ventilation, has little to recommend it except simplicity, it is still used to some extent at climatological stations. For this purpose it is usual to suspend the thermometers vertically, with the wick from the wet bulb dipping into a water can, usually of copper. The best arrangement and the best form of can are shown in Fig. 53. The can is of such a form that freezing will not damage it, and has a narrow mouth, to prevent the air in the neighbourhood being made moister by evaporation. Note that the mouth of the can is at the same level as the top of the wet thermometer bulb, the wick being horizontal. If the wick slopes down towards the bulb, water may drop continuously off the latter, which is unnecessary; while if it slopes upwards, the bulb may not receive enough water

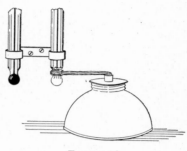

FIGURE 53
Simple psychrometer.

in dry weather. The common practice of putting the can beneath the bulb, with the wick dangling down, and touching the latter, is to be avoided. In freezing weather the wick is removed, and the bulb with the muslin on it dipped into water some time before the observation. A *thin* coating of ice should be aimed at.

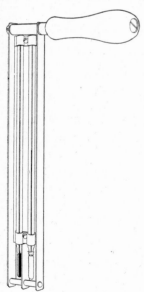

FIGURE 54
Sling psychrometer.

Of the ventilated psychrometers, the simplest and cheapest is the *sling psychrometer* (Fig. 54), also called the *whirling psychrometer*. This consists essentially of two thermometers, mounted in a frame which can be rotated rapidly about an axis at right-angles to its length. The construction of the handle requires special attention, especially for use in maritime locations, where corrosion has to be prevented. Furthermore, as the instrument has to be swung for some time, it should be comfortable to the hand—many handles are too small.

The sling psychrometer has to be stopped in order to read it. With a little practice, a technique of stopping the instrument smoothly and in the proper position for reading will easily be developed. Nevertheless this is a disadvantage, and there are many superior types of psychrometer in which the thermometers are held stationary and the air drawn past them.

Of all these, the instrument which has been regarded as standard for many years is the ventilated psychrometer of Assmann

(Fig. 55).[12] By means of a motor (clockwork or electric), a fan is caused to draw air past the thermometer bulbs in the double-walled chambers A and B, one of which is shown in section. At intervals, the wet bulb is moistened with distilled water by means of a special applicator shown at C. The thermometer bulbs are cylindrical, and usually small, the muslin being supplied sewn or woven into tubes to fit.

These instruments are recommended[13] for routine observations at sea, especially on naval ships. For permanent installations on land, however, a more rugged type of psychrometer, which can be installed in a Stevenson screen, may be preferred, since the Assmann psychrometer is very expensive and not sufficiently durable to leave out in the weather. Such an instrument[14] is illustrated in Fig. 56. It consists essentially of a centrifugal exhaust fan with a special inlet duct, mounted directly on the end of a standard split-phase induction motor of the capacitor type, which has no brushes and cannot interfere with radio reception. Suitable holders for the thermometers are provided, the dry bulb, of course, being nearer the outer end of the duct. The wick from the wet bulb goes through a hole to the water container. This instrument is intended to be controlled by means of a switch in the office, so that it can be turned on a few minutes before an observation, and turned off when the observer again goes indoors.

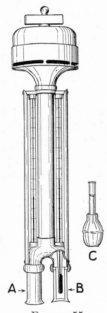

FIGURE 55
Assmann psychrometer.

For portable use, an excellent hand-aspirated psychrometer is available,[15] which employs a venturi tube to produce a vacuum for sucking air over the bulbs. Air is forced through the venturi by means of a rubber bulb.

Recording psychrometers have been developed, and are entirely successful if proper precautions are observed. One of the best makes use of two mercury-in-steel thermometers, strongly ventilated by an exhaust fan; the only serious defect of this instrument is its very great lag coefficient, rendering the maximum temperature (and the minimum relative humidity) somewhat doubtful, and emphasizing the considerations developed on page 89 above.

The Kew photographic thermograph referred to on page 68 is really a recording psychrometer. It has given long and honourable service at many stations; but it is doubtful whether any more such instruments will ever be installed—the reduction of the records is too tedious.

[12]See also p. 54.

[13]*Admiralty Weather Manual.*   London 1938, H.M. Stationery Office.

[14]MIDDLETON, W. E. K., Bull. Amer. Met. Soc., **21**:63-65, 1940.

[15]Made by Julien P. Friez & Sons, Baltimore.

Resistance thermometers can be used. A special bridge circuit has even been developed, which gives an approximate record of the relative humidity directly on the chart of a recording potentiometer. But all such instruments fail to function during frost, owing to the difficulty of keeping a film of ice continuously on the wet bulb. Probably the mercury-in-steel psychrometer is the simplest and most satisfactory recording instrument for use in warm climates or in the warmer parts of the year, and does not represent as tremendous an investment as an elaborate double recording resistance thermometer.

FIGURE 56
Motor psychrometer.

(d) *Maintenance of the wet bulb: Sources of error*

It is of interest that all the errors of a psychrometer, apart from errors in the thermometers themselves, operate in such a direction as to increase the observed relative humidity. These errors may be classified as

(1) Errors due to conduction of heat down the thermometer stem

(2) Errors due to insufficient ventilation

(3) Errors due to the muslin (or the covering of ice on the bulb) being too thick

(4) Errors due to dirty muslin or impure water.

The conduction of heat down the stem is not usually important in glass thermometers, though it has an effect on the value of the psychrometric constant and its variation with ventilation.[16] In short, the tables have taken this into account, and unless a thermometer is of unusual construction this error is not likely to be important. With metal bulbs, however, conduction is a serious matter. By sinking small thermocouples flush with the surface of a model of a mercury-in-steel thermometer bulb, the writer found a temperature gradient of more than a degree Fahrenheit from one end of the bulb to the other. It was found necessary to cover the stem with wet muslin for a distance equal to the length of the bulb, to get rid of this gradient in the bulb itself.

The errors due to insufficient ventilation are really due to using the wrong tables—but to save trouble it is better to have an air speed of at least 4 metres per second (9 m.p.h.). Attention should be drawn to the fact that this involves about 4 revolutions per second of a sling psychrometer a foot long.

---

[16]SPILHAUS, *l.c.*

As to the remaining errors, their amount is various, but they always operate in the same direction.   The muslin should be a fine cotton fabric, thin but very closely woven, and should be held tightly to the bulb.   For cylindrical bulbs

a tube of muslin should be sewn up, leaving as little in the hem as possible.   For spherical bulbs, which are standard in British meteorological practice (though not in the United States), a very convenient means of installing the muslin is provided by having circles ready cut and threaded with a linen thread (Fig. 57), which can be pulled tight and wrapped once or twice around the stem of the thermometer above the bulb, then tied.   These are very cheap, and the observer is encouraged to change the muslin at least once a week, more often near the sea or in dusty places, such as many airports.

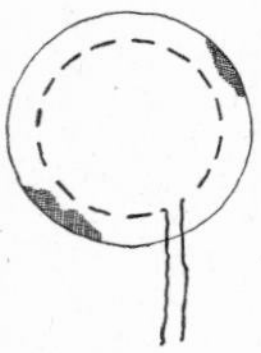

FIGURE 57
Muslin circle, for wet bulb.

If we suppose that everything is in proper condition, there remains the uncertainty in the thermometers themselves, and in reading them.   The following table shows the approximate error dU in relative humidity, caused by an error of 1.0°F. in the difference between the two thermometers, for various dry-bulb temperatures, according to the U.S.W.B. tables:

Temperature °F.................	−20	0	20	40	60	80	100
dU for 1.0°F., %.................	−90	−33	−15	−8	−6	−4	−4

While an error of one- or two-tenths of a degree is not serious at summer temperatures, it may render the measurement absurd in winter.

4. The Hair Hygrometer

(a) *General principles*

The hair hygrometer is the leading example of a class of instruments for measuring humidity by means of the changes in dimensions suffered by hygroscopic substances when their moisture content varies.   It was invented by H. B. de Saussure in the eighteenth century, and forms the subject of a remarkable book, *Essais sur l'hygrometrie*,[17] a monument to an experimenter of almost superhuman patience.   The instrument came in for a good deal of criticism from the inventors of rival hygrometers, and in 1788 de Saussure published at Geneva his *Defense de l'hygromètre à cheveu*, a delightful chapter in the history of science.

In appraising de Saussure's work, it must be remembered that the idea of relative humidity had not yet occurred to anyone.   This idea makes the behaviour of the hair *seem* very simple; actually it is a surprising fact that the length of a hair is a function of *relative* humidity, and not of the actual amount of water-vapour in the air.   For example, it is a cause for some astonishment that a change of 0.1″Hg in vapour-pressure at the freezing point produces the same effect as a change ten times as large at a temperature of 98°F.   This

[17]Neuchatel, 1783.

behaviour makes the hair a very useful substance for the measurement and control of relative humidity.

The increase in length of a human hair as the relative humidity is changed from 0 to 100 per cent is about $2\frac{1}{2}$ per cent of the original length. From the results of X-ray analysis it is deduced that the water is adsorbed on to the surfaces of minute crystals, much longer (in the direction of the length of the hair) than they are wide. However, the details are not fully understood.

While the human hair is generally used, hair from various species of animals is also of service. Before being used, hair of any kind should be put in ethyl ether for approximately one hour at room temperature, to remove fats. Too long treatment deteriorates it.[18] It is then washed thoroughly in distilled water and dried without artificial heat.

Different specimens of hair will extend different amounts, but there is a fairly constant relation between the relative humidity and the elongation of the hair as a fraction of its total change of length. The following[19] are the accepted figures:

R. H. (per cent)	0	10	20	30	40	50	60	70	80	90	100
Elongation (per cent)	0	20.9	38.8	52.8	63.7	72.8	79.2	85.2	90.5	95.4	100

(Between 20 and 100 per cent R. H. the relation is not far from logarithmic.) This uniformity makes it possible to replace the hair in an instrument without changing anything except the magnification.

Besides altering its length with increase of relative humidity, the hair expands with increasing temperature. The determination of this effect is extremely difficult, but its magnitude seems to be about 1/15th as much per degree centigrade as the mean change of length for 1 per cent R. H. It is certainly a function of the relative humidity, being greater under moist conditions. There is another temperature effect on the hair, which is presumed to correspond to the freezing of the adsorbed water between the crystals; namely, the sudden increase of length that sometimes occurs at very low temperatures, especially with hairs that have been prepared too long in ether. It has been suggested that only hairs which have been found not to exhibit this effect should be used for aerological work.

(b) Lag of the hair

Changes in the indication of the hair do not follow the simple first-order law noted above for thermometers (page 56). The most complete investigation of this has been made by Spilhaus,[20] who shows that the curve connecting the time t and the indication r satisfies the differential equation

$$\left| \frac{1}{r} \frac{dr}{dt} \right| = K \left| r - r_f \right|^n \qquad \ldots\ldots\ldots(4.16),$$

[18]SPILHAUS, A. F., *M.I.T. Met. Course Prof. Notes*, no. 8. Cambridge, Mass., 1938.
[19]KLEINSCHMIDT, E., *Beitr.z.Phys. d. f. Atm.*, 2:99, 1908.
[20]SPILHAUS, *l.c.*

r_f being the actual R. H. of the air and K and n constants for a given hair at a given temperature. Since the change in length of the hair is proportional to the logarithm of r, we may write

$$\left|\frac{dl}{dt}\right| = K_1 \left| r - r_f \right|^n \qquad \ldots\ldots\ldots(4.17).$$

For increasing r, n is not far from unity, but seems to be greater for r decreasing. The value of K varies widely, but depends especially on temperature and on the tension of the hair.

It has been observed by many workers that the hair responds very slowly at low temperatures, the lag becoming almost infinite at $-40°$C. This is a very serious limitation of the usefulness of the hair as a humidity indicator for aerological purposes, and is noticeable at ground stations in the arctic regions. As to the effect of tension, Spilhaus contends that K is increased by increasing the force on the hair, and advises greater tension than the few grams per hair commonly used; but a full investigation of the effect of tension on the permanence of the zero is needed before such a recommendation could be adopted.

(c) Modern hair hygrometers and hygrographs

Hair hygrometers are not much used in meteorology as indicating instruments. When they are, they are generally of the form shown diagrammatically in Fig. 58, the mechanism consisting of a bell-crank pivoted at O, one arm of which is a balanced pointer, the other being attached to the hair at A. Means are provided of adjusting the distance OA. The hair is kept under approximately constant tension by the weight W. The zero of the instrument may be adjusted by means of a screw B at the far end of the frame.

FIGURE 58
Diagram of
hair hygrometer.

Hair hygrographs are more common, and are made in many different constructions, nearly all of them using either a bundle of hairs or a "harp" of hairs held parallel and side by side. The mechanical arrangements fall into three general classes, shown as (a), (b), and (c) in the diagrams of Fig. 59. In this figure the hair is represented by a double line, and pivots by small circles.

The first of these is fundamentally the same as the hygrometer of Fig. 58, except that a pen-arm is substituted for the pointer. It has the great advantage that only one axis is required, and the further advantage that the magnification is not changed by adjusting the zero. Its disadvantage is that the scale is non-linear, and this seems a great defect to some people; actually it is of no importance whatever unless it is desired to obtain the mean relative humidity from the record by means of a planimeter. Since the mean relative humidity is a quantity of very little significance, it is probable that this is almost never done.

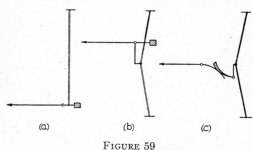

FIGURE 59

Three arrangements for a hygrograph.

The second type has a somewhat more nearly (though not accurately) linear scale, but has the disadvantage that the zero adjustment changes the form of the scale somewhat. The third uses two cams to ensure a linear scale; the frictional resistances are, of course, larger and more uncertain than in the other types, and any corrosion of the cams would be serious. It is the opinion of most authorities[21] that the simpler the mechanism of a hygrograph, the better; and those who have used instruments of the first class do not find that the non-linear scale causes any trouble. Such an instrument is shown in Fig. 60.

The change in length of the hair can also be used to turn the rotor of a self-synchronous motor (see below, page 121) for making records of the relative humidity at a distance. The principle of this is further discussed in chapter VI.

(d) Maintenance of the hair hygrograph

(i) Changes in the zero

Various causes, some of them not completely understood, can operate to change the zero of a hygrograph. One of these is stretching of the hair due to sticking of the hygrograph mechanism when the R.H. is decreasing, or to moving the pen up instead of down when making time-marks. The hair should never have excess force applied to it. But the zero can also change if the hair is exposed for long to a very dry atmosphere. Such a change is likely to be *reversible*; that is to say, the hair will usually return to its or-

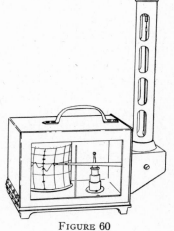

FIGURE 60

Hair hygrograph.

(Courtesy of Negretti and Zambra)

iginal state when it has been kept in saturated air for a time. The general accuracy of hair hygrometry in dry regions could undoubtedly be improved by the practice of exposing the hair to a saturated atmosphere for a few hours once a month.

The hair hygrometer is at its best as an instrument for the *control* of relative

---

[21]See FERGUSSON, S. P., "The errors of absorption hygrometers," *Ann. Astr. Obs. Harvard Coll.*, vol. 58, part II, appendix. Cambridge, Mass. 1906. KLEINSCHMIDT, *Handbuch*, p. 240.

8

humidity, especially in applications where the temperature is also maintained constant. It behaves better if large variations do not occur, and is used with little attention to control relative humidity in countless thousands of buildings.

(ii) *Removal of dust*

Most kinds of dust ruin the accuracy of the observations.[22] At frequent intervals, therefore, the dust should be brushed off with a soft, clean, dry brush (a camel's-hair brush is very suitable), after which the brush should be washed out in *distilled* water and the hair washed down from top to bottom with a full brush. The hair should on no account be touched with the fingers at any time. After being wetted, a properly adjusted hair should indicate about 95 per cent R.H., not 100 per cent as might be expected.

(iii) *Life of the hair*

With proper attention and regard to cleanliness, the hair should last several years in temperate climates, except in places polluted by acid fumes or ammonia. When it is replaced, a complete recalibration of the instrument is necessary, and usually the magnification will have to be adjusted.

(e) *Calibration of the hair hygrograph*

It is usually a waste of time to attempt to calibrate a hygrograph by direct comparison with instantaneous values of the relative humidity outdoors, unless perhaps the times of maximum or minimum R.H. can be watched for. It is better to calibrate it in a special chamber, or failing that, in the reasonably steady conditions of an ordinary room at a time when the room temperature is fairly constant.

First the instrument should be covered with a wet cloth (or put in a box lined with a wet cloth) and left until its indication has ceased to rise. This gives the 100 per cent point. It may then be exposed to the air of the room, and when the new indication is steady, a *series* of readings (say five) should be taken with a sling- or Assmann psychrometer. Any necessary adjustment of the zero or of the magnification can now be made, and the tests repeated. It should be mentioned that the saturation of the air within a box can be hastened and made more certain if a small fan is installed.

A routine method of control used in some countries is to plot the readings at term-hours as ordinates against simultaneous readings of a psychrometer as abscissae. The points should lie about a straight line through the origin and inclined at 45° to the axes; there will be a good deal of scatter, but with a large number of observations any trend away from this line may be discovered. The superposition of graphs for consecutive months affords a means of investigating the constancy of the zero of the instrument.

Periodic checking of the hygrograph is essential to accuracy; and this should generally be done on a cloudy day when the temperature is nearly

[22]GRUNDMANN, W., *Met. Zeits.*, **50**:106-108, 1933.

steady, or, if convenient, near the time of minimum temperature. In summer the instrument might better be calibrated indoors; but in winter this procedure might lead to errors larger than those it is desired to detect.

5. The Dew Point Hygrometer

(a) General principles

When a solid body is cooled to the dew point, small drops of water begin to condense on it. If the temperature of the surface of the body can be observed at the inception of this phenomenon, this temperature will be the dew point.

In practice, however, two circumstances must be considered before any great accuracy can be attained: (1) It is not usually possible to measure the temperature of a body exactly at its surface, (2) it is difficult to see the very beginning of condensation. In consequence of these difficulties the dew point is usually taken to be half way between the temperature at which dew is first observed when the temperature of the body is falling, and that at which the dew disappears when the surface is warming up. If we suppose that the beginning of dew formation is as easy to see as the last vestiges of existing dew, the right result will be obtained if the rate of fall and the rate of rise are equal. It is not always feasible to ensure this.

(b) Dew point apparatus

In order that the incidence of dew shall be as easy to observe as possible, the surface on which it is to be formed is highly polished, and the dew is observed rather by the dulling of reflections than as a thing in itself. The details of the various instruments differ, but most of them derive from that of Regnault, a modern form of which is shown in Fig. 61. In this instrument, one of the two silvered tubes is cooled by bubbling air through the ether contained in it; a thermometer dipping into the ether gives its temperature, which is supposed to be that of the polished surface. The other polished tube is for comparison, and to obtain the dry bulb temperature. It should be pointed out that partial immersion thermometers ought to be used, to avoid stem errors (see page 63).

To use such an instrument, it should preferably be set up several feet from the observer and looked at through a telescope, air being bubbled through the ether by means of a suction bulb on a long rubber tube. If the telescope is not used, the observer's breath may cause false readings. It will be easier to see the formation of dew if the reflection of a boundary between light and dark areas is visible.

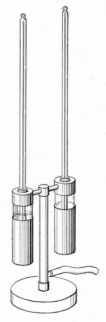

FIGURE 61

Dew point hygrometer.

The use of ether as a means of cooling is costly and somewhat dangerous, being practically impossible indoors. A great improvement in dew-point apparatus has recently been described by Thornthwaite and Owen,[23] which uses either an ordinary freezing mixture, or solid CO_2, contained in a Dewar flask. Through the stopper of such a flask (Fig. 62) passes a copper rod having on its end a polished plane metal surface, with one junction of a thermoelectric circuit attached to it, the other being elsewhere at a standard temperature. Just beneath the polished surface is a small heating element. If this is not functioning, the surface will be cooled well below the dew point; but by switching it on, the temperature of the polished surface can be raised at any speed desired.

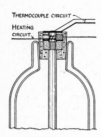

FIGURE 62

The dew point hygrometer of Thornthwaite and Owen.

The instrument can be made to give a record by observing the surface photoelectrically; that is to say, by allowing it to reflect a parallel beam of light to a photoelectric cell. The change of photo-current which occurs when dew forms is used to switch on the heater, and the reverse change when the dew vanishes is used to turn the heating current off.

The temperature, which can be recorded by a recording potentiometer, fluctuates over a short range about the dew point.

The dew point hygrometer is not used to any extent in meteorology except as a research tool. It seems possible that the apparatus of Thornthwaite and Owen might have a place at first-order meteorological stations in winter, possibly with the photoelectric method of observation, but without the recording feature.

6. Absorption Hygrometry

Absorption hygrometers may be divided into two classes—chemical and electrical. The former are used scarcely at all in meteorological practice.[24] Briefly they consist of an apparatus for exposing a known quantity of air to a drying agent, and either (1) weighing the moisture taken up by the dryer, (2) measuring the change in volume of the air at constant pressure, or (3) measuring the change in pressure at constant volume. The first of these is the most accurate, is indeed the most accurate of all methods of measuring humidity; but it takes much time, and can only be used accurately to give a mean value over an hour or so.

The electrical method was developed in connection with the investigation of the upper air, as an attempt to overcome the defects of the hair hygrometer for that purpose, and will be treated in that connection (page 199).

---

[23]THORNTHWAITE, C. W., and J. C. OWEN, *U.S. Mon. Wea. Rev.*, **68**:315-318, 1940.
[24]But see below, p. 116.

7. A Hygrometer Calibration Chamber

One of the most satisfactory methods of maintaining a constant humidity is to circulate the air in a closed system over saturated solutions of hygroscopic salts. A very convenient apparatus for this purpose has been developed by Jacobsen at Toronto, and is shown in its essential features in Fig. 63.

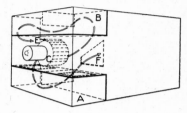

The hygroscopic salts ($CaCl_2$, NH_4Cl, $Ca(NO_3)_2$, etc.)[25] are contained in trays in the removable boxes A and B. Several pairs of these boxes are provided, and when not in use each pair are held together by their fasteners, forming practically airtight containers for the salts. This is very convenient for routine calibrations (meteorographs, etc.), since the salts can be interchanged quickly.

FIGURE 63
Hygrometer calibration chamber

A simpler scheme could be devised for occasional work.

The air is circulated over the salts by a motor fan C of the centrifugal type, which draws air in from the main chamber and forces it over the trays to the ports E, F, along the paths indicated by the double arrows. In front of one of these ports is a psychrometer, with a means of keeping the wet bulb supplied with water. The curved partitions which separate the two streams of air are not shown in the drawing.

The work done on the air by the motor would cause the temperature inside the box to rise fairly rapidly. A cooling coil is therefore provided in the inlet duct, through which cold water may be circulated at a rate sufficient to keep the air temperature constant.

The entire box is made of weather proof (resin-bonded) plywood, and painted thoroughly inside and out to prevent absorption of moisture. The instruments being calibrated can be observed through a double-glazed door, which closes against a gasket. This door is in the end of the box opposite the motor.

---

[25]Tables in *Handbook of Chemistry and Physics*, 24th ed. Cleveland 1939, Chemical Rubber Publ. Co.

CHAPTER V

THE MEASUREMENT OF PRECIPITATION AND EVAPORATION

1. General Considerations[1]

(a) *Purpose of the measurements*

Water falls upon the earth in the form of rain, snow, hail, etc., and condenses upon it as dew.   In order that this process may continue, just as much water must leave the surface of land and sea by evaporation.   A complete and successful measurement of these quantities over the whole earth might be said to determine the water economy, or water balance, of the atmosphere.

Leaving out of consideration, for the moment, the measurement of evaporation, it is obvious that the amount of precipitation falling upon the earth is not very accurately known.   Apart from the fact that wide stretches of land are uninhabited by civilized man, we have practically no measurements over the much greater area of ocean.

Even in more limited endeavours, such as the determination of the water economy of a valley or a watershed, our best efforts involve an extrapolation of very great extent.   There are probably few regions of any size which are covered by a network of rain-gauges so dense that every ten square miles has its gauge; but let us imagine such a region.   If each of the supposed gauges has a diameter of 8 inches, its area is only one eight hundred millionth of that of the region which it is taken to represent.   Or, to take another illustration, suppose a slight shower to leave half a cubic inch of water in the 8-inch gauge; if the shower has been uniform over the ten square miles it will have poured on this area no less than 7,000 tons of water!   It is rather as if we were to estimate the amount of water in a fair-sized lake from the result of one sounding near the middle.

Fortunately this last analogy is not entirely fair, at least in flat country. We have every reason to expect a fair degree of uniformity in the rainfall of such regions, just as we might have other reasons to believe that our hypothetical lake was uniformly deep.   It therefore behoves us to make our sample "sounding" as accurate as we can, and in particular to keep it free from purely local sources of error.

(b) *Units of precipitation*

It is the universal practice to distinguish between rain, snow, and total precipitation.   All these are measured on the basis of depth; i.e., the depth to which a flat surface would be covered if no water were lost by run-off or evaporation.   The units are

---

[1]The student who wishes to go further in this subject should not omit to consult the annual volumes of *British Rainfall* (H.M. Stationery Office).

(i) The *inch*—stated to 0.01 inch for rain and total precipitation, 0.1 inch for snow. Used in Canada, Newfoundland, and the United States.

(ii) The *millimetre*—stated to 0.1 mm for rain and total precipitation, whole millimetres for snow. Used in practically all other countries (including Great Britain since 1915).

A conversion of more-than-ample accuracy is: 1 inch = 25.4 mm.

As we shall see later, snow is sometimes measured as such, and sometimes melted and measured as water. If the former course is taken, the depth of snow is usually stated in terms of inches or millimetres, and then divided by 10 to obtain the water equivalent for the purpose of calculating the total precipitation. This divisor assumes that the density of snow is 0.1—an assumption very far from the truth in individual instances, but statistically a fair approximation in many localities, though certainly not in all.

2. The Ordinary Rain-Gauge

The ordinary (non-recording) rain-gauge consists essentially of a right cylinder of known cross-section, having a fairly sharp upper edge and provided with means for ensuring the collection and measurement of all water falling into it. It is installed so that the upper edge is in a horizontal plane. Each meteorological service has its own preferred design of rain-gauge, and it would serve no useful purpose to describe many gauges which differ only in matters of detail. We shall therefore describe three gauges only:

(1) The 5-inch gauge of the Meteorological Office (London)—

                                           Fig. 64(*a*)

(2) The standard gauge of the Canadian Meteorological Division—

                                           Fig. 64(*b*)

(3) The 8-inch gauge of the United States Weather Bureau—

                                           Fig. 64(*c*).

Certain of the differences between these gauges are due to the fact that in the British Empire all rain-gauges are intended to have their rims 12 inches above level ground, while in the United States no such limitation is imposed. We shall return to this in sec. 5 below.

The 5-inch M.O.-pattern gauge is made of sheet copper with a brass rim, details being sufficiently indicated in the figure. It will be noted that the upper edge of the funnel is nearly one diameter below the rim. This is to prevent raindrops splashing out of the gauge. The funnel discharges into a clear glass bottle, which is placed inside a copper pail to catch the water if the bottle overflows or breaks. In use, the top section of the gauge is lifted off, and the water in the bottle measured in the measuring glass, which is graduated in hundredths of an inch, or millimetres, of rain. If the bottle has overflowed into the copper pail, this is also taken out.

The Canadian gauge is smaller, having an *area* of 10 square inches (3.57 inches diameter). The whole gauge is of brass and copper,[2] and the entire

---

[2]Older gauges had a cast-iron base and a galvanized outer body.

height of the instrument is only $10\frac{1}{2}$ inches, permitting its installation on the end of a buried post projecting $1\frac{1}{2}$ inches from the ground. A measuring glass, suitably graduated in hundredths of an inch, is provided. In the Canadian gauge the funnel is placed well below the rim to prevent splashing.

The 8-inch gauge of the United States Weather Bureau differs greatly from the other gauges, both in its size and shape, and in the manner in which the readings are taken. The construction of the gauge will be clear from the figure, and it will be noted that the cylindrical wall above the funnel is comparatively shallow, just a little over one-quarter of the diameter, in fact. The whole gauge is supported by an iron tripod, the total height being about 30 inches.

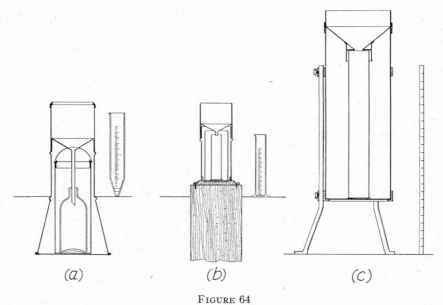

FIGURE 64

Three types of rain-gauge (see text).

A measuring glass is not used with this gauge. Instead, the inner cylinder has an area just one-tenth that of the gauge, and a thin measuring stick is provided, graduated in inches and tenths, corresponding to tenths and hundredths of an inch of rain. This is plunged into the inner cylinder through the hole at the apex of the funnel, and its wetted height gives the amount of rain. If the inner tube is full, it is emptied, the outer vessel taken up, and the overflow poured into the inner tube and measured.

In various places, experiments have been made to determine whether the measured rainfall varies with the size of gauge.[3] These show little evidence of such an effect, provided great care is taken to expose the various gauges in

[3]See PURI, H. R., India Met. Dept., *Sci. Notes*, **3**, no. 23, Calcutta 1931.

exactly the same way. The recent report[4] by F. Napier Denison on comparisons of the Canadian and United States gauges is therefore of great interest. In observations at two stations, the Canadian gauge was found to record 2.3 per cent and 2.9 per cent more than the United States gauge. Now Kadel[5] and others have shown beyond reasonable doubt that of two rain-gauges having the same diameter, the one with the deeper rim catches the most rain, presumably because some of the drops splash out of the shallower funnel. (The angle at the apex of the funnel should also be of some importance.) Denison's investigation should be repeated for a longer period. In the opinion of the writer, the Meteorological Office (London) is entirely correct in recommending the abolition of gauges with shallow rims, since it seems more probable that the shallow rim would *lose* rain by splashing out, than that the deeper rim would *collect* any water that does not belong to it.

3. Recording Rain-Gauges

(a) Classification

The very large number of recording rain-gauges which have been designed can be classified into five types, as follows:

(1) Float types, without automatic siphon
(2) Float types, with automatic siphon
(3) Weighing gauges (balance gauges)
(4) Tipping-bucket gauges
(5) Combination types.

Many variations of each of these types can be found in the catalogues of instrument-makers and in the scientific literature; here we shall merely illustrate the principles of each type by a reference to designs which are likely to come to the attention of English-speaking readers.

It should be understood that the primary function of the recording gauge is not to provide an accurate record of the *amount* of rain, but rather of its *time* of beginning and ending and its *rate* of fall. If a recording gauge is used as the standard gauge for a station, it must be of a type which retains the rainwater for measurement independently of the recording mechanism.

(b) The float gauge

This type of gauge, which is not common, may be represented by the "Hyetograph" of Negretti and Zambra. The principle of this instrument is shown in Fig. 65. The rain collected by the funnel A passes down the tube B to the float-chamber C, causing the float to rise. The rod E, which is attached to the float, is provided with eight studs F, at equal intervals. These engage a pallet G on the pen-arm H. The pallet is of such dimensions that when the pen arrives at the top of its travel it drops to the next stud, giving eight traverses of the pen for the 4 inches of rain which the instrument holds. The

---

[4]DENISON, F. N., *Bull. Amer. Met. Soc.*, **22**:65-67, 1941.
[5]KADEL, B. C., *U.S. Mon. Wea. Rev.*, **58**:282-283, 1930.

chamber is emptied by a siphon which is actuated by pressing the float down by hand.

The advantages of such a gauge are the absence of cumulative error, and the utter simplicity of the mechanism. Its disadvantage, shared with all gauges having a float, is that the float can be irreparably damaged by frost. Such instruments are suitable for cold climates only if automatic heating is installed.

(c) The automatic siphon gauge

The necessity of emptying the float chamber by hand naturally suggested the installation of a self-starting siphon to empty it when it is filled up to a certain level, at the same time returning the pen to zero. The problem of making a siphon with a perfectly regular action has been solved in several ingenious ways, of which the one[6] due to W. H. Dines is referred to here because of its adoption by the Meteorological Office for use in the British Isles.

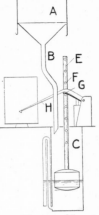

FIGURE 65
The "Hyetograph."

In this instrument the float-chamber A (Fig. 66) together with the float B and the siphon D, are mounted on knife edges at C. When the float rises to the top of its travel, it strikes a lever attached to the trigger E, which releases the entire assembly and allows it to tip towards the right, emptying out just enough water to allow the float to return to zero. At that point the counterweight F returns the mechanism to its original position, where it is held by the trigger E until the float again releases it. One traverse of the pen corresponds to 0.20 inches or 5 mm of rain.

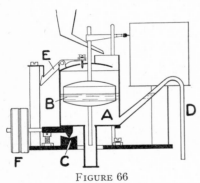

FIGURE 66
The Dines tilting-siphon rain-gauge.

Another form of siphon is shown diagrammatically in Fig. 67. In this construction the siphon is arranged coaxially. The upper end of the outer tube is formed by a polished glass cap, and the thick inner tube nearly touches this, forming a very narrow annular aperture with all its area compressed into a very short vertical distance. The area is large enough to carry away the water rapidly and without preliminary dribbling.

Gauges of these forms are preferred in Western Europe because they give a continuous indication of very light rain. They ought to find a field of application on the Pacific coast of North America.

(d) Weighing or balance rain-gauges

For detailed precipitation records in cold climates, the weighing type of

---

[6]DINES, W. H., *Met. Mag.*, **55**:112-113, 1920. *Collected papers*, p. 112.

rain-gauge has much to recommend it. The best-known gauge of this pattern is that of Fergusson,[7] a diagram of which is shown in Fig. 68. It has the advantage that any form of precipitation is weighed and recorded as soon as it falls into the gauge.

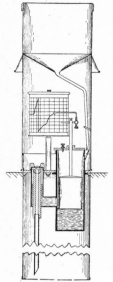

Under the opening F a receiver R is supported on a platform carried by a special spring balance. The platform is attached to a vertical frame B, supported by a helical spring which is hung from the adjustable arm E. The frame B is constrained to move nearly in a straight line by the two lattice-work levers L, L, which are hinged to B and to the stand A. The movements of D are transmitted to the pen-arm P by means of the arm C and the slotted links K_1, K_2. The pen-arm is overbalanced so that it tends to move the pen upwards, and the link K_1 is heavier than K_2; this causes the pen to traverse the sheet four times, alternately up and down, as the frame B moves continuously down under the weight of the collected precipitation.

To prevent snow or rain from getting to the mechanism, the upper part of the gauge H is provided with a skirt G which is slightly smaller than the receiver R. A funnel may be attached to this in order to discourage evaporation during periods when snow is not expected.

One of the difficulties of such gauges is that oscillations of the balance can be caused by the wind. The Fergusson gauge is fitted with a large oil damper which can be seen in part at M.

FIGURE 67
Natural siphon rain-gauge.
(Courtesy of Negretti and Zambra)

(e) *Tipping-bucket gauges*

The principle of the tipping-bucket gauge is very simple. A bucket of the shape shown at B, Fig. 69, is balanced in unstable equilibrium on the axis D. It is divided by a partition C into two halves. When a definite amount of water has been added, the bucket tips suddenly to the other position, spilling out the water. The other side then begins to fill. The bucket is usually designed to hold an amount of water corresponding to 0.01 inch of rainfall; adjustment is provided by the stop screws E.

In the particular gauge to which Fig. 69 refers,[8] a fork G is rigidly attached to the bucket. When the fork has well begun its travel, one prong of it engages the arm H, which is attached to a mercury switch capable of oscillation about the axis J. As this switch passes its central position a mo-

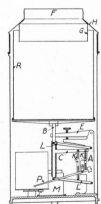

FIGURE 68
Fergusson weighing rain- or snow-gauge.

[7]FERGUSSON, S. P., *U.S. Mon. Wea. Rev.*, **49**:379-386, 1921.

[8]Designed in the Meteorological Service of Canada. All the working parts are of nickel alloys, to resist corrosion.

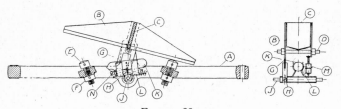

FIGURE 69
Mechanism of the tipping-bucket rain-gauge.

mentary contact is made, operating a chronograph in the office.

Gauges on this principle have the advantage of recording at a distance, avoiding trouble due to chart paper becoming wet.[9]   Since no record is made until 0.01 inch of rain has fallen, however, they are not recommended for use in maritime climates where very light drizzle is the rule.

The tipping of the bucket takes a finite time, of the order of 0.2 sec. While the bucket is going through the first half of its motion, water is still running into the full side; therefore the amount of water collected for each tip of the bucket will be a linear function of the rate of rainfall, as shown in Fig. 70, which is the result of experiments on the M.S.C. gauge. The error is not serious except for rates in excess of 2 inches an hour, an exceedingly heavy rain.

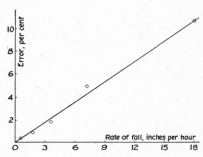

FIGURE 70
Rate error of the tipping-bucket rain-gauge.

(f) *Other types*

A very ingenious gauge has been devised by F. Nilsson,[10] which is a com-

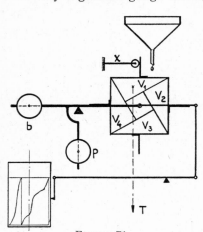

FIGURE 71
Nilsson rain-gauge, diagram
(from a brochure issued in 1939 by Sievert in Stockholm).

bination of the tipping bucket and weighing types. As will be seen (Fig. 71), it has a wheel of four buckets V_1 to V_4, restrained from turning by a stop X, which bears against any one of the four radial prongs. The whole system is balanced by the weight b, and moves downwards as rain falls into the top bucket, raising the weight p and causing the pen-arm to rise on the chart. When 3 mm of rain has fallen, the stop X releases the wheel, which moves in a counter-clockwise direction, emptying out the water and lightening the wheel, which is arrested with the next bucket in position. Thus a greatly magnified record is obtained.

(g) *Heating of gauges*

By installing electric lamps or heating

---

[9]Waterproof chart paper is supplied by some English firms.
[10]NILSSON, F., *Met. Zeits.*, **54**:72-75, 1937.

elements inside a gauge, it is possible to prevent frost damage to such components as a float or a float chamber, and to record *rain* during the winter months. Heating a gauge with the idea of measuring both rain and snow is not, however, a very satisfactory procedure, since if the funnel is heated strongly enough to melt the snow as fast as it falls, a good deal of evaporation will take place. It is better to use a simple cylinder properly shielded (see sec. 7 below).

4. Totalizers

A totalizer is a gauge for use at stations which can be visited only infrequently. It is usually a large vessel, having a mouth of known area, and sometimes provided with some form of water gauge on the outside. It is partially filled with a fairly strong solution of calcium chloride, which has a low freezing point; and a thin layer of oil is added to suppress evaporation. A record is kept of the amount of $CaCl_2$ solution originally in the gauge, and the amount of rainfall or snowfall can be found by subtraction.

5. Rate-of-Rainfall Recorders

The relation of the rate-of-rainfall recorder to the recording rain-gauge is the same as that of the dp/dt variometer to the barograph. Only one type of instrument has found much use—the rate-of-rainfall recorder of Jardi.

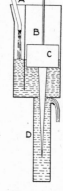

In this instrument the water from a large receiver falls through the tube A (Fig. 72) into the float chamber B. The float C has an appendix of diminishing cross-section extending through an aperture into a lower chamber D. The water can flow into D only through the annular space between the bottom of B and the tail of the float. The higher the float rises, the larger will this space be, and the float will continue to rise until as much water flows out of B as enters at A. The motion of the float is transmitted to a pen by a system of levers. By Torricelli's principle, the volume W of water flowing out is proportional to the area of the opening and to the square root of the depth h. Let us calculate the shape of the tail of the float to give a linear relation between W and h. Let R be the radius of the aperture in the floor of B, r that of the tail in the plane of the aperture (r is a function of h).

FIGURE 72
Jardi rate-of-
rainfall recorder.

Then
$$W = c_1(R^2 - r^2)\sqrt{h} \qquad \dots\dots\dots (5.1).$$

But by hypothesis
$$W = c_2 h$$

and therefore
$$r = (R^2 - ch^{\frac{1}{2}})^{\frac{1}{2}} \qquad \dots\dots\dots (5.2)$$

is the required relation. The constant c is best determined empirically.

Such an instrument responds to varying rates of fall much as the dp/dt variometer does to varying changes of pressure. It may be left as an exercise to the student to formulate the precise relation.

6. Measurement of Snow

It will be shown in the next section that the amount of snowfall can be measured by means of certain rain-gauges, such as the weighing types, if proper precautions are taken. At many stations, however, these precautions are not taken for one reason or another, and we must therefore discuss other methods of measuring snowfall.

Snow falling under completely windless conditions will lie as it falls on any horizontal surface, and it is easy to take a hollow cylinder with a sharp edge and cut out a sample, which can be weighed at once, or melted and measured in a graduate. If the snow has fallen on top of old snow, it will be necessary to cut a section near the point where the sample is taken, to determine the depth to which the cylinder should be inserted. If the snow has drifted, but not badly, it may be possible to use the average of several samples over as large an area as possible.

For snow surveys in mountainous regions, special snow-sampling tubes are provided, usually 3 inches in diameter, and having a sharp cutting edge. They are used with a spring balance graduated directly in inches water equivalent.

In many places the only measurement of snow is to measure with a ruler the total depth that has fallen. The water equivalent is then assumed to be one-tenth of the depth. The pros and cons of this, not being an instrumental matter, will not be treated here.

7. Exposure of Rain- and Snow-Gauges

(a) General[11]

As was mentioned at the beginning of this chapter, the ideal installation of a precipitation gauge would measure the amount falling on unit area of level ground. Given a gauge of proper design, arranged in such a way that raindrops will not splash in or out, it is almost self-evident that in the complete absence of wind this result would be automatically attained. The discussion of the exposure of rain-gauges,[12] therefore, is *entirely* a discussion of the effect of wind on the catch.

It was found more than a century ago that the catch of rain became less, the higher above the ground the gauge was placed. This was correctly ascribed to the increase of wind with height. In England these investigations resulted in the almost universal practice of installing the gauge with its mouth one foot above the ground, the ground being supposed to be covered with short grass. This height was sufficient to prevent water splashing into the gauge, and was kept as small as possible in order that the wind speed over the mouth of the

---

[11]See Puri, H. R., *l.c.*

[12]*Rain-gauge* is used as a general term in this section, for rain- and snow-gauge.

gauge should be low.   The sole disadvantage of this rule, as far as the collection of *rain* is concerned, is that it imposes rather severe limitations on the design of gauges.   It obviously was not designed with snow-measurements in view.

In order that at least the average wind velocity should be in a horizontal plane near the gauge, this should not be installed on sloping ground.   On the windward side of a hill the catch will be less; on the leeward side, greater.   Flat ground near a cliff is equally to be avoided.

The ordinary rule for installing a gauge is that it should not be closer to an obstruction than the height of the obstruction.   This is much too close, if a better exposure can be obtained.   Three times the height of the obstruction should be a safe distance, even if the object is a solitary tree; though a telephone pole might be allowed somewhat closer in view of the turbulence always associated with wind.

(b) The shielding of gauges from wind

A rain-gauge is an obstruction to the free flow of the wind, if it projects above the ground at all; hence one would expect to find a generally rising current on the windward side of the gauge, and a descending current to leeward, besides a complicated pattern of eddies about the gauge.   The problem is to modify the surroundings in such a way that the wind above the mouth of the gauge will be accurately horizontal.

Devices for this purpose[13] are of three general forms:

        (1) Pits
        (2) Fences, or an arrangement of posts
        (3) Shields, usually of metal.

The first form, while apparently excellent for rain, drifts full of snow.   The second appears to be inferior to the third.   Therefore in the interests of brevity we shall describe, first, the original form of shield, due to Nipher,[14] and second, the latest form recommended by Brooks.

Nipher's original shield (Fig. 73a) consists of two cones of copper, the lower one having a semi-angle of about 20° and the upper one of 45°.   At the rim of this is a ring of copper-wire gauze, which deflects the air but prevents the splashing of rain into the gauge.   The upper cone is braced to the gauge by metal strips set on edge.   Decades of experience suggest that this is the best general form, requiring two modifications; a space for snow to slide out at the bottom, and the substitution of a very flat cone for the upper cone and horizontal gauze, to add to the stiffness and stability of the construction.   The final recommendations of Brooks[15] are as follows (Fig. 73b): ". . . the outer 5 inches of their radius slopes inward at only 10° [to the horizontal], and there joins a 60° slope occupying 4.5 or 5.5 inches in radius.   This steep portion

[13]For a very complete discussion see Brooks, C. F., International Association of Hydrology, *Bulletin 23*, Riga 1938.   This paper contains an excellent bibliography.

[14]Nipher, F. E., *Zeits. f. Met.* 14:250-254, 1879.   All screens of this general form are called Nipher shields.

[15]*l.c.*, p. 20.

joins a vertical pipe 5.5 inches in radius at 8.7 inches below the top of the shield. The flat outer rim is covered by raised fine wire screening, against splash. These dimensions are suitable for an 8-inch gauge 2 ft. high. Such a shield can be varied proportionally for other sizes, though not to reduce the distances from shield to gauge." It would seem that for a gauge differing greatly from 8 inches in diameter, the proportions would be a matter of experiment.

The catch of such a gauge should be little affected by wind, and it should give reasonably good results with snow. For this purpose it should, of course, be placed much higher than the standard 1 foot of British gauges, or the approximate 2 feet 7 inches of those in the United States. To avoid snow-drift, it might be placed on a pole over level ground, the higher the better according to Brooks; not on a building.

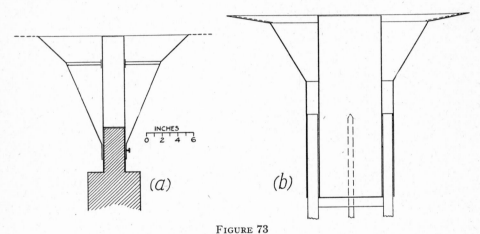

FIGURE 73
(a) Original Nipher shield.   (b) Shield as recommended by Brooks (1938).

The precipitation measurements of most countries are greatly at fault in regard to the shielding of gauges. Let us hope that, in time, it will be realized that an accurate knowledge of the amount of rain or snow which falls on a country is as important as many other statistical activities of government. A few thousand dollars would improve the exposure of all the rain-gauges in any half dozen states or provinces.

8. Measurement of Dew: Drosometers

In some parts of the earth, an important part of the precipitation occurs as dew. Naturally, attempts have been made to devise instruments to measure this quantity, and such instruments are called *drosometers*. Their general principle is to weigh the dew deposited on a suitably exposed plate. Perhaps they may render it possible to say that more dew condensed on one night than on another; but the actual amount of water deposited on the earth in this manner depends on the surface characteristics, especially on the vegetation, as anyone can see for himself on a dewy morning. Such instruments are not very widely used except in special researches, and detailed descriptions will be omitted here.

9. Measurement of Evaporation

(a) General considerations

The evaporation of water from land and sea and vegetation is obviously a process of tremendous importance in meteorology. It may seem surprising, therefore, that direct measurements of this quantity have not been made, and that only recently has an indirect method been devised, the full value of which is still to be ascertained.

The reasons for this are twofold. First of all, the terrestrial surfaces from which evaporation might take place are of all kinds, and have various amounts of moisture available for evaporation. At one end of the scale we have surfaces of water, and at the other, hard dry rock. Under given conditions of the atmosphere and of surface temperature, a certain maximum amount of water will evaporate from unit area of water surface in unit time. Somewhat less will evaporate from other surfaces. Hence we are led to make a distinction between *evaporation* and *evaporating power of the air*.

Now in order to obtain comparable results with various instruments, each would have to have an evaporating surface of the same "wetness," the same roughness, the same exposure to wind and to sun. In practice this means that actual measurements of evaporation are purely relative, and in order that they may be comparable they must be made with *identical* instruments. Conversion between the scales of different instruments is seldom of value unless the instruments are of the same type; are, in fact, intended to be identical.

Relative measurements of this sort are made by means of instruments known as *atmometers*.[16]

(b) Relative evaporation gauges (atmometers)

Atmometers may conveniently be divided into four main classes, as follows:

    (1) Large evaporation tanks sunk into the ground or floating on protected waters
    (2) Small evaporation pans
    (3) Porous porcelain bodies
    (4) Wet paper surfaces.

Each has its advantages and disadvantages.

(i) Large evaporation tanks

Large evaporation tanks are used at main observatories fairly widely, and are commonly 6 feet square and 2 feet deep, though there seems to be no standard universally adopted. They are usually lined with copper or zinc, and filled with water up to within a few inches of the top, the level at any

---

[16]Also evaporimeters, etc. Atmometer is the senior word (1813), has an unmixed etymology, and is official.

instant being measured by means of a hook-gauge (Fig. 74), placed on a stand-pipe in the tank. Rain falling into the tank is allowed for, on the assumption that the catch of a nearby rain-gauge represents the added depth of water due to the rain. A box-shaped cover of coarse netting protects the tank from animals.

Such a tank must be kept clean. A small amount of copper sulphate in the water discourages the growth of algae. The results are of value only in comparison with other precisely similar tanks, and do not indicate the true evaporation from large water surfaces, much less that from the ground. A better approximation to the evaporation from lakes can be obtained by floating the entire tank by means of pontoons, which ensures that the temperature of the water is not far from that of the lake.

(ii) *Small evaporation pans*

Most *recording* atmometers use small evaporation pans, drawing a graph of the variation of either weight or water-level with time. They are not very widely used. For eye-readings, however, a simple cylindrical pan with a pointed wire soldered to the bottom makes the cheapest and most robust atmometer. Such instruments were used for years by Wright[17] in a large-scale investigation (Fig. 75). Care was taken to specify the paint, the stand, and the cover, in order to obtain comparable results; but of course these have practically no relation to results obtained by any other instrument.

(iii) *Porous porcelain bodies*

Porous porcelain spheres, cylinders, or plates have been used by various workers since the time of Sir John Leslie (1813), but are nowadays generally associated with the name of Livingston,[18] who established a laboratory at Baltimore for their standardization. The sphere (Fig. 76) is much used in botanical and forest investigations; it is about 5 cm in diameter and 3 mm thick, and has a stem which is varnished or otherwise rendered waterproof. In use it is attached to a brass or glass tube which extends into a reservoir bottle; the sphere and tube are filled with *distilled* water and remain full because of the pressure of the atmosphere on the surface of the water in the bottle.

This type of atmometer is much used by plant physiologists because it is felt to give a good representation of the evaporation from the organs of plants. Its disadvantage is that it is easily broken by frost.

(iv) *Atmometers with wet paper surfaces*

This type is represented by the Piché atmometer (Fig. 77), which consists of a graduated tube with one end closed and the other ground flat, the flat end being covered by a circular piece of filter paper pressed against it by a disk. In use the vessel is filled with distilled water, the paper circle and disk put on, and the whole instrument inverted. The results from this atmometer are very sensitive to wind speed.

---

[17]WRIGHT, J. G., Dept. of the Interior, Canada, *Forest-fire Hazard Paper no. 2*, Ottawa 1932.
[18]LIVINGSTON, B. E., *Mon. Wea. Rev.*, **43**:126-131, 1915.

(c) *Absolute evaporation measurements*

All the devices described above are suitable for the sort of *ad hoc* researches for which they were designed, but do not contribute very much to the solution of the fundamental problems of meteorology. Recently a brilliant attempt to put evaporation measurements on an absolute basis has been made by Thornthwaite and his collaborators,[19] which, while an indirect method, is full of promise.

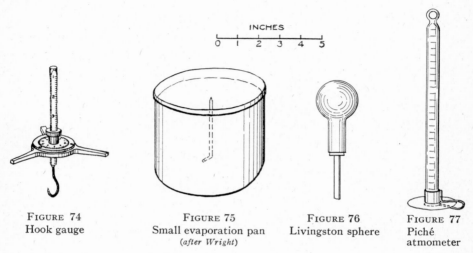

INCHES

0   1   2   3   4   5

FIGURE 74	FIGURE 75	FIGURE 76	FIGURE 77
Hook gauge	Small evaporation pan *(after Wright)*	Livingston sphere	Piché atmometer

Briefly, the method depends on the measurement of the vapour pressure (or specific humidity, etc.) at two levels, and the simultaneous measurement of the wind speed at the same two heights. The formula is

$$E = \frac{K_0^2 \rho (q_1 - q_2)(u_2 - u_1)}{\log_e \left(\dfrac{h_2}{h_1} \right)^2} \qquad \dots\dots\dots (5.3),$$

in which K_0 is von Karman's coefficient (0.38)

ρ is the density of the air (gms cm^{-3})

q_1 is the moisture concentration at the lower level (gms per gm)

q_2 is the moisture concentration at the upper level (gms per gm)

u_1 is the wind speed at the lower level (cm sec^{-1})

u_2 is the wind speed at the upper level (cm sec^{-1})

h_1 is the height of the lower level (cm)

h_2 is the height of the upper level (cm)

E is the evaporation in cm sec^{-1}.

The measurement of evaporation in this manner, therefore, involves two hygrometers of some sort, almost necessarily recording instruments, and two anemometers. The recording dew-point meter referred to above (page 100)

---

[19] THORNTHWAITE, C. W., and B. HOLTZMANN, *Mon. Wea. Rev.*, **67**:4-11, 1939, and other papers.

was developed with this application in mind, but more recently Thornthwaite[20] has constructed a double absorption hygrometer that seems ideally suited to the purpose.   This consists of a pump of known displacement, which draws air, on alternate strokes, through two absorption tubes.   A counter shows the number of strokes, and if the pump is left running at constant speed, two weighings of each absorption tube will give a *mean* vapour-pressure for the period.   Such an installation would seem to be a practicable means of measuring the evaporation from large lakes, flat country, and possibly from the ocean. The heights h_1 and h_2 used by Thornthwaite and Holtzmann were 2.0 and 28.6 feet respectively, but the upper level has now been reduced to 16 feet.[21]

[20]THORNTHWAITE, C. W., at Washington meeting of Amer. Geoph. Union, May 1, 1941.
[21]Private communication.

CHAPTER VI

THE MEASUREMENT OF WIND NEAR THE SURFACE

1. General Considerations: Units

Wind is air in motion; this motion is a *vector* quantity, a directed magnitude. Consequently it is to be expressed by two numbers, representing *direction* and *speed*—not "direction and velocity," since the term "velocity" includes both properties of the vector.

The direction of the wind is universally considered to be the direction *from which* it is blowing. There are two ways in which the direction of the wind may be stated:

(1) In terms of eight, sixteen, or thirty-two compass points.

(2) In degrees from north, measured clockwise; or in tens of degrees.

The first of these alternatives is used for most climatological purposes, and in airways practice in Canada and the United States. For simple climatological records, hourly records in particular, the eight directions N, NE, E, etc., are sufficient. In airways observations the sixteen directions N, NNE, NE, ENE, E, etc., are in general use. Thirty-two directions, employed in weather telegraphy in some countries, are usually given by number, "32" corresponding to N, "05" to NE by E, for example. "00" signifies *calm*, not N.

For navigation, both marine and aerial, the specification of wind-direction in tens of degrees is coming more and more into use. In this system the numbers 01 to 36 represent tens of degrees from north; "27," for example, would indicate a west wind. Calm is "00."

This system is not suitable for statistical work, since nobody wishes to construct wind-roses to 36 directions; and there is no *simple* means of converting the results into the eight- or sixteen-point system without emphasizing either the cardinal or the intermediate points. This will be obvious if we consider that N on the 16-point system covers the angles between $348\frac{3}{4}°$ and $011\frac{1}{4}°$, NNE $011\frac{1}{4}°$ and $033\frac{3}{4}°$, and so on.

The speed of the wind is indicated in any one of the following units:

> Metres per second (especially for upper winds—see chapter VII)
> Miles per hour (English-speaking countries)
> Kilometres per hour (Europe, for aviation and popular use)
> Feet per second (engineering use in English-speaking countries)
> Knots (nautical use).[1]

Conversion tables are available, but it is useful to remember that

---

[1] The expression "knots per hour," often seen in the newspapers, is nautically illiterate. The knot is one nautical mile per hour, and a knot per hour would be, not a speed but an acceleration.

(a) One metre per second = 2.2 miles per hour approximately
(b) One mile per hour   = 1.6 kilometres per hour approximately
(c) 60 miles per hour   = 88 feet per second.

In addition to the above units, a *scale of wind force*, called after Admiral Beaufort, its inventor, is used for non-instrumental observations at sea, and a revised form of it on land. Its thirteen numbers, depending on the effects of wind on the sea or on terrestrial objects, have been related to ranges of wind speed as measured by the use of instruments.

Besides speed and direction, a third characteristic of the wind is of importance in meteorology. The flow of air over the ground or over the sea is not smooth, but turbulent; and the degree of turbulence may be indicated by a quantity known as the *gustiness*. At least six definitions have been suggested for this quantity; that used by English authors[2] is convenient for use with the records of many anemometers. It is

$$G = \frac{V_{max} - V_{min}}{V_{mean}} \qquad \dots\dots\dots (6.1),$$

the values being taken over a period of 10 minutes.

It is comparatively easy to build an instrument which will make some sort of record each time the wind speed changes by one unit (e.g., 1 mile per hour). Given such an instrument, a useful measure of gustiness would be the number of times per hour that this change takes place. In symbols

$$G = \frac{\Sigma |\Delta V|}{T} \qquad \dots\dots\dots (6.2).$$

Note that the direction of the change does not matter.

A special problem is involved in measuring or estimating wind from a ship in motion. The observed wind will be the *relative wind*, that is to say the velocity relative to axes moving with the ship. In vector notation, the true wind CB (Fig. 78) is equal to the sum of the relative wind CA and the velocity of the ship AB. Thus if we construct a figure such as that shown, the scale of AB and that of CA being equal, the speed of the true wind will be given by the length CB and its direction by the angle NBC. Note that the angle CAB is that between the relative wind and the ship's course; in the example, the wind appears to be on the port bow, but is really on the quarter.

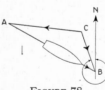

FIGURE 78
Estimation of wind
on board ship.

2. Wind Vanes

(a) Types of wind vane

The instrumental measurement of wind direction is done by means of a wind vane, almost certainly the oldest meteorological instrument. Funda-

[2] See, for example, SCRASE, F. J., M. O., London, *Geophys. Memoirs* no. 52, 1930.

mentally, a wind vane is a body mounted unsymmetrically about a vertical axis, on which it is free to turn. The end offering the greatest resistance to the motion of the air goes to leeward.

Of the numerous types of vane which have been constructed, we shall indicate only four (Fig. 79). The first of these (a) is simply a flat plate mounted on suitable bearings. The plate may take almost any form, according to the fancy of the maker, but is usually counterbalanced by a weight of much smaller surface, as shown.

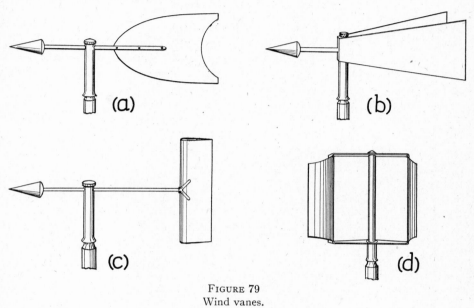

FIGURE 79
Wind vanes.

A somewhat superior form known as the splayed vane is shown at (b), and consists of two flat plates at a slight angle. It follows small changes in wind direction rather better than the single plate, but not nearly as well as the vane of airfoil section, shown at (c). The best modern vanes are of this general type, the span sometimes being three or four times the chord, as in the one shown.

The vane shown at (d) is not common, but is favourably mentioned by several authors, and will serve to illustrate the possibility of unconventional design. Its moment of inertia is obviously much smaller than that of other types.

A substitute for the wind vane, which has the advantage of being easily visible from the air, is the *wind sock* used at airports. This consists of a cloth bag in the shape of the frustrum of a cone, open at both ends, the larger end fastened to a ring which is free to turn about a vertical axis. The cone is extended by the wind, forming a tube several feet long. The convergence of the air within it tends to stabilize the flow and makes it unresponsive to small-scale turbulence.

Large *wind-tees*, roughly in the shape of an aeroplane, are used at important airports. They are usually arranged to carry lamps for night indication. A recent type is provided with a small anemometer which, when the wind drops below a chosen speed, makes an electric contact. The whole wind tee is then rotated by a motor to point in the direction of whichever runway has been selected by the traffic-control officer. If the wind increases, the wind tee is automatically unlocked and points in the direction of the wind.

(b) Constructional requirements

Nowadays it is much easier than in the past to construct a wind vane which maintains its sensitivity over long periods. The use of a shaft carried in ball bearings ensures a negligible resistance to motion, provided the entire vane is balanced about the axis. It need only be added that the resistance offered by reasonably well-constructed ball bearings will be very small, that of the transmitting or indicating mechanism being much more important. Provision must be made for lubricating the bearings at intervals, and it is highly desirable that the entire apparatus should be easy to take apart for cleaning.

A wind vane is often combined with an anemometer. Examples of this combination are described below (pages 130, 135).

(c) Methods of transmitting the indications of a wind vane

Even if the wind vane is provided with stationary arms pointing to the cardinal directions, serious errors in reading the wind direction may occur, and nearly all vanes nowadays are made to indicate or record at a distance.

If the vane is mounted on a mast which is on the roof of a building, a simple extension of the vane shaft will provide a *mechanical* means of indicating the wind direction indoors. A pair of mitre gears may be used to transform the motion of the vane into rotation about a horizontal axis, so that a dial may be placed vertically. However, such an installation is likely to be more expensive than the simpler kinds of *electrical* indicator.

The position of the wind vane may be indicated electrically by any one of three general procedures:

    (i) By a number of lights, operated by a contact mechanism
    (ii) By a meter with a battery, and a resistance which is varied by the motion of the vane
    (iii) By a pair of self-synchronous motors.

(i) The circuit of a sixteen-point direction indicator is shown in Fig. 80. To the shaft of the vane is fixed a transmitter A, having two spring plungers B, which make contact with one or two of the bronze octants C. The transmitter is so proportioned that the angle subtended at the shaft centre by the *outside* tangents to the plungers is equal to $22\frac{1}{2}°$ plus that corresponding to the width of the slot between each pair of octants. Thus the transmitter will make contact with one octant at a time over half the entire circle, and with two octants at a time over the remainder. In the drawing it is shown indicating NNE, being in contact with both the N and the NE sectors.

Nine wires connect the vane to the receiver, which is simply a ring of lamps. The eight principal directions are indicated by one lamp being lighted, while the intermediate directions, such as NNE, are indicated by two lamps.

(ii) An arm attached to the vane can make contact with a ring-shaped resistance coil (Fig. 81), varying the current in a meter in series with the resistance and a battery.

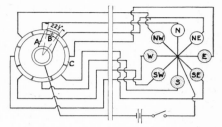

FIGURE 80
Sixteen-point direction indicator.

This has the advantage that only two wires are required, and the indication of direction is practically continuous. However, it has three drawbacks: (1) the voltage must be regulated, (2) there is a discontinuity at whatever direction corresponds with the ends of the scale, so that if the wind oscillates about this direction, the meter will swing over its entire range, and (3) contacts of this sort are not entirely reliable over long periods. The method is not much used in English-speaking countries.

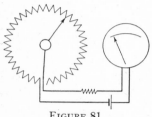

FIGURE 81
Resistance indicator.

(iii) By far the most satisfactory method of distant indication involves the use of *self-synchronous motors*. These are small motors with a single-phase rotor and three-phase stator (or *vice versa*), and are sold under such names as "Autosyn" (Bendix), "Selsyn" (General Electric), and "Synchrotie" (Westinghouse). When two or more motors of this kind are properly connected and supplied with single-phase A.C., their shafts do not rotate continuously like that of an ordinary motor, but any rotation which is imposed on one is followed by the others with an exactitude which depends on the torque they have to develop, on the voltage, and on the number of "receiving" motors connected to one "transmitter." For the purpose of indication, an accuracy of about 2° can be assumed.

The fundamental circuit is shown in Fig. 82 (for the three-phase stator). The rotor of the "transmitting" motor is turned directly by the wind vane, and a pointer is attached to the shaft of the receiver. The distance between the units can be as great as desired, provided the leads have not more than a certain resistance (about 20 ohms), and as long as the stators can be fed from the same supply network.

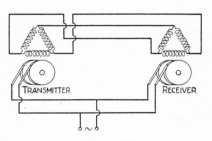

FIGURE 82
Connections of self-synchronous system

Self-synchronous motors can be used for the remote indication of any motion that can be converted into rotation.

(d) Methods of recording wind direction

It is convenient to classify the methods of *recording* wind direction according to whether they record a finite number of directions (usually 8, less frequently 16) or whether they record all the fluctuations of wind direction as a function of time.   The former are exclusively electrical; the latter may be either electrical or mechanical.

(i) Contact direction recorders

For the sake of clearness, we shall confine ourselves to those instruments which record the wind to eight directions.   All of these consist fundamentally

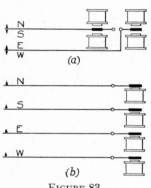

(a)

(b)

FIGURE 83
Contact direction recorders.

of a set of pens, either 2 or 4 in number, operated by 4 electromagnets. In the arrangement shown in Fig. 83 (*a*), the upper pen indicates N if pulled upwards, S if pulled downwards; the lower one, E if pulled upwards, W if pulled downwards.   The intermediate directions are indicated by the four possible ways in which two pens can be moved simultaneously.   The electromagnets are controlled by a transmitter similar to that shown in Fig. 80, except that its contacts subtend 45° and move over four quadrants.

A similar result is obtained with 4 pens in the arrangement shown in Fig. 83 (*b*).   Each pen moves only in one direction from its rest-position.   The mechanical arrangements are much simpler to make and to adjust than in the other type, but there are twice as many pens to maintain.[3]

Instruments of this sort are usually combined with some form of wind-speed recorder (sec. 4), and give a record of the direction either for each mile of wind, or at equal intervals of time.

(ii) Continuous direction recorders

Mechanical direction recorders have been in use for about two centuries, and have been given many ingenious forms.   At the present time the twin-pen recorder of Dines is the most generally used, but the single-pen recorders of Baxendall and of Rooker are sometimes employed.   They are most frequently built in connection with pressure-tube anemometers (see sec. 5).

No description of the peculiar double helical cam of the Dines twin-pen recorder is likely to be at all clear; and it is difficult to make its operation understood by means of a drawing.   Briefly, it consists of two helices, each one revolution long, formed as steps on the surface of a cylinder.   The upper arm is counterbalanced to press its follower up against the upper helix, and the lower arm to press its follower down against the lower one.   In operation,

---

[3]The mechanical details are too various to be treated here.   Reference to instruction books is essential to the practising meteorologist.

one pen is always at rest at one extremity of the chart. The way in which the transfer is made from one pen to the other is extremely ingenious, but must be seen to be understood.

An equally ingenious single-pen mechanism is used by Negretti and Zambra and by Friez. Official experience seems to indicate that the twin-pen recorder is more durable, but it involves the maintenance of two pens instead of one. The single-pen recorder depends on the proper action of springs and a dash-pot.

The Baxendall recorder interchanges the usual arrangement of the time and direction axes (Fig. 84). This instrument consists of a long, narrow drum which revolves with the wind vane, and a pen which is moved parallel to the axis of the drum at a uniform rate. It is a much simpler mechanism than the other types, but does not lend itself to a simultaneous speed record on the same chart.

A continuous record of wind direction can be made *electrically* at a distance by means of self-synchronous motors, in conjunction with any of the above mechanisms. As there is a good deal of friction, a rather larger type of motor is required than is necessary for the distant *indication* of wind direction.

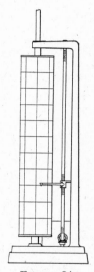

FIGURE 84
Baxendall recorder.

3. The Measurement of Wind Speed: Classification of Anemometers

Instruments for the measurement of wind speed are called *anemometers;* those which make a record, *anemographs*. Brazier[4] classifies anemometers according to whether they make use of the pressure, the kinetic energy, or the cooling-power of the wind. Since pressure-operated anemometers are of very diverse types, we shall use the following classification, which seems preferable for the present purpose:

(1) *Rotation anemometers*
    (*a*) Propellor or windmill anemometers
    (*b*) Cup anemometers
    (*c*) Special types

(2) *Pressure-plate anemometers*
    (*a*) Plate allowed to swing
    (*b*) Plate held normal to the wind

(3) *Bridled anemometers*

(4) *Pressure-tube anemometers*

(5) *Anemometers depending on cooling*

---

[4]BRAZIER, C. E., *Annales du Bureau Central Mét. de France*, 1914, Mémoires, pp. 157-300. Paris 1920, Gautier-Villars.

(*a*) The hot-wire anemometer

(*b*) The Kata-thermometer

(*c*) The heated-thermometer anemometer.

Anemometers will be discussed in this order.

4. Rotation Anemometers

(*a*) *General*

The first record of a rotation anemometer bears the date 1752, when Schober devised a means of indicating the rate of rotation of a small windmill. Nearly a century later, the cup-anemometer was described by Robinson (1846), who ascribed the fundamental idea to Edgeworth (1783). These two types suggest a classification according to the direction of the axes of rotation, whether horizontal or vertical.

(*b*) *Rotation anemometers with horizontal axis (windmill anemometers)*

While windmill anemometers are not very much used in meteorology nowadays, they have certain properties which make it possible that their use will undergo a renaissance. The most important of these properties is the nearly linear relation between the speed of the wind and the angular velocity of the windmill, which obtains if the frictional resistances are kept reasonably low.[5]

There are two types of windmill anemometers, having flat and helicoidal vanes respectively. The former is represented by the "air meter" (Fig. 85),

FIGURE 85
Air meter.

(*Courtesy of the Taylor Instrument Co.*)

commonly used for measuring the flow of air in large ducts, etc. The vanes in such instruments are usually of mica, so that the moment of inertia of the system is very small; this enables the air meter to give good results in an unsteady wind. The indication is usually by means of a train of gears and several dials. A relatively large correction is required at very low wind speeds.

Experiments with helicoidal (propellor) anemometers have been made at intervals in various countries.[6] The chief difficulty seems to lie in making the instrument durable enough for ordinary service, without adding too much to its weight. Probably a suitable rotor could be made out of some of the modern plastics, and the modern methods of measuring frequency might be used to count its revolutions. The problem of directing the axis of rotation into the wind still remains, with its attendant mechanical and electrical complications.

---

[5]See FERGUSSON, S. P., *Bull. Amer. Met. Soc.*, **15**:95-99, 1934.

[6]See BRAZIER, *l.c.*

(c) Rotation anemometers with vertical axis: I. The cup anemometer

(i) *General description*

The original cup-wheel consisted of four plain hemispherical cups with their diametral planes vertical, and disposed radially at equal angles about a vertical axis.   Later, after the investigations of Patterson,[7] the wheel of three cups came to be preferred.   Still more recently the edges of the cups have been beaded, and finally the cups have lost their hemispherical form and become conical (Fig. 86), with a gain in strength and probably also in performance.

In recent years there has been a general tendency to reduce the size and weight of the cup wheel.   The latest wheels are made of aluminium alloys and are about a quarter the size of that of the "Kew" anemometer which was standard in the British Isles for many years.   Whatever else may be said about this change, there is no doubt that the accuracy of the instrument in gusty winds has been improved thereby.   Nearly all natural winds are gusty to some extent.

FIGURE 86
Modern small cup anemometer.
(Courtesy of Julien P. Friez and Sons)

The essential parts of a cup anemometer are the cup wheel, a vertical shaft running in suitable bearings, and the necessary mechanism for (1) counting the revolutions of the shaft, or (2) indicating its instantaneous speed of rotation.   It is in the details of this mechanism that the various types and makes of anemometer chiefly differ, and we shall endeavour to indicate the main forms in a later paragraph.

(ii) *Theory*

Robinson[8] assumed, wrongly, that the ratio of the speed of the wind to that of the centres of the rotating cups was constant and equal to 3.   It was not long before it became evident that this ratio, which is called the *factor*, not only was not equal to 3, but was not constant either.

If V is the speed of the wind, assumed steady, and v the linear speed of the cups, then it is possible to express the relation between V and v by a power series

$$V = a' + b'v + c'v^2 + \qquad \cdots\cdots\cdots (6.3)$$

or, with Brazier[9]

$$V = a + bn + cn^2 + \qquad \cdots\cdots\cdots (6.4)$$

for a given anemometer, if n is the number of revolutions of the cup wheel in unit time.   The factor F is, from (6.3)

---

[7]PATTERSON, J., *Trans. Roy. Soc. Canada*, sec. III **20**:1-54, 1926.
[8]ROBINSON, T. R., *B.A. Report*, 1846, p. 111.
[9]BRAZIER, *l.c.*, Brazier uses the term *factor* for V/n, not V/v.   This is not a happy choice, as it renders the factors of different instruments difficult to compare.

$$F = \frac{a'}{v} + b' + c'v + \qquad \ldots\ldots\ldots (6.5).$$

Brazier set himself the problem of finding the conditions under which c' (or c) should be zero or very small. His results, which have not received attention from later writers, show that this is so when d/D is made approximately 0.5, where d is the diameter of a cup and D that of the circle described by the cup centres. This corresponds to a cup arm equal in length to the radius of the cup—rather shorter than in any standard anemometer of which we have knowledge.

Spilhaus[10] suggests a hyperbolic equation

$$\left(\frac{V}{v} - h\right)\left(\frac{V}{V_0} - 1\right) = k \qquad \ldots\ldots\ldots (6.6),$$

in which h and k are non-dimensional constants and V_0 is the wind speed at which v is very nearly zero. This quantity can be calculated from the dimensions of the instrument and a measurement of the bearing friction; and h and k can then be found from a calibration of any particular instrument. It is shown that both h and k depend not only on d/D but also on the size of the instrument. The treatment is interesting as the first successful theoretical attempt to relate V/v to the various dimensions of the cup wheel; but the practically important part of the paper is as follows:

Suppose we arrange the gear train or other indicating or recording mechanism so that a wind speed
$$V_i = Fv$$
is *indicated*, and let $F = h$; then $V_i = hv$, and if we solve (6.6.) for V, we obtain

$$V = \frac{V_i + V_0 \pm \sqrt{(V_i + V_0)^2 - 4(h-k)V_0 v}}{2} \qquad \ldots\ldots\ldots (6.7).$$

Taking the positive sign before the root, we see that when $h = k$, $V - V_i$ (the correction to the anemometer) is independent of v and equal to V_0. Thus by plotting h and k against d/D for the chosen size and design of cups, the value of d/D where the curves intersect should give an anemometer with a constant additive correction. It is interesting to note that for fairly large cups d/D has to be much less than for very small ones.

Comparing these results with the above-mentioned findings of Brazier, it would seem that a different size of cup would have led to a different value of d/D for the linear relation which he found.

(iii) *Experimental work*

Early experiments on the cup anemometer were performed on a whirling machine. This has serious disadvantages; and since about 1914 all the significant work has been done in wind tunnels. The experiments of Brazier have already been referred to. A very important research was undertaken

---

[10]SPILHAUS, A. F., *M.I.T. Prof. Notes* no. 7, 1934.

during the years 1921-4 by J. Patterson,[11] and similar work has been done on cups of more recent form by Brevoort and Joyner,[12] Spilhaus,[13] and several others.   The main lines of experiment are:

    (1) Calibration tests—determination of V/v
    (2) Static torque tests on one or more cups
    (3) Dynamic torque tests.

It would lead us too far afield to go into all the details of these tests, but it is important that Patterson found the static torque to be a maximum when the diametral plane of the cup was inclined at an angle of 45° to the wind direction. This conclusion was verified by Brevoort and Joyner, who found an actual discontinuity at this point in the curves connecting torque and angle.   One of their curves for a plain hemispherical cup is plotted in Fig. 87, together with one for a beaded conical cup under similar aerodynamic conditions.

Patterson found that the torque on the entire 3-cup wheel was more uniform around the entire revolution than that on the 4-cup wheel, and argued from this that the 3-cup wheel is preferable.   A much better reason for this prefer-ence is that, with the same materials of construction, the 3-cup anemometer gives a greater torque per unit weight, and is thus more sensitive to changes in wind speed. This has been discussed by Fergusson.[14]   In view of the work of Spilhaus, it is probable that the primary reason given by Fergusson and Patterson for preferring the 3-cup anemometer (namely the constancy of V/v) was the result of a careful choice of propor-tions rather than a fundamental property.

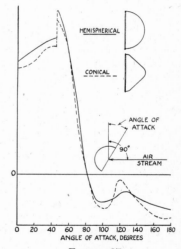

FIGURE 87
Static torque on cups.
(*After Brevoort & Joyner, N.A.C.A. Rept.*
513.)

(iv) *The cup anemometer in a gusty wind*

It has been recognized for a long time that in a variable wind the cup anemometer will register too high a mean wind, since the cup wheel accelerates more quickly than it loses speed.   Thus there is a very great doubt whether the calibration of the cup anemometer in the steady wind of a wind tunnel gives a reasonably good representa-tion of its behaviour in the open air.

Numerical data have been obtained by Fergusson,[15] by Schrenk,[16] and by

[11]PATTERSON, *l.c.*
[12]BREVOORT, M. J., and U. T. JOYNER, *N.A.C.A. Report* no. 513.   Washington 1935.
[13]SPILHAUS, *l.c.*
[14]FERGUSSON, *l.c.*
[15]*Ibid.*
[16]SCHRENK, O., *Zeits f. techn. Phys.*, **10**:57-66, 1929.

Schmidt,[17] using an artificially gusty wind. The error varies inversely as the period of the gusts and directly as the variability (gustiness) of the wind. It is of course greater, the greater the moment of inertia of the cup wheel, and can easily reach 10 per cent for wheels of ordinary dimensions.

(v) *Methods of registering the wind speed with the cup anemometer*

On the assumption that the cup wheel itself is satisfactory, we must now consider the various methods of indicating or recording the wind speed. This is simply equivalent to counting the revolutions of the cups; and a mechanical counter can be geared directly to the cup shaft as in the instrument shown in Fig. 88. This method is, however, obsolete except for portable anemometers.[18]

FIGURE 88
Anemometer with counting dials.

(Courtesy of Julien P. Friez and Sons)

An especially ingenious counting mechanism for this latter purpose has been described by Sheppard.[19] A small 3-cup wheel revolves a shaft in which there is an eccentric section of hardened steel. The rotation of the shaft causes this eccentric to rock a forked lever, the other end of which operates the escapement of a stop watch with its balance-wheel removed. Thus every revolution of the cup wheel causes the sweep hand of the watch to advance by one tick—usually one-fifth of a division. The great merit of this construction is that all the power for the operation of the counter is supplied by the mainspring of the watch.

Indication or recording at a distance is most conveniently effected by the *contact anemometer*. Part of the vertical cup shaft is formed into a worm which engages a worm wheel, and a further gear-reduction may follow, the ratio being chosen so that the final gear makes one revolution for some convenient quantity (1 mile, $\frac{1}{10}$, $\frac{1}{60}$, or $\frac{1}{120}$ mile, for example) of air motion. A contact is operated, either directly or by means of a cam, one or more times in each revolution of this gear. The number of times the contact is made can be counted visually by means of a lamp, aurally by means of a buzzer, or automatically by means of some form of chronograph.

If a contact is made for every 1/60th mile of wind, the number of contacts in one minute will give the wind speed in miles per hour, that is to say, its average value during that minute. Similarly 120 contacts per mile can be

[17]SCHMIDT, W. *Ann. d. Hydr.*, **62**:326-339, 1934.
[18]The instrument shown in Fig. 88 is also provided with electrical contacts.
[19]SHEPPARD, P. A., *J. Sci. Instr.*, **17**:218-221, 1940.

counted for half a minute, with a gain in convenience but less certainty of obtaining a good average.

A new application of the contact anemometer has recently been made by the Instrument Division of the United States Weather Bureau. By means of the circuit shown schematically in Fig. 89, the small condenser C_1 is discharged into the large condenser C_2 every time a contact is made. Between contacts the small condenser is charged from the regulated voltage V. The charge on C_2 is continually leaking off through the microammeter A and the resistance R, and the reading of A is proportional to the potential of C_2. This in turn is a linear function of the rate at which contacts are being made, provided that the time constant of the combination C_2, R is sufficiently great. In practice the elements of the circuit are so chosen that the indication of A gives the mean wind speed for the minute just past.

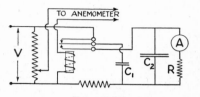

FIGURE 89
Condenser discharge anemometer.

This arrangement seems ideal for indicating wind speed at secondary stations, especially for airways use. It can be operated with a relatively inexpensive anemometer.

Contact anemometers with mile contacts are most frequently used in connection with chronographs to give a *record* of the wind speed, usually combined with a record of wind direction (see above, page 122). Three methods of doing this are shown in Fig. 90. At (a) is shown a pen operated by a heart-shaped cam, the latter being turned by an electromagnet through a given fraction of a revolution each time a contact is made. The record is in the form of ascending and descending steps, say 50 up and 50 down (as in the standard Canadian instrument).

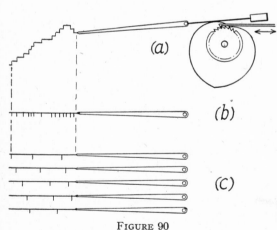

FIGURE 90
Recording wind speed with a chronograph.

A simpler method, needing no explanation, is shown at (b). The paper speed must be sufficiently great to separate the strokes of the pen even at high wind speeds. The labour of abstracting such a record is severe.

A third method (c) has recently been brought into use in the United States. Five pens are used, operated by separate electromagnets and connected to the anemometer in succession by a *stepping switch*, a standard piece of equipment used in automatic telephone service.   This arrangement makes it easy to count the miles of wind in fives.

At this point it may be well to show the complete circuit of a wind speed and direction recorder operating with six wires between the outdoor instrument and the chronograph.   This gives the number of miles of wind and also records the direction to 8 points whenever a wind-speed contact is made (Fig. 91).   The speed magnet also acts as a relay.

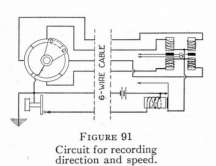

FIGURE 91
Circuit for recording
direction and speed.

In the Canadian Service a combined contact anemometer and wind vane is used, which illustrates the general design of such instruments (Fig. 92).   The combination is called an *anemovane*, a convenient term, even if not linguistically elegant.   The main features of the instrument will be clear from the drawing, but a few points may be enlarged on a little.

The direction transmitter consists of a circle A divided into four quadrants, insulated from each other and from the frame.   The tubular shaft B, fixed to

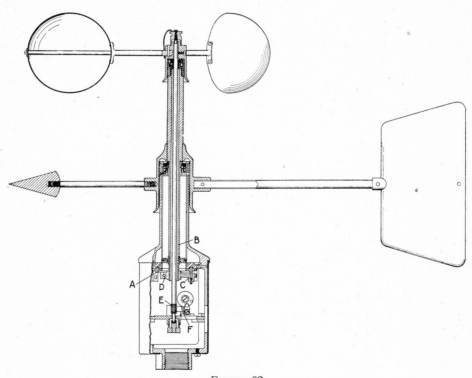

FIGURE 92
Combined contact anemometer and wind vane.

the vane, carries a casting C which bears a pair of spring contacts subtending 45°. The casting is clamped to B by the screw D. To facilitate adjustment, a hole is drilled in the middle of the north quadrant and a corresponding hole in C; it is therefore necessary only to point the vane to the north and rotate C in relation to B until a pin can be passed through both holes; the screw D is then tightened and the pin removed.

The contacts which make the wind-speed record are operated by the train of worm gearing E F. One contact is grounded to the frame, making it possible to use a common wire for this and the contacts on C.

Instead of recording the direction of the wind every time the speed record is made, as in the circuit of Fig. 91, it is possible to record it at any desired interval of time by means of a contact on a clock, usually the clock which drives the chart. This has an advantage at low wind speeds.

Where an indication and not a record of the instantaneous value of the wind speed is desired from a cup anemometer, several electrical methods are available. The *magneto anemometer* is the simplest. A permanent magnet with 6 or more poles[20] is rotated by the cup shaft within a wound laminated stator. This generates an alternating current of which the voltage and frequency are both nearly proportional to the wind speed. The A.C. is rectified by a full-wave dry-disk rectifier, and measured on a direct-current meter. The scale is linear for moderate and high wind speeds, but not at the lower end.

A recent anemometer[21] operates with a frequency meter in a somewhat similar manner, except that practically no energy is supplied by the cups. Details of the circuit are not available, but the final output is read on a milliammeter. A recording meter may also be used to give a continuous record of the wind speed, within the limitations of the cup anemometer itself.

II. *Special rotation anemometers with vertical axis*

The normal design of cup anemometer has been drastically modified for the recording of high winds on Mount Washington by Mann.[22] The special anemometer developed for the purpose resembles a Pelton wheel with 6 shallow buckets (Fig. 93). To prevent the accumulation of ice it is heated by internal stationary heating coils which can dissipate as much as 700 watts, a surprising power requirement considering that the drum is only 6 inches in diameter. This anemometer has recorded a wind speed of 216 miles per hour on Mount Washington, but is not satisfactory for low speeds, as might indeed be expected.

FIGURE 93
Heated anemometer
for mountain use.

[20]Such magnets are possible because of the remarkable magnetic properties of a new alloy called *alnico* (aluminum-nickel-cobalt).

[21]CORWIN, E. F., *Bull. Amer. Met. Soc.*, **21**:337-340, 1940.

[22]MANN., D. W., *U.S. Mon. Wea. Rev.*, **62**:189-191, 1934.

5. Pressure-Plate Anemometers

(a) General

The wind exerts a pressure upon any solid body placed in it; and if we have a body whose motion from a reference position varies with the pressure exerted on it by the wind, we have an anemometer. This is the oldest kind of anemometer; the idea is said to have occurred to Leonardo da Vinci, and a description of such an instrument was published by Robert Hooke in 1667.

Pressure-plate anemometers may be divided into two classes: (1) pendulum anemometers, (2) normal pressure-plate anemometers.

(b) Pendulum anemometers

The pendulum anemometer consists essentially of a plate, free to swing about a horizontal axis in its own plane and above its centre of gravity. The whole assembly is kept facing the wind by a wind vane. The theory of this instrument is not at all simple, and in fact only an experimental calibration is possible. Unless great care is taken in the design, resonance between the swinging plate and the gusts and lulls of the wind may completely falsify the indications of the anemometer. Such instruments are scarcely used at all in English-speaking countries, and elsewhere chiefly for special researches. Therefore we shall depart from our general rule in this book, and give an illustration (Fig. 94) of Hooke's anemometer of 1667, because it was the first real anemometer of any kind, and because it illustrates the principle of all instruments of this class.

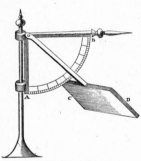

FIGURE 94
The first anemometer
(Hooke, 1667).

(c) Normal plate anemometers

We could equally well neglect the normal plate anemometer on the grounds of desuetude, were it not for a modern form of the instrument which is the most satisfactory anemometer yet devised for the detailed study of wind gusts. The wind force on a plate held normal to the wind is

$$F = cA\rho V^2/2 \qquad \ldots\ldots\ldots (6.8),$$

where A is the area of the plate, ρ the density of the air, V the speed of the wind, and c a coefficient depending on the shape and size of the plate, but not greatly different from unity.

The anemometer referred to above was described by Sherlock and Stout[23] in 1931, and is remarkable in that its natural period of oscillation is of the order of 0.01 sec. It consists of a plate A (Fig. 95) forming the front end of a tapering chamber B oriented by a vane C. The plate is 9×8 inches in size. It is supported on flexible spring hinges at its lower edge, and its motion under wind pressure is opposed by the stiff spring D. To this spring is attached an

[23]SHERLOCK, R. J., and M. B. STOUT, *Univ. of Michigan Engineering Res. Bull.* no. 20, Ann Arbor 1931.

iron armature E, which moves near the U-shaped iron core of a coil F, so that the impedance of the coil varies with the position of the armature and of the pressure plate.

To make a record, this coil is made one arm of an A.C. bridge (540 cycles per second), a similar fixed reactor being the adjacent arm, and a centre-tapped transformer secondary forming the remaining two. The out-of-balance current is rectified by a copper-oxide rectifier and recorded on a string oscillograph.

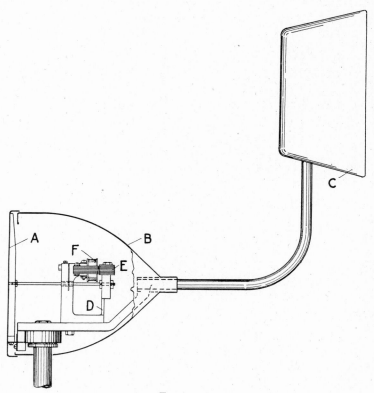

FIGURE 95
The normal-plate anemometer of Sherlock and Stout.

Sherlock and Stout had 12 of these instruments connected to an oscillograph with 12 elements, and were able to get a clear picture of the wind structure over a cross-section of the atmosphere 500 feet long and 250 feet high—certainly the most monumental programme of anemometry in all history.

6. Bridled Anemometers

The rotation anemometers, described in section 4 above, turn by virtue of the pressure of the wind on their rotating parts. Thus if they are prevented from turning, the force necessary to prevent rotation is a measure of the wind speed. In order that such an instrument may be independent of the direction of the wind, it is necessary to adopt some such construction as that due to Friez (Fig. 96), which has a wheel of 32 cups.

We shall not insist on the mechanical details of this instrument, beyond drawing the attention of the reader to the set of springs which make the displacement of the cups approximately proportional to the square-root of the wind-force, and hence to the speed of the wind. (We shall meet this use of springs again in the next section.) The angular displacement of the wheel is transmitted to a self-synchronous transmitter (see page 121). Such an instrument is useful when several records have to be made at various places from one anemometer, as at a large airport.

FIGURE 96
Bridled anemometer.
(Courtesy of Julien P. Friez and Sons)

7. Pressure-Tube Anemometers

(a) *General principles*

It has been known since early in the eighteenth century that the wind blowing *into* the mouth of a tube causes an excess of pressure in the tube, and that a current *across* the mouth causes a suction. Either of these effects may be used in connection with a suitable manometer, to measure the speed of the wind; or both may be employed in combination.

The pressure in a thin tube facing the wind is $P_s + \frac{1}{2}\rho V^2$, where P_s is the barometric pressure, ρ the density of the air, and V the wind speed. The suction in a transverse opening depends greatly on its shape and dimensions, but for a given system the pressure beneath such an opening will be $P_s - \frac{1}{2}c\rho V^2$ where c is a constant less than unity. The total difference of pressure will therefore be

$$\Delta p = \frac{1}{2}\rho V^2(1+c) \qquad \ldots\ldots\ldots(6.9),$$

and this may be read on a manometer connected to the two openings.

For meteorological purposes the use of this combination is to be preferred, since it forms a system which can be isolated from the room in which the manometer is placed. If we try to measure the pressure or the suction alone, we can never be sure that the pressure in the room (to which one side of the manometer is open) is equal to the barometric pressure;[24] and very serious errors can occur.

(b) Design of the anemometer head

Since one of the two tubes, the pressure tube, has to be kept pointed into the wind, it is necessary to provide it with a wind vane. Since the suction in the other tube is very sensitive to its orientation if a plain tube is used, some form which is insensitive to wind direction must be found. The double problem

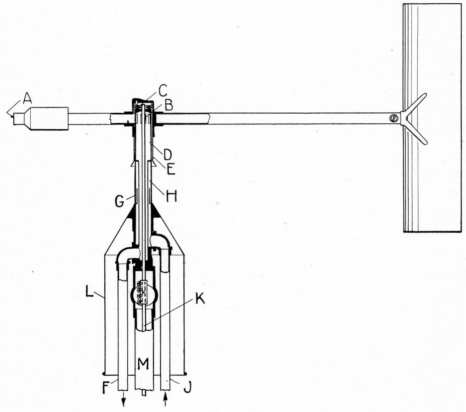

FIGURE 97
Head of the Dines anemometer.

was first solved by W. H. Dines,[25] whose pressure-tube anemometer is in use at important stations in most countries.

The head of the Dines anemometer consists essentially of a large wind vane of airfoil section having a tubular shaft and a tubular support. The pressure opening is at A (Fig. 97), and communicates with the interior of the tubular support by means of the slots B. The weight of the vane is carried on a ball-

---

[24]See the discussion on p. 13 above.
[25]DINES, W. H., *Q.J. Roy. Met. Soc.*, **18**:165-183, 1892. *Collected Papers*, p. 32.

bearing C. The seal between the vane and its support owes its efficiency to the provision of an excellent fit between the stationary tube D and the rotating one E.

The pressure is carried down D and out through F. The suction is produced by an arrangement of 96 small holes in 4 staggered rows at G; these communicate with the annular space H and the outlet J.

The entire assembly is supported on a pipe mast M, down the centre of which may pass a rod K which is fastened to the vane at the top, if a direction recorder is to be used also. The pipe connections, etc., which are not symmetrical about the mast, are covered by a cone and cylinder L, made of sheet metal.

The value of c (equation 6.9) for this head is 0.490, according to the Meteorological Office,[26] provided that the specifications for its construction are followed exactly. This value is rather sensitive to variations in the dimensions of the annular space. For the standard head in an atmosphere of $\rho_0 = 1250 \, gm.m^{-3}$, the above value leads to the formulae

$\Delta p = \quad 0.0186 \ V^2$ (Δp in mm of water, V in miles per hour)

$\Delta p = 0.000731 \ V^2$ (Δp in inches of water, V in miles per hour)

$\Delta p = \quad 0.093 \ V^2$ (Δp in mm of water, V in metres per second).

For air of any other density, the true wind speed V is related to the indicated speed V_0 by the formula

$$V = \sqrt{\frac{\rho_0}{\rho}} \, V_0 \qquad \dots\dots(6.10).$$

The pressures involved are small; for example, a wind of 20 m.p.h. gives a pressure of only 7.4 mm of water (less than 1 mb). Hence the manometers used to measure the pressure must be very sensitive. Three types are in use: liquid manometers, float manometers, and diaphragm manometers.

(c) Liquid manometers

Liquid manometers are used chiefly for laboratory purposes, and not to any great extent in meteorology. The ordinary U-tube manometer is scarcely sensitive enough, and special instruments, such as the tilted manometer and the Chattock gauge, are used. For ordinary wind speeds it is desirable to be able to read them to 0.05 mm of water, or better.

(d) Float manometers

(i) *The Dines float manometer*

In the ingenious float manometer invented by W. H. Dines,[27] the shape of the float is designed to convert the pressure readings into a linear scale of wind speed. The instrument is shown schematically in Fig. 98.

In a cylindrical tank A floats a bell of the form shown.[28] This bell is in two

[26]*Meteorological Observer's Handbook*, 1939 ed. London, H.M. Stationery Office, p. 122.

[27]DINES, *l.c.* (*Collected papers*, p. 35). The present instrument is greatly modified from the one first described, but the principle remains unchanged.

[28]Normally in water; but if it is impracticable to keep the temperature of the instrument above freezing point, a mixture of glycerine and alcohol, of unit density, may be used.

parts, the inner part B open at the bottom, and the outer part C completely closed and having rather more than sufficient buoyancy to float the entire bell. A pipe D extends up above the water level into the space B; this is connected through the valve E to the pressure-tube of the head. The suction-tube is connected through the valve F to the space G above the float. Thus the total difference of pressure acts to raise the float when these valves are open. The valves are so arranged that when they are closed, the spaces B and G are connected through small openings to the air of the room, reducing the difference of pressure to zero.

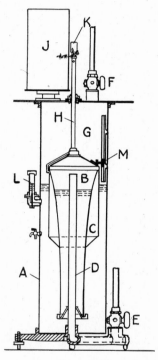

FIGURE 98
The Dines float manometer.

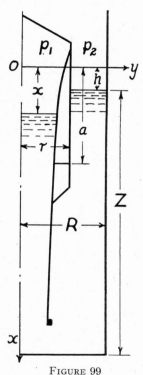

FIGURE 99
Illustrating the theory of
the Dines float manometer.

To the top of the float is attached a light rod H, which runs through a very accurately machined sleeve in the top of the tank. To this rod is attached the pen, recording on the chart J, and also a small cup K in which shot may be placed to adjust the zero. A wheel M, running in guides, prevents the float rotating. A water-gauge L enables the water-level in the tank to be kept constant.

It is an interesting property of this apparatus that the level of the water in the tank outside the float is independent of the pressure difference between the space B and the space G. This depends upon the fact that no external forces act on the float.   To demonstrate this property, we need only remember that the weight of the float, which is a constant, is equal to the weight of the water displaced.   Thus the volume of water displaced is constant; but this is equal to the total volume of the tank up to the water-level, minus the total volume of water in the system.   Since this latter quantity is constant, the total volume of the tank up to the water-level, and thus the water-level itself, will not change.   It will aid in understanding this minor paradox if we reflect that as the float rises, the reduced displacement of the float chamber C is exactly matched by the increased volume of the space B.

We may now calculate the shape of the doubly-curved surface forming the interior of the float chamber.   Since this is a surface of revolution, we need to find only the equation of the generating curve.   Let this be

$$y = f(x)$$

the origin of co-ordinates being fixed to the float and moving with it, and x being counted positive downwards, y radially outwards from the centre line of the float.

The diagram (Fig. 99) shows a half-section of the apparatus with the necessary notation.   Let the generator of the outside of the float be $y = r$ down to a point below any possible water-level, and at some level $x = a$ place an imaginary plane, cutting off a constant volume V_0.

Let the pressure inside the float be p_1, that outside it p_2; and let $x = h$ be the water-level outside the float.   If we consider a point (x, y) at the intersection of the inside water-level with the float, and write

$$p = p_1 - p_2 \qquad \qquad \dots \dots (6.11),$$

we may note that both x and h are functions of p.   Finally let w be the density of water, R the radius of the tank, and Z its height up to the outside water-level.

The pressure difference is

$$p = w(x - h) \qquad \qquad \dots \dots (6.12).$$

Now the total volume of water in the system is

$$\pi R^2 Z - V_0 - \pi r^2 (x - h) - \pi \int_x^a (r^2 - y^2) dx,$$

which is constant; so that under varying p

$$r^2 (x - h) + \int_x^a (r^2 - y^2) dx = \text{const.} \qquad \dots \dots (6.13).$$

Also we wish h to be given by

$$h = k \sqrt{p}$$

which locates the y axis at the water-level when $p = 0$; k is simply the scale value of the instrument.   This may be written

$$p = h^2 / k^2 \qquad \qquad \dots \dots (6.14).$$

Now let us differentiate (6.12), (6.13), and (6.14), obtaining

$$dp = w(dx - dh) \qquad \text{(a)}$$
$$r^2(dx - dh) - (r^2 - y^2)dx = 0 \qquad \text{(b)}$$
$$dp = 2hdh/k^2 \qquad \text{(c).}$$

From (b) $$dx = \frac{r^2}{y^2} dh \qquad \dots\dots\dots(6.15).$$

Substituting in (a) with (c) in mind, we have

$$\frac{2hdh}{k^2} = w \cdot \frac{r^2}{y^2} dh - wdh$$

$$\therefore \quad \frac{2h}{wk^2} = \frac{r^2}{y^2} - 1$$

Differentiating, $$\frac{2dh}{wk^2} = -\frac{2r^2}{y^3} dy$$

But from (6.15), $$dh = \frac{y^2}{r^2} dx$$

and therefore $$\frac{dx}{wk^2r^4} = -\frac{dy}{y^5} \qquad \dots\dots\dots(6.16).$$

Integrating, $$\frac{x}{wk^2r^4} = \frac{1}{4y^4} + \text{const.}$$

Now if we change the origin so that $y = r$ when $x = \frac{1}{4} wk^2$,

the constant of integration becomes zero, and

$$xy^4 = wk^2r^4/4 \qquad \dots\dots\dots(6.17)$$

is the equation of the required curve.

(ii) *The anemobiagraph*

The anemobiagraph is a modification in which the scale is made linear in wind speed by means of springs, acting as shown in Fig. 100, the float being cylindrical inside and out. In this instrument the level of the liquid in the tank is not constant, since the float is acted on by a varying external force. Glycerine solution (density 1.16) is used instead of water; this has the advantage of remaining liquid at low temperatures, but it must be kept at the proper density or both the zero and the scale value of the record will be altered. It has a tendency to take up water and become less dense. The instrument is certainly less accurate than the Dines anemograph.

(e) *Diaphragm manometers*

Diaphragm manometers are, in effect, large, sensitive aneroid chambers, and operate in the same manner and have the same characteristics (see chapter II). For use with

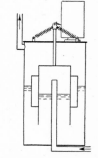

FIGURE 100
The anemobiagraph
—principle.

the pressure-tube anemometer, however, it is necessary that the entire apparatus should be in an air-tight case which is connected to the suction side of the anemometer head.

A typical instrument of this sort is that of Negretti and Zambra (Fig. 101), which has much the same mechanism as the precision aneroid of the same firm (see p. 40). No attempt is made to make the scale linear, though it is improved somewhat by a special control spring which comes into operation at higher wind speeds.

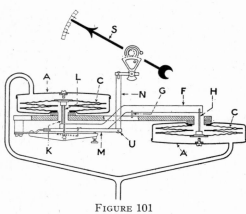

FIGURE 101
Diaphragm manometer.
(Courtesy of Negretti and Zambra)

Such instruments are most frequently indicating instruments, and may be combined with a pitot tube to form a portable anemometer, especially for use at sea.[29] But they are also built for use as recording anemometers, examples being made, especially for naval use, by Munro in England and by Friez in the United States.

The advantages of the diaphragm manometer are: (1) it has a small volume and short natural period of oscillation; (2) it can be made insensitive to changes of attitude, so that it may be used at sea; (3) it has no liquid to freeze. On the other hand, (1) the forces available are very small, (2) the thermal and mechanical properties of springs and membranes are involved (see chapter II). It is probable that, on the whole, the float manometers are to be preferred for land stations.

(f) The mounting of the pressure-tube anemometer

It will be well to give a few indications concerning the mounting of the instrument. Since in most instances a direction record is required, it is necessary to place the anemograph directly beneath the anemometer head. At large observatories a special hut is usually erected in an open space, with a mast above it; but this is not always feasible at airways stations where readings may be needed at any time; the mast is often put on the roof, and the exposure suffers in consequence. A hut might easily be heated electrically in winter.

Nowadays the best material for the connecting pipes is undoubtedly the copper tubing which is being used to a great extent for domestic plumbing. This may be obtained in coils or in lengths of about 20 feet, and is connected up by soldering, with no screw threads. Tubing not less than 1 inch in diameter should be used. This tubing is much smoother inside than iron or even brass pipe, besides being much lighter.

---

[29]*Admiralty Weather Manual*, p. 33.

(g) *Errors of the pressure-tube anemometer*[30]

If we may assume that the connecting tubes are tight, the instrument correctly adjusted, and the head clear of ice and snow, the chief errors of the pressure-tube anemometer are three in number: (1) the error due to changes in air-density, (2) the errors in an unsteady wind, (3) the error due to a change in the weight of the float.

(i) For stations near sea-level the annual variation of the temperature may amount to about 20 per cent of the mean (absolute) temperature, so that a range of 10 per cent in the readings may be expected. If a 5 per cent error is important, a correction should be made in very cold or very hot weather. Anemometers installed at stations above 1,000 feet or so should be provided with a special scale based on the mean density of the air at the level of the instrument.

(ii) Whenever the wind speed changes, a good deal of air has to flow in and out of the connecting pipes, and the float itself has to be accelerated. Two effects follow from this; first, the recorded wind fluctuations are out of phase with the actual ones, the phase angle being greater the shorter the period of the fluctuations,[31] and second, the amplitude of the recorded fluctuations is much reduced. The following table from Giblett[32] shows what is to be expected with a Dines float manometer connected to the head with 50 feet of 1-inch pipe on each side:

Mean speed 21 m/hr

Period (sec.)....................................	10	4	2
Indicated speed range ÷ applied speed range........	0.963	0.700	0.465

The conclusions reached by Giblett are, that means of very short periods are untrustworthy, and that the gustiness is always somewhat greater than that recorded.

It is also possible that the float moves up more easily than down, so that the *mean* wind speed tends to be a little high in gusty winds.

(iii) The float may change in weight by the condensation of drops of water on it. Giblett gives a table showing the error due to an increase in weight of 10 grams for various wind speeds, for a standard Dines float:

Speed (mi/hr).................	3	6	10	20	40	60	80
Error (mi/hr).................	3.7	2.0	1.4	0.9	0.6	0.5	0.5

and suggests that a film of medicinal paraffin on the water would remove this source of error by preventing evaporation.

[30]A very full discussion in GIBLETT, M. A., *et al.*, M.O. *Geophys. Memoirs* no. 54, 1932, pp. 26-33.

[31]SCHMIDT, W., *Ann. d. Hydr. u. marit. Met.*, 62:326-339, 1934.

[32]GIBLETT, M. A., *l.c.*

This error will not occur with diaphragm gauges, and because of the small volume and short natural period the second source of error should be reduced; nevertheless it seems probable that the absence of springs renders the Dines anemograph the more accurate over a long period.

(h) Distant indication with the pressure-tube anemometer

Self-synchronous motors can be used to give a distant record of wind speed and direction with a pressure-tube anemometer, or simply to give a continuous

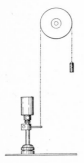

indication on distant dials. If a record is needed, the motor which moves the direction pens must be of rather large size, but the wind-speed motors must be kept small to minimize the reaction of the transmitting motor on the float. For distant *indication*, both pairs of motors may be of the smallest size.

An accurate method of converting the linear motion of the float into a rotation of the transmitting motor is suggested in Fig. 102. On the motor shaft is mounted a pulley with a shallow, half-round thread cut in its edge. A fine gold-plated chain is fixed to an arm which is clamped to the float rod; this chain passes one and a half times round the pulley, and has a weight of about 10 grams attached to its free ends.

FIGURE 102
Distant indication of wind speed with Dines anemometer.

The panel shown in Fig. 103 is used in the Canadian Service for remote indication in connection with a Dines anemometer. Besides the large dials for wind direction and speed, it carries a clock and an aneroid "station barometer" (altimeter) for use in giving altimeter settings to aircraft.

8. Anemometers Making Use of the Cooling Power of the Air

(a) The hot wire anemometer[33]

The connection from a heated wire in an air stream was exhaustively studied by King, who applied his results to the construction of a sensitive anemometer. In his apparatus a fine platinum wire (0.003 inch diameter) is heated to a constant temperature, this condition being determined by making the wire part of a Kelvin bridge. If i is the current through the wire when a balance is obtained, and V the wind speed,

FIGURE 103
Distant indicating panel

$$i^2 = i_0^2 + K\sqrt{V} \qquad \ldots\ldots\ldots (6.18),$$

where i_0 and K are experimental constants. To make the anemometer rea-

[33]See KING, L. V., *Phil. Trans. Roy. Soc. Lond.*, A **214**:373-432, 1914; *Phil. Mag.*, VI, **29**: 556-577, 1915.

sonably independent of the air temperature, the wire is heated to about 1000°C. Wind speeds of from a few centimetres per second up to about 10 metres per second can be measured in this way.

Hot-wire anemometers are not much used in meteorology, but could be of great service in micro-climatological studies.[34] For such purposes a direct-reading circuit is desirable; the only thoroughly satisfactory circuit of this sort seems to be due to Albrecht.[35]

(b) The Kata-thermometer

The Kata-thermometer is derived from the work of Leslie (1804), but was developed as a meteorological instrument by Hill[36] more than a century later. It is a spirit-in-glass thermometer with a large bulb, and only two marks on the stem, corresponding to temperatures of 35° and 38°C. The thermometer is warmed to over 40°C., and the time taken by the spirit column to fall from 38° to 35° is measured by a stop-watch. The wind speed V can then be derived from the formula

$$B^2 V = \left(\frac{F}{(36.5-t)\,T-A}\right)^2 \qquad \ldots\ldots\ldots(6.19),$$

where F is an instrumental constant, T the time in seconds, t the air temperature, and A and B experimental constants varying slightly for different instruments. This apparently complicated procedure has the advantage that it will measure very low wind speeds with fair accuracy.

(c) The electrically-heated thermometer

An ingenious anemometer on these principles has been devised by Yaglou.[37] A heating coil of fine wire is wound round the bulb of a mercury thermometer, and connected in series with a battery and rheostat. The voltage across the coil is held constant, and the excess over air temperature measured. This anemometer will measure wind speeds between 5 cm/sec. and about 30 m/sec., and is almost independent of ambient temperature and humidity, nearly unaffected by radiation. The equation connecting wind speed and temperature is similar to that of the hot-wire anemometer, and may be written

$$Q/(\theta_h - \theta_a) = K_0 + K_1 V^{-\frac{1}{2}} \qquad \ldots\ldots\ldots(6.20),$$

where Q is the heat input in milliwatts, θ_h the temperature of the heated thermometer, θ_a that of the air, K_0 and K_1 constants.

9. Exposure of Wind Instruments

Whatever types of anemometer and wind vane are employed, it is essential that they be suitably exposed for the purpose in hand. In special researches,

[34]See GEIGER, R. Das Klima der Bodennahen Luftschicht. Braunschweig 1927, Vieweg. Such instruments would not function during rain.

[35]ALBRECHT, F., in KLEINSCHMIDT, Handbuch, p. 393. A full description and theory does not seem to have been published.

[36]HILL, L., O. W. GRIFFITH, and M. FLACK, Phil. Trans. B 207: 183-220, 1915.

[37]YAGLOU, C. P., J. Industrial Hygiene and Toxicology, 20:497-510, 1938.

special arrangements will suggest themselves; we shall therefore confine our remarks to the ordinary exposure of wind instruments for climatological and synoptic purposes.

There is little doubt that deficiencies in the exposure of anemometers cause more serious errors than imperfections in the instruments themselves. For example, although the speed of the wind varies greatly with height, little attention is paid to standardizing the height at which anemometers are exposed. A height of 10 metres has been suggested as a standard, but anemometers are to be found on hangars, on airport offices, even on skyscrapers.

In rural installations, the anemometer should be installed as far away from trees as possible, but if there are trees at no great distance, the instrument should be as far above their tops as it would be above bare ground. A location near the edge of a cliff, or anywhere on a steep hill, is of no use unless it is desired to measure the effect of the hill on the wind. For the determination of the general movement of air, the exposure must be almost free from obstructions.

The installation of an anemometer above a large building practically ensures that it will record a fictitiously high speed, because the streamlines are crowded together as the wind passes the building. In such an exposure, the gustiness recorded by a Dines anemograph will also be high, and, unless the building is symmetrical, will vary widely with wind-direction.

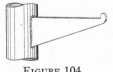

FIGURE 104
Step for an
anemometer mast.

The actual support of an anemometer is usually either a wooden pole, a steel pipe mast, or a lattice tower. For installation on the ground, a light steel tower is to be preferred, as it needs no guys; but a roof installation calls for a steel pipe mast, provided with steps and a horizontal safety ring at the top, into which the observer can climb and leave both hands free. A satisfactory and cheap form of step is shown in Fig. 104. It is cut out of 5/16-inch steel plate and welded to the mast in the shop.

Surprisingly large forces can act on the guys of a mast during high winds. Whenever a mast more than 15 feet high is to be installed on a roof, the services of a structural engineer or architect should be obtained to determine the adequacy of the roof structure and to design the attachments.

CHAPTER VII

THE MEASUREMENT OF UPPER WINDS BY MEANS OF PILOT BALLOONS

1. General Remarks

The process of making a pilot balloon observation is, briefly, as follows: A small balloon is inflated with a gas lighter than air, and released. Its flight is followed by means of either one or two theodolites, which are instruments for measuring vertical and horizontal angles. By graphical methods or by direct computation, the path of the balloon is determined from the angles observed at known intervals of time.

A balloon rising through the air partakes of the horizontal motion of the layer in which it happens to be at the moment, no matter what the vertical speed of its ascent—at least to a degree of approximation much higher than the errors of the experiment. The surface area of a balloon is so high, and its inertia so low, that its acceleration to the speed of the wind is practically instantaneous. Thus in order to measure the upper winds, we need know only (1) the height of the balloon at the beginning and end of suitable intervals, and (2) the position of the foot of the perpendicular from the balloon to the ground at the same instants. The means of obtaining this information is the subject of this chapter.

It is not our intention to enter into competition with the various official handbooks[1] designed for the instruction of civilian or Service personnel. It is rather our purpose to present the general principles and describe the apparatus involved, without entering into the details of routine.

2. Balloons

(a) Materials and manufacture

Balloons for meteorological purposes have been made of paper, oiled silk, goldbeaters' skin, and rubber; but the advantages of rubber balloons are so overwhelming that no other material is used to any extent at the present day. It is probable that artificial rubber will find an increasing use in the future.

Rubber is a compound of carbon and hydrogen which occurs as a long chain molecule; its structure gives it many interesting properties. While it can be deformed greatly without rupture, its compressibility (change of *volume* under pressure) is very small indeed. Many of the engineering applications of rubber depend on this property.

Nowadays balloons are manufactured chiefly from a suspension of rubber

---

[1]Air Ministry, Meteorological Office, *M.O. 396*, London 1936; *M.O. 354*, 1932. Canada, Department of Transport, *Pilot Balloon Instructions*, 3rd ed. 1940. U.S.W.B. *Circular O* (W.B. no. 1278), 1940.

latex—the uncured juice of the rubber tree.   For the sizes used in pilot-balloon work, there are two common methods of manufacture:

(1) The dipping process, wherein a "mould" made of polished metal, glass, or glazed earthenware is dipped repeatedly into the latex emulsion.   The balloon, after some drying, is pulled off the form, making it necessary for the neck to stretch a good deal.   The difficulty of obtaining uniform thickness limits the process to balloons not much greater than 9 inches diameter (uninflated).

(2) The hollow-mould process.   A measured amount of latex emsulsion is placed inside a divided hollow mould, and the mould shaken and revolved automatically in such a fashion as to distribute the material evenly over its surface.   The mould being taken apart, the soft, hollow mass is somewhat inflated, and dried in this state.   This process is used chiefly for larger balloons, and has the advantage that it makes possible a close control of the weight of the finished article.

For the measurement of upper winds, balloons of approximately 30 grams weight are commonly used.   Larger balloons with a weight of 100 grams are useful for high ascents, since a greater vertical speed can be obtained with them, and they are visible at a greater distance.   Balloons of 20 grams weight or less are often used when there is low cloud.

Balloons are made in various colours—white (or clear), red, dark blue, and black.   Clear balloons are more easily visible against a blue sky, appearing as a bright spot in the sunlight.   Red balloons are used with broken cloud (and in Canada with overcast skies also), blue or black balloons with overcast skies.

(b) The bursting thickness

When a balloon is inflated, its surface increases, but the volume of rubber remains practically unchanged.   Consequently the wall gets thinner in direct proportion to the square of the diameter of the balloon.   The very small thickness of the wall before the balloon bursts can be seen by a numerical example. Suppose we have a pilot balloon weighing 30 grams; since the density of rubber is 0.935, its volume will be $30/0.935 = 32$ cm³.   Now such a balloon will often stand inflation to more than a metre in diameter without bursting; at this diameter it has a surface area of 31400 cm².   Hence the average thickness of the rubber is only 1/1000 cm, or 10 microns.   Actually this is an over-estimate, since some of the volume is in the neck, which remains relatively unstretched.

It is obvious that the manufacture of a balloon of such quality demands the complete exclusion of dust or other impurities in the latex emulsion from which it is made.

(c) The gases used for inflation

Except in the United States, hydrogen is universally employed for filling meteorological balloons, because it is the lightest of all gases, and therefore imparts the greatest buoyancy per unit volume.   In the United States, an abundant supply of helium is available, which is used in preference to hydrogen because of its perfect safety.

Commercially, hydrogen is usually a by-product of the electrolytic manufacture of oxygen, and is available in steel cylinders into which it is compressed to a pressure of about 120 atmospheres (100 atmospheres for use in the tropics). Shipping it in this way is an absurdly inefficient process, as will appear when it is noted that the ordinary cylinder weighs 125 to 180 pounds and contains about one pound of hydrogen. Yet its convenience recommends this method of supply.

With slightly more trouble, hydrogen can be prepared by the action of caustic soda on silicon, the latter being available in the form of ferro-silicon containing about 90 per cent of the desired element. The advantage of this reaction is that it can be carried out at high pressure in an autoclave (of the general shape and size of a hydrogen cylinder), yielding about 100 cubic feet of hydrogen at a charge. Only about 20 pounds of chemicals are required for each pound of gas, so that there is a great saving in freight over the shipping of cylinders, especially as the latter also have to be returned. A small building should be erected to house the autoclave and keep the chemicals dry.

There is also the possibility of producing hydrogen electrolytically on a small scale at very low cost. The technical problems of the small electrolytic cell are rather special, but not insuperable. Unfortunately it is impracticable to produce hydrogen in this way at a pressure sufficient to fill a rubber balloon (see below); this necessitates either a small gas-holder and a compressor, or a larger one and a low-pressure pump. Great care has to be taken to maintain the purity of the gas at not less than 97 per cent, to keep clear of the range of mixtures which is explosive.

Helium is available in the United States, compressed into cylinders similar to those used for hydrogen. As it is an elementary substance, there is no way of producing it from other materials. It occurs as a constituent of natural gas.

Hydrogen should be treated with great respect, since mixtures with air or oxygen are violently explosive. The danger from cylinders in storage is, however, greatly exaggerated. Any compressed gas should be kept away from hot radiators, and out of the sun, to prevent a dangerous increase in pressure, and the cylinders should not be allowed to fall off a truck or to fall over; but the actual bursting of a cylinder in shipment or storage is very rare, because of the rigorous tests imposed by the shipping authorities. When it has come out of the cylinder into a balloon, hydrogen is much more dangerous.

Although helium is twice as dense as hydrogen, its buoyancy is only about 7 per cent less, volume for volume, since both are very much lighter than atmospheric air. The buoyancy of the two gases in air at N.T.P. (pressure 760 mm Hg, temperature 0°C.) is as follows, in various units:

Hydrogen		Helium
1.203	grams per litre	1.115
1.203	kilograms per cubic metre	1.115
0.0751	pounds per cubic foot	0.0696
34.0	grams per cubic foot	31.5

The hybrid unit in the last line is of use because the buoyancy of meteorological balloons is usually measured in grams, their dimensions often in feet and inches.

To give an idea of the buoyancy, or *total lift*, as it is called, of balloons of various diameters, the following short table is presented. It should be noted that the net buoyancy, or *free lift*, of a given balloon inflated to a certain diameter will be obtained by subtracting the weight of the balloon itself from the value obtained from the table. The buoyancy at a pressure p (mm) and an absolute temperature T will, of course, be obtained by multiplying the tabular value by $273\ p/760\ T$.

TOTAL BUOYANCY OF A SPHERICAL BALLOON AT N.T.P.

Diameter (inches)	Buoyancy if filled with hydrogen (grams)	Buoyancy if filled with helium (grams)
12	18	16
14	28	26
16	42	39
18	60	56
20	82	76
22	110	102
24	142	132
26	181	168
28	226	210
30	278	258
32	338	313
34	405	375
36	481	445
38	565	524
40	659	611

(d) Inflation of balloons

It is generally desirable, and indeed essential for simple pilot-balloon methods, to know the rate of ascent of a balloon, and to be able to predict it in advance with sufficient accuracy in terms of the following known quantities:

$W =$ the weight of the balloon (and its attachments, if any);

$L =$ the free lift, that is to say the weight that the inflated balloon, carrying any attachments, will just support without rising or sinking.

The construction of a satisfactory formula relating the rate of ascent v with W and L can be approached theoretically, even if the determination of the constants involves specially designed experiments. Hesselberg and Birkeland[2] have provided the following theoretical basis. The total lift $L+W$ is equal to the weight of the air displaced, or $\rho.V$ where V is the volume of the balloon and ρ the density of the air. Since the excess pressure inside the balloon is very small

[2] HESSELBERG, TH., and B. J. BIRKELAND, *Beitr. z. Phys. d.f. Atm.*, 4:196-216, 1912.

$$V \sim RT/p \qquad \dots\dots\dots(7.1),$$

but
$$\rho = p/RT \qquad \dots\dots\dots(7.2),$$

and therefore　　　　$L + W = \text{const. at all heights.}$

Since W does not change, the free lift L also remains constant, except for any possible escape of gas by diffusion or otherwise.

In ascending freely, after a few seconds the balloon attains a vertical speed v, when the air resistance R has become equal to the free lift L. Now R is a function of v, ρ, and the horizontal cross-sectional area of the balloon, A. From wind-tunnel experiments on spheres we may conclude that

$$R = b_1 \rho v^2 A \quad [= L = \text{const.}] \qquad \dots\dots\dots(7.3),$$

in which b_1 is approximately constant. It follows that

$$(v/v_0)^2 = \rho_0 A_0 / \rho A \qquad \dots\dots\dots(7.4),$$

where v_0, ρ_0 and A_0 refer to conditions near the surface. But

$$A_0/A = (V_0/V)^{\frac{2}{3}} = (\rho_0/\rho)^{-\frac{2}{3}}$$

and therefore　　　$v/v_0 = (\rho_0/\rho)^{\frac{1}{6}} \qquad \dots\dots\dots(7.5).$

Thus the rate of ascent is not constant, but varies with the air density and therefore with the height. The variation is not great, however, as may be seen from the following table, which represents mean values for temperate latitudes:

Height in km	0	2	4	6	8	10
$(\rho_0/\rho)^{\frac{1}{6}}$	1.00	1.04	1.08	1.11	1.15	1.19

The unknown loss of gas by diffusion tends to correct the change in speed, and in view of the many uncertainties of the entire procedure the rate of ascent is usually considered to be constant.

Now $A \sim V^{\frac{2}{3}}$, and at $\rho = \rho_0$, $V \sim L + W$. It follows, therefore, from (7.3) that

$$L = b_2 \cdot v^2 (L + W)^{\frac{2}{3}} \qquad \dots\dots\dots(7.6),$$

where b_2 is a product of several constants. Solving for v we obtain the formula

$$v = b \cdot \frac{L^{\frac{1}{2}}}{(L + W)^{\frac{1}{3}}} \qquad \dots\dots\dots(7.7).$$

The determination of b is a matter of experiment; it has been shown to vary with the Reynolds number.[3]

The Meteorological Office (London) uses the formula (7.7), with the constant $b = 275$ if L and W are in grams and v in feet per minute. If v were in

---

[3] R. FROST (Q.J. Roy. Met. Soc., **66**:367-369, 1940) has proposed a formula
$$v = b(WL)^{1/14} L^{\frac{1}{2}} (L + W)^{-\frac{1}{3}},$$
where b is said to be invariant. Experience with this formula is not reported.

metres per minute b would be 84.   But others[4] have doubted the adequacy of the exponents in the formula, and have preferred to write

$$v = bL^x/(L+W)^y \qquad \dots\dots(7.8),$$

and to determine the constants b, x, and y by experiment.   The formula used in the Canadian Service and the United States Weather Bureau is

$$v = 72L^{0.63}/(L+W)^{0.42} \quad [\text{metres/min}] \ \dots\dots(7.9);$$

and in order to recognize the influence of turbulence in the lowest layers of the atmosphere,

20 per cent is added to v for the first minute
10 per cent for the second and third minutes
5 per cent for the fourth and fifth minutes of the ascent.[5]

In the Canadian Service the balloon is released half a minute after the zero of time, and at the end of four and a half minutes it is assumed to have risen to a height equal to five times the final speed per minute.   This simplification does not introduce any serious error.

The above formulæ apply to balloons inflated with hydrogen.   Because of the greater size of a balloon filled with helium to give the same free lift, different constants will be necessary if helium is used.   Larger balloons than the normal 30-gram size, for example the newer 100-gram balloon, also need somewhat different constants.   In general, the formula seems to be a good approximation over a considerable range of L, but not over a very great range of W.

The adjustment of the free lift is made in one of two ways.   Either a simple nozzle of known weight is used, to which various weights may be attached; or the nozzle is attached to one pan of a "trip-scale" (such as is used in physical laboratories for many purposes) and the lift of the balloon balanced against rider weights and, if necessary, weights in the pan.   Such a balance makes it possible to allow for balloons of different weights from the average.   However, the formula is not very sensitive to reasonable changes in W, and modern balloons of good quality are fairly uniform; so that the simpler method is entirely adequate if (as is usually the case) one or two standard rates of ascent are always employed.

In dry, cold climates, the static electricity which is produced by the escape of hydrogen into the balloon may not easily leak away.   In the Canadian Service in winter it is the practice to ground the balance thoroughly, the observer standing on a metal plate which is also grounded.   Before the balloon is filled, it is dipped into a weak solution of glycerine to render it conducting. This practice greatly reduces the risk of fire.

The actual inflation of a balloon is a surprisingly complex and interesting phenomenon.   The excess of pressure inside the balloon has been investigated

[4] See KLEINSCHMIDT, Handbuch, p. 448, for a collection of formulæ.
[5] SHERRY, B. J., U.S. Mon. Wea. Rev., 48:692-694, 1920.

by Väisälä,[6] who found that the excess pressure Δp is related to the thickness d_0 and the radius r_0 of the balloon just before stretching starts, by the formula

$$\Delta p = \frac{2d_0}{r_0} P(n) \qquad \dots\dots\dots(7.10).$$

The parameter $n = r/r_0$, where r is the radius of the balloon at any time during the inflation. $P(n)$ is characteristic of the material and is a complicated function, empirically determined to be

$$P(n) = (\tau_1/n^3)e^{a(n-1)-b/(n-1)} \quad \dots\dots(7.11),$$

in which τ_1, a, and b are constants for all balloons made of the same material. For the Finnish balloons used by Väisälä, the trend of $P(n)$ is shown in Fig. 105. The circles are experimental points.

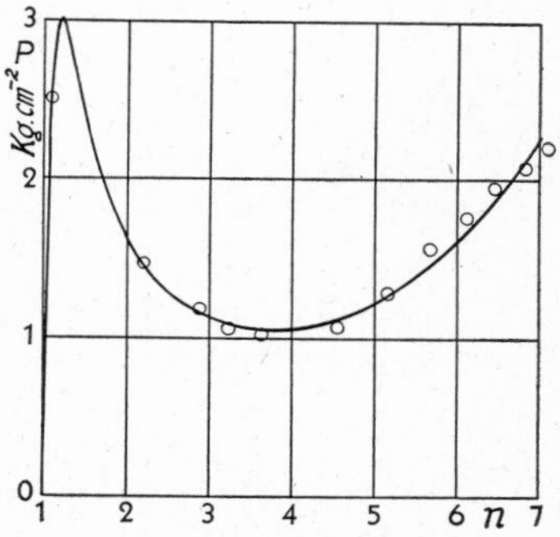

It will be noted that the maximum pressure occurs just after the balloon has begun to expand, and that the pressure falls off thereafter until n is about $3\frac{1}{2}$, when a new rise begins.

FIGURE 105
Values of $P(n)$.

(*After Väisälä*)

The maximum pressure required depends on the size of the balloon, as well as its thickness. The following table is given by Väisälä for a thickness of $d_0 = 0.04$ cm:

Diameter at start (cm)	0.5	5	7.5	10	13	17	30	70
Maximum pressure (cm of water)	960	96	65	48	37	28	16	7
Second minimum (cm of water)	340	34	22	17	13	10	6	2

Note that the ordinary "six-inch" pilot balloon weighing about 30 grams comes somewhere between the fifth and sixth columns of the table. It is not surprising that such balloons cannot usually be filled from commercial illumi-
nating-gas lines.

After being inflated, the balloon is usually tied at the neck with soft string, and a loop tied in the string so that the balloon may be carried out to the theodolite.

(e) Illumination for night flights

For night flights, it is necessary to have a light carried up with the balloon in order that its position may be observed. Two forms of light source are used, (1) a candle in a "Chinese Lantern" of translucent paper, (2) a small electric battery and bulb.

Of these the lantern and candle is the most efficient as well as the cheapest and lightest. It is not quite safe to use it in agricultural or forest areas in

[6]VÄISÄLÄ, V., *Ann. Acad. Scient. Fennicae*, series A, **48**, no. 8, 1937.

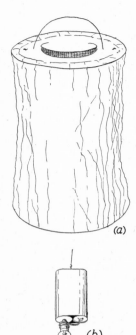

FIGURE 106

Night lighting devices.
(a) Paper lantern.
(b) Electric unit.

summer, however, on account of the rather remote possibility of the balloon floating down with the candle still alight.

The usual form of lantern is shown in Fig. 106a. It is about 8 inches high and $4\frac{1}{2}$ inches in diameter when extended, and is made of white tissue paper with cardboard bottom and top. About $\frac{3}{4}$ inch of a standard candle is stuck to the bottom of the folded lantern, the candle lighted and the lantern pulled quickly and smoothly out. It is attached to the balloon by about 10 to 20 feet of thin string.

A typical battery and lamp is shown in Fig. 106b. This assembly consists of two small flashlight cells connected in series, and a special lamp rated at 2 volts, the entire unit weighing about 35 grams. It gives much light at first, but the intensity rapidly falls off, and it cannot be followed as far as the lantern and candle. The battery is usually attached, lamp downwards, below a small parachute (about 12 inches in diameter) made of tissue paper. From the apex of the parachute a thin string runs to the balloon.

When inflating the balloon for a night flight, the weight of the lighting unit should simply be added to the free lift calculated for the balloon alone. As far as can be determined from recent experiments in various parts of Canada, this procedure gives the correct rate of ascent to the combination.

A completely different method of making night ascents has been suggested by Spilhaus.[7] This makes use of a series of flashes, obtained by means of a number of charges of flash-powder fired at predetermined intervals by a fuse. A camera with a very wide angle lens is directed vertically, and all the flashes are photographed on the same plate, the shutter being left open until the flight is completed. The method does not seem to have come into use, possibly because of a certain danger of fire; but it might be of interest for a very detailed study of the wind near the ground, because the flashes could be caused to occur at very short intervals, and observations could thus be obtained more frequently than with a theodolite (see sec. 3).[8]

3. Theodolites for Following Balloons

(a) General

The theodolite is an optical instrument for measuring horizontal and vertical angles, and is used largely for that purpose by engineers (in North America under the name *transit*). The balloon theodolite is exactly the same in prin-

---

[7] SPILHAUS, A. F., *Bull. Amer. Met. Soc.*, 18:154, 1937.

[8] The same result could be obtained, with more accuracy as to timing, by photographing the scales of a theodolite with a motion-picture camera.

ciple as the engineering instrument, but has its optical system so arranged that the axis of the eyepiece remains horizontal no matter where the telescope is pointed. Since the order of accuracy of the readings is very different from what is required in surveying, the arrangements for reading the angles are also somewhat special.

In the last thirty-five years a great many designs have been produced, both in Europe and in North America. Several of these have been *registering* theodolites, that is to say, theodolites equipped to make a record of the angles observed; but these have not been used to any extent in English-speaking countries. We have not space to describe all the various constructions, or even all the representative types. We shall therefore restrict this section to a description of three instruments:

(1) The Theodolite Mark I of the Meteorological Office, by Watts, of London

(2) The new Gurley Pilot-balloon Theodolite

(3) The shipboard theodolite of Keuffel and Esser, used to some extent by ships of both Great Britain and the United States.

A familiarity with the general features of surveying instruments will be assumed.

(b) *The Theodolite Mark I of the Meteorological Office, London*

This theodolite, now standard in the British Empire, was designed[9] at the Meteorological Office in collaboration with Messrs. E. R. Watts & Son, Ltd

Its general appearance is shown in Fig. 107a, and a cutaway drawing, illustrating some features of the mechanism, in Fig. 107b. It may be considered a good example of the "totally enclosed" type of instrument.

In common with all other balloon theodolites for use on land, it has a telescope with a bent optical axis, the horizontal part of which coincides with the horizontal axis of rotation. A secondary, wide angle telescope is also provided, having the objective A, and using the same eyepiece D as the main telescope. This is brought into use by rotating a mirror into the line of sight by means of a small lever B (the diagram (Fig. 108) will make the matter clear), and makes it easy to keep a balloon in view during the

FIGURE 107a
Watts' Theodolite. General view from eyepiece side.
(*Courtesy of E. R. Watts and Son Ltd.*)

[9]CRANNA, R., *Q.J. Roy. Met. Soc.*, **64**:613-615, 1938.

first minute of a flight, when its motion is likely to be irregular and rapid. It will be noted from the diagram that a pentagonal prism is used in the main telescope; this has the advantage that the perpendicularity of the two parts of the optical axis is independent of the exact position of the prism, but the disadvantage that the quality of the reflection depends on the silvering of the two reflecting faces, neither reflection being total.

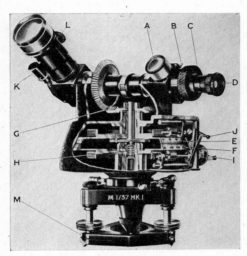

FIGURE 107*b*
Watts' Theodolite. Cutaway view.

(Courtesy of E. R. Watts and Son Ltd.)

A graticule having 100 divisions is placed at the focus of the eye-piece, the entire assembly being moved along the axis by the knurled ring C (Fig. 107b). The eyepiece itself can be moved independently, in order to focus the graticule.

The remainder of the instrument consists largely of arrangements for moving the telescope about vertical and horizontal axes and indicating its position by means of scales. The construction of the sub-base M, levelling screws, and vertical axis is not special. It is in the arrangement of the scales that the instrument is original.

In order to bring the vertical circle E into close proximity with the horizontal circle F, it is connected to the telescope by a pair of miter gears G. A spring H pushes the gears into contact in order to avoid backlash and take up wear. Both scales are visible through one window directly under the eyepiece. Both circles are driven in slow motion by handwheels, one of which is shown at I in Fig. 107b. These handwheels, which are graduated in tenths of a degree, operate worms engaging with accurate 360-tooth wheels attached to the circles. The worms can be disengaged by the levers (J) near the hand-wheels, so that the telescope may be moved rapidly in azimuth or altitude.

In a very recent model, the worm wheel moving the telescope in altitude is in a vertical plane and attached directly to the telescope. Only the circle is driven by the bevel gearing.

The whole degrees of both altitude and azimuth are read against a fiducial line engraved

FIGURE 108
Watts' Theodolite —
diagram of telescopes.

on the glass window, and the tenths of degrees on the handwheels. (Many observers, however, estimate the tenths on the scales without reference to the wheels.)

A lamp is provided to illuminate the scales, and another to throw an adjustable amount of light into the field of view. This second lamp is carried in a shield K, and illuminates a small inclined reflecting surface carried on a stem projecting into the telescope barrel. The stem can be turned by the knurled head L, enabling the illumination in the field to be varied continuously from zero. This device is simple and elegant, but it is questionable whether it would not be better to illuminate the graticule than to light up the whole field.

The batteries for illumination are carried in the top part of the instrument. This is very convenient, but not practicable in cold climates, and it has been necessary to fit these theodolites with a slip-ring and brush system for use under Canadian conditions.

(c) The Gurley theodolite

The balloon theodolite made by W. and L. E. Gurley, of Troy, N.Y., is an excellent modern example of more conventional design, and is about as simple as such an instrument could well be. The two scales have been brought into sufficiently close proximity for easy reading by the observer, and the slow motion of the circles is extremely simple, being performed by friction gearing attached to milled heads at A and B (Fig. 109). If the telescope is turned by hand it will drive the friction gearing, so that no disengagement is required. There is no secondary telescope, but open sights are provided for picking up the balloon. A lamp C illuminates the scales, and the "crosswires" are illuminated by a second lamp at D. The electrical connections are made to a bayonet connector E, the idea being that the observer will carry a flashlight battery in his pocket.

FIGURE 109
Gurley theodolite.
(Courtesy of W. and L. E. Gurley)

(d) The Keuffel and Esser shipboard theodolite

The problem of making pilot-balloon observations from the deck of a ship is obviously complicated by the motion of the vessel. In order to keep the theodolite approximately level, it is attached to the top of its tripod by a Cardan suspension, a long rod carrying a heavy weight serving to put the centre of gravity just below the point of support. Even with such a mounting, however, it is impossible to use an ordinary theodolite, and an instrument is used which is really a combination theodolite and sextant.

The general principle of such an instrument[10] is shown in Fig. 110.   The
telescope which is directed at the balloon consists of the eyepice E, the prism
P_1, and the objective O_1, together with a rotatable mirror M attached to a

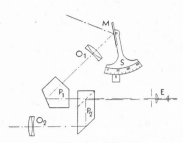

scale S which moves past an index.   At the
same time two narrow strips of the horizon
are thrown into the field of view by the objective O_2 and the prism system P_2.   When the
image of the balloon coincides with the horizon
and with a vertical cross-hair, the elevation
angle is read from the scale S and the horizontal
angle (usually with reference to the ship's
head) on a circle similar to the horizontal circle
of an ordinary theodolite.

FIGURE 110
Principle of the shipboard
theodolite.

For use when a natural horizon is not visible, provision is made for throwing the image
of a level-bubble into the field of view.   For use at night, illumination is provided for both the scales and the bubble.

Several other methods for following balloons are possible on shipboard,
especially on naval ships; for instance, by means of the telescopic sight of a
high-angle gun; but such methods can be used only when the ship is reasonably
steady, and the shipboard theodolite is to be preferred.

(e) Light filters for theodolite observations

Coloured light filters are often used with theodolites to increase the visibility of the balloon against its background, especially by reducing the brightness of the light scattered by the haze, or if the sky is blue, by the use of a
highly selective filter that makes it appear very dark.[11]   For use with clear
balloons against a blue sky, a red filter is the best, the balloon appearing as a
red speck against a dark background.   A neutral filter for very bright white
clouds, and a red-absorbing one for use near sunrise and sunset, may also be
desirable.

(f) The mounting of theodolites

The mounting which is normally used for surveying instruments, namely
a tripod, was used for pilot-balloon work for many years.   At fixed stations
there is no good reason for the use of such an unhandy support, and an
adjustable stand was adopted in the Canadian Service about 1928, in the
United States about ten years later.   The Canadian stand (Fig. 111) is made
of brass, and has a vertical range of about 1 foot.   A stainless steel pin
working in a groove maintains the azimuth adjustment of the theodolite

---

[10]The best-known type is made by the Keuffel & Esser Co., Hoboken, N.J.
[11]WATT, R. A. WATSON, *M.O. Prof. Notes* no. 16, London 1931, H.M. Stationery Office.

even if it is raised or lowered, though not certainly with such accuracy that a re-check can be dispensed with. The lower end of the brass part has a 2-inch pipe thread, and a 3-inch pipe stand is generally used, with a reducing coupling.

The stand used in the United States is similar in principle, but is raised and lowered by a rack, pinion, worm, and wheel arrangement.

Early in the history of pilot ballooning in Canada, it was recognized that some protection for the observer was essential in winter. A good shelter should not be any larger than is required to allow sufficient room to walk around the theodolite; otherwise the wind is more likely to form eddies within the structure. The Canadian shelter is extremely simple and effective (Fig. 112). It consists of a square enclosure, $4\frac{1}{2}$ feet on a side and $5\frac{1}{2}$ feet high, with a low door in one (usually the south) side. Each wall is surmounted by a hinged flap 10 inches wide, normally fastened by a chain so as to incline inwards at an angle of 30° to the vertical. The observer takes note of the direction of the surface wind, and throws down the appropriate flap, or two flaps, leaving the remaining flaps to windward to deflect the breeze well over his head. If the wind is very light, it may not be necessary to release any of the flaps.

FIGURE 111
Theodolite stand.

A rather better looking structure can be made on the same principles, but octagonal.

4. Methods of Observation and Computation

FIGURE 112
Pilot-balloon shelter.

(a) *The single-theodolite method*

(i) *Theory*

The single-theodolite method of pilot-balloon observation depends for its validity entirely on the constancy of the ascensional rate of the balloon (see sec. 2d above). If this is assumed, so that we may suppose that we know the height Z_1 of the balloon at any instant, then the horizontal distance (OP′, Fig. 113) from the theodolite to the point below the balloon is

$$r = Z_1 \cot H_1 \qquad \ldots\ldots\ldots (7.12).$$

H_1 is the elevation angle. In addition the azimuth A_1 is read, so that the polar co-ordinates (r_1, A_1) of the projection of the balloon's position can be written down.

In some convenient time, say one minute, let the balloon move from P to Q, and let the new elevation angle and azimuth be H_2 and A_2, respectively, the new height Z_2. Then the position of Q' can be found as was that of P'; and the magnitude and direction of P'Q' gives the horizontal motion of the balloon in the elapsed interval. The direction of Q'P' is therefore the mean direction *from which* the wind is blowing in the layer of air between Z_1 and Z_2, and the magnitude of P'Q' gives its movement during the minute, in the units used for Z_1 and Z_2, OP' and OQ'.

There are many methods of expediting the calculation of the vector Q'P'. We shall refer to three, one arithmetical, using a slide-rule, the other two graphical.

(ii) *The slide-rule method*[12]

The Meteorological Office, London, uses a slide-rule method of computing the ascent. It is not our intention to reproduce the instructions in detail, but the following is the simple theory.

Fig. 114 is the horizontal projection of the path of the balloon, the theodolite being at O, the projection of the balloon's position at the *n*th minute at P' and at the $(n+1)$th minute at Q'. The direction ON is north and OE east. We wish to find P'Q'; let us resolve it into components along OE and ON.

The component along OE is $V_E = OE_2 - OE_1$, which is clearly

$$V_E = Z_2 \cot H_2 \sin A_2 - Z_1 \cot H_1 \sin A_1 \quad \ldots\ldots(7.13).$$

Similarly the component along ON is

$$V_N = Z_2 \cot H_2 \cos A_2 - Z_1 \cot H_1 \cos A_1 \quad \ldots\ldots(7.14),$$

and thus the direction of P'Q' is given by

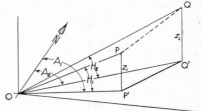

FIGURE 113
Geometry of the
single-theodolite method.

$$\tan \phi = V_E / V_N \quad \ldots\ldots(7.15),$$

and the magnitude P'Q' by

$$P'Q' = V_E / \sin \phi \quad \ldots(7.16).$$

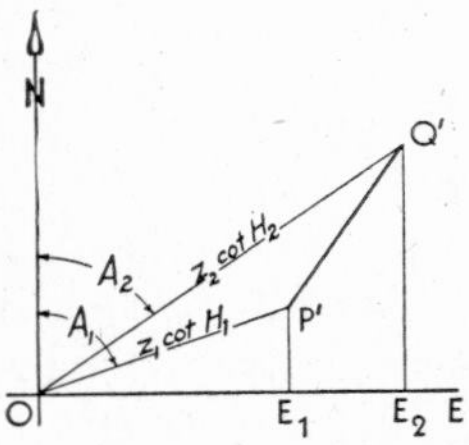

FIGURE 114
The slide-rule method
of computation.

The chief opportunity for error in this computation, so fundamentally simple, lies in the possibility of ascribing the wrong *sign* to one or more of the quantities $\sin A_1$, $\sin A_2$, $\cos A_1$, $\cos A_2$. It is abundantly clear that an observer with a good knowledge of trigonometry, who comprehends exactly what is being done, will

[12]Air Ministry, Meteorological Office, *M.O. 396*, London 1936, p. 14.

make far fewer mistakes than one who merely follows rules imperfectly understood.

(iii) *The graphical methods*

The so-called graphical methods of plotting the projection of the path of the balloon, and deriving the wind velocity from the diagram, are really semi-graphical, the computation of OP', OQ', etc., being performed on the slide-rule or by means of tables before any plotting is done. These methods stem from the work of Jonas,[13] and surprisingly little change has occurred even in the details.

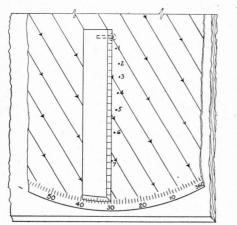 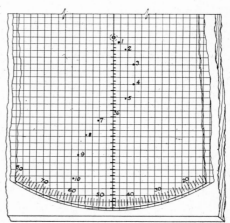

FIGURE 115

Plotting boards. (*a*) Canadian, (*b*) U.S. Weather Bureau type.

Two variations of the graphical method, differing chiefly in the construction of the plotting board, are employed in the United States and in Canada. The board used by the United States Weather Bureau has a transparent disk of plastic with a fixed sheet of cross-section paper beneath; the Canadian one has an opaque disk, ruled with parallel lines, and a graduated arm swinging about the centre of the board. The two constructions are shown in Fig. 115.

In each of these, the circular disk is graduated around the edge in degrees, making it possible to plot a point in azimuth. The radius from the centre to the point is determined by (7.12), either by slide-rule or by tables. It is here that the two methods become somewhat different.

In the Canadian method, the horizontal scale of the plot is determined by the ascensional rate of the balloon, each centimetre being equivalent to the distance (e.g., 180 metres) that the balloon rises in one minute; or to some simple fraction of this. Thus one set of tables giving values of $n \cot H$ ($n = 1, 2, 3, \ldots$) suffices for all rates of ascent.[14] It is necessary only to turn the page between readings, to pass from one value of n to the next.

[13]JONAS, G., *Beitr. z. Phys. d.f. Atm.*, **4**:1-12, 1912.

[14]As in JONAS, *l.c.*; but the idea seems to have arisen in several quarters.

In the United States method, two scales, 1 cm = 200 m and 1 cm = 400 m, are printed on the fixed cross-section paper along a radial index line; the value of r having been calculated in metres, the transparent disk is turned until the azimuth angle A is over the index line, and the point plotted.

In either method, a number of points are obtained, corresponding to A and H for every minute of the flight, which when connected form the locus of the horizontal projections of the successive positions of the balloon. Clearly the distance between successive points will represent the number of metres the balloon has moved with the wind during the minute, on the scale of the plot. A special measuring scale enables the *wind speed* to be read off in miles per hour or other desired units.

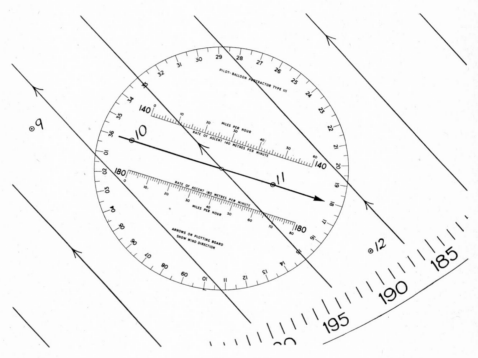

FIGURE 116
Protractor used with Canadian plotting board.

To obtain the *direction* with the United States board, the disk is turned until the two points under consideration are on one of the vertical lines of the cross-section paper. The direction is then given by the reading of the angular scale at the index line (the points 3 and 4 in Fig. 115b are in this position—the wind direction is 46°). This result is obtained because in the United States Service the theodolite is set to point south at $A = 360°$, automatically performing the reversal implied in the definition of wind direction as that from which the wind is coming.

The Canadian board is ruled with a number of parallel lines with arrows pointing toward "north." A special protractor (Fig. 116) is used to determine the angle between one of these lines and the line joining two plotted points. This protractor is shown with its arrow "flying with the wind" and its centre on the most convenient of the parallel lines; the wind direction, 330°, is read in the direction of the "north" end of the board. Note that this arrangement requires that the angles on the protractor be numbered counter-clockwise.

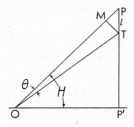

FIGURE 117
Illustrating the theory
of the tail method.

(iv) *The tail method*

The tail method is a single-theodolite method, and differs from those which have been described solely in the manner of determining the height of the balloon. Instead of assuming this to be known, it is calculated from the angle subtended by a tail attached to the balloon.

In Fig. 117, which represents the vertical plane through the theodolite O and the balloon P, T is the end of the tail and P' the point directly beneath the balloon and at the same elevation as O. Drop a perpendicular, TM, on OP.

Let the angle TOP [= the angle TOM] = θ radians;
then since θ is small, $TM/OM \doteq \theta$.
Let PT, the length of the tail, be l;
Then since the angle MTP = the elevation angle, H,

$$MT = l \cos H.$$

Hence $$OM = (l \cos H)/\theta,$$

and since $$OM >> MP,$$

$$OP \doteq (l \cos H)/\theta$$

and $$PP' = (l \cos H \sin H)/\theta$$
$$= (l \sin 2H)/2\theta \quad \text{(height of the balloon)} \quad \dots\dots\dots(7.17);$$

also $$OP' = (l \cos^2 H)/\theta \quad \text{(horizontal distance of balloon)} \dots\dots\dots(7.18).$$

In order to measure the angle θ, the theodolite is fitted with an eyepiece scale or a micrometer eyepiece. The tail is a sheet of paper stiffened with wire, at the end of about 30 metres of thread. A launching drum is useful.

The tail method is chiefly useful in correcting for the effects of rough terrain and turbulence in the first few minutes of the flight. It is obviously not going to be very accurate after the balloon reaches a distance of a mile or so.

(b) *The two-theodolite method*

For special purposes, such as researches in mountain valleys where vertical motion of the air may be important, two-theodolite observations are made. This technique makes it possible to dispense with all assumptions about the rate of ascent of the balloon.

12

The use of two theodolites necessitates a base line which must be carefully surveyed. It should be about a mile long, and lie in a direction approximately at right angles to the prevailing wind. Computation is simplified if the two stations are at about the same elevation. If at all possible they should be connected by telephone or radio, in order to assure the exact synchronism of readings on which the accuracy of the method depends.

It simplifies matters if the two theodolites are adjusted so that they point either (1) in the same direction along the base line, or (2) towards each other, when the azimuth circles read 360°. In the analysis below, the first of these alternatives will be assumed.

The computation is performed either graphically or by means of a slide-rule. As long as the balloon is not too near the vertical plane containing the base line, a horizontal triangle is solved first, to obtain the projection of the balloon and its horizontal distance from one of the stations. Graphically this may be done by having a large plotting board and two fixed protractors with long thin arms (Fig. 118). The protractors are fixed at a distance corresponding to the length of the base line on the scale chosen for plotting. After the projection of the balloon (C) has been obtained, its height above the level of A will be calculated by the relation $Z = AC. \tan e$, where e is the elevation angle measured at A. This last computation is better done arithmetically on a slide-rule. The elevation above B may be calculated as a check; it is $Z' = BC. \tan e'$.

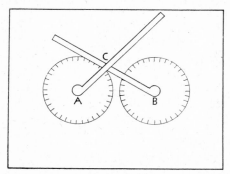

FIGURE 118
Plotting board for two theodolites.

The entire process can be performed fairly simply with a slide-rule; in fact the graphical method is used chiefly where a very large programme of observations makes it worth while to set up the board. The theory of the arithmetical procedure is simple. AB (Fig. 119) is the base line of length b; P is the position of the balloon, and C its projection on the horizontal plane through A. The angles measured from A are a and e, those measured from B, a' and e'.

Now $\angle ACB = a - a'$,

∴ $AC/\sin a' = b/\sin (a - a')$.

∴ $AC = b \sin a'/\sin (a - a')$

Similarly

$BC = b \sin a/\sin (a - a')$ $\qquad \qquad \dots \dots (7.19),$

also

$Z = b \sin a' \tan e/\sin (a - a')$

and

$Z' = b \sin a \tan e'/\sin (a - a')$ $\qquad \qquad \dots \dots (7.20).$

If A and B are on the same level, Z and Z' should be equal.

If B is not in the same horizontal plane as A (Fig. 120) b will be the projected distance AB'. Since BC = B'C', the formulae (7.19) and (7.20) may be used without change; but Z', being the height of the balloon above B, will be expected to differ from Z by a constant amount h, where $h = $ B'B.

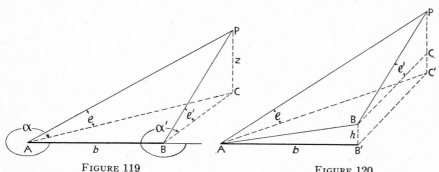

FIGURE 119
Perspective of two-theodolite triangulation.

FIGURE 120
Stations at different heights.

When the balloon is near the vertical plane containing the base line, a small error in α or α' will cause a large error in the computed position of the balloon. In this event it is better to solve the vertical triangles ABP, ACP (Fig. 121).

It will easily be seen that

$$AC = b \sin e' \cos e / \sin (e \pm e') \quad \ldots \ldots (7.21),$$

$$Z = b \sin e' \sin e / \sin (e \pm e') \quad \ldots \ldots (7.22),$$

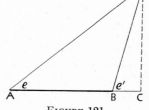

FIGURE 121
Solution of vertical triangles.

with similar formulae for BC and Z'. The positive sign will be used when C lies in AB, the negative sign when it lies in AB produced.

It may be left as an exercise for the student to work out suitable formulae for use when A and B are at notably different elevations.[15]

(c) *Observations at sea*

Observations at sea are always single-theodolite observations; and if they are worked out by any of the methods referred to above, the result will be a graph of the path of the balloon relative to the ship considered as the origin of co-ordinates. If the slide-rule method is being used, it is necessary only to add to the components V_E and V_N the components of the ship's velocity, say S_E and S_N, to obtain the components of the true velocity. It is probable that this method has the balance of advantages in its favour for marine work, especially in view of the difficulty of finding space for an adequate plotting board.

---

[15]See United States Weather Bureau *Circular O*, Instrument Division, Washington 1940.

A graphical method of plotting presents no other difficulty, however. From an origin O (Fig. 122) lay off the various positions $S_1, S_2, S_3 \ldots S_n$ of the ship, O being its position at the start of the flight. Fom each of these points lay off the total horizontal distance of the balloon in its true direction, for example S_1B_1, S_2B_2. Then $OB_1B_2 \ldots B_n$ will be the path of the balloon, and the direction of the wind in the nth minute will be the direction B_nB_{n-1} (*towards* O); its speed, the length of B_nB_{n-1} on the scale in use.

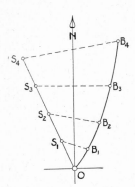

FIGURE 122
Plotting of observations at sea.

(d) *Reporting the wind at definite heights*

The wind is usually desired at even thousands of feet, or half kilometres, above sea-level; and in general these elevations will not coincide with the heights attained by the balloon in the middle of the equal intervals between observations. It is therefore necessary to make graphs of wind speed and direction against height, and pick off the values at the heights required. An apparatus used in the Canadian Service (and in the United States in essentially the same form) is shown in Fig. 123. It consists of an ordinary clip-file board fitted with a reversible transparent scale of vinylite[16] at the right-hand edge. On the board is placed a sheet of special cross-section paper in such a position that the axis of Z coincides with the edge of the scale and the zero of the scale falls at the proper height above the base line to correspond with the elevation of the station above sea-level. The scale is graduated to correspond with the heights attained by the balloon in the middle of each interval, supposing a standard rate of ascent; by pulling out two pins the scale may be reversed for use with a second standard rate. A vinylite triangle with appropriate graduations makes the plotting of the points very rapid and certain. The successive points are joined by smooth curves and the method has the very considerable advantage of showing up any real mistakes in the observations or computations.

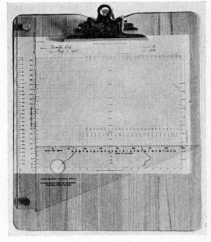

FIGURE 123
Graphing board.

---

[16]Vinylite is one of the newer plastics. These scales, triangles, etc., are made of 3 layers cemented together, 0.005, 0.050, and 0.005 inches thick respectively, the printing being sandwiched between the two lower layers.

5. General Accuracy of Pilot-Balloon Results

It is very difficult to predict the accuracy obtainable from a pilot-balloon ascent. Apart from actual mistakes in reading angles, the most important source of error is the uncertainty in the rate of ascent of the balloon, both on account of errors in inflation and on account of vertical currents in the atmosphere. Even if two theodolites are used, eliminating this uncertainty at low altitudes, no great precision can be expected at heights of more than 3 or 4 kilometres. It is probably unwise to trust even the best observations to give the true wind more closely than ±2° in direction, ±1 metre per second (2.2. m.p.h.) in speed, even at low altitudes; while at 5 km these figures may certainly be doubled.

CHAPTER VIII

INSTRUMENTS FOR INVESTIGATING CLOUDS

1. The Measurable Attributes of Clouds

A century ago, the observation of the motions of clouds was the only means of investigating the winds of the upper air, if we except the infrequent ascents in manned balloons. It is not surprising that a great deal of ingenuity was employed in devising means of measuring the height and velocity of clouds. Nowadays the pendulum has swung the other way, and there is a disposition to observe only those clouds, or those attributes of clouds, which are of direct importance to the aviator or the forecaster. It is possible that at some future time the old interest may revive.

The measurable, or at least observable, attributes of clouds are: (1) the amount of cloud, (2) their direction of motion, (3) their speed, (4) their height—usually the height of the lower surface of the cloud-layer, (5) their structure, and (6) their form. The first and the last of these are only rarely instrumental observations; the remainder may involve the employment of instruments.

2. Cloud Amount

It is the universal practice to express the amount of cloud—either of all the cloud present, or of a particular layer—by stating how many tenths of the sky are covered. This is nearly always an eye observation, and the reader must be referred to instruction books and to special works on clouds[1] for an account of the aids to observation and sources of error. Instruments for improving the accuracy of the estimation have been suggested; but the plain fact is that with one exception they are used practically nowhere.

The one exception is the *polestar recorder*, which consists simply of a very long-focus camera—a photographic telescope—pointed at the north pole of the heavens. One used at Chicago had a focal length of 75 inches.[2] This is exposed throughout the night, and if the night is perfectly clear, the small apparent motion of Polaris will be recorded as an unbroken circular arc. Clouds will interrupt this; and while the results for a single night may not agree with eye observations, on the average the agreement is probably fairly close. Such instruments are not at all common nowadays.

3. Cloud Direction

The direction of motion of a cloud is the direction from which it appears to be coming. This again is often an eye observation, and well it may be where

---

[1]Particularly SÜRING, R., *Die Wolken*, Leipzig 1936, Akad. Verlag.
[2]COVERT, R. N., *J.O.S.A. and R.S.I.*, **10**:351, 1925.

low clouds are concerned; but the direction of high clouds is not often to be determined accurately without the use of instruments.   There are two kinds of instrument suitable for this purpose—nephoscopes and theodolites.

Nephoscopes may be divided into two classes, direct-vision and mirror nephoscopes.   Representative of the first class is the comb nephoscope, originally due to Besson, and modified by the Norwegians into the grid nephoscope (Fig. 124).   This consists of a grid of steel bars, mounted on a vertical axis about 10 feet long, which can be turned by means of two ropes.   An index shows the direction in which the longer members of the grid are pointing.   To use this instrument, the operator moves about until a cloud feature is behind one of the intersections of the grid; he then rotates the grid until the cloud appears to move along the long member.   It is essential that he should stand quite still during this procedure; and a stick about 6 feet long, sharply pointed at each end, is suggested as a useful accessory.   This could be stuck into the ground and left undisturbed during the measurement, and the eye kept in line with it, the grid, and the cloud.

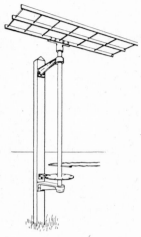

FIGURE 124
Grid nephoscope.

A more convenient type of nephoscope is that due to Finemann.   This consists of a disk of black glass mounted on a tripod stand fitted with levelling screws (Fig. 125).   A compass needle is sometimes built in for purposes of orientation.   A vertical pointer is arranged so that it can be rotated around the centre of the disk, and set at various known distances above the reflecting surface.   The disk is engraved with concentric circles a known distance apart.

In use the pointer is placed in such a position that the image of a cloud appears in line with the pointer and the centre of the disk.   The image is then

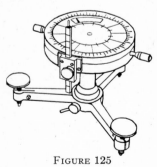

FIGURE 125
Mirror nephoscope.

(Courtesy of Negretti and Zambra)

watched, being kept in line with the pointer, and the direction of motion of the cloud read from the graduations on the edge of the disk. It need scarcely be said that if the instrument is set up with the 180° graduation pointing due north, the direction from which the cloud is moving will correspond to the graduation toward which its image moves.

A theodolite (which may be very simple, since open sights are better for the purpose than a telescope) affords another method of measuring the direction of motion of clouds.   Observations are made at intervals, and the position of the cloud worked out by any of the means described in the preceding chapter, considering the height to remain constant.   The reliability of the results may be judged from whether three or four successive points are collinear or otherwise, since a sudden change of direction is virtually impossible. The determination of the direction of motion of any upper clouds might well follow each pilot-balloon observation as a routine matter.

The accuracy of all these methods is limited by the constant changes in the shape of clouds. A feature which was prominent at the beginning of an observation may change so as to be unrecognizable, or may be covered by newly formed cloud. The method is not suitable for uniform layers of cloud without surface structure.

The only way of determining the direction of such a layer of cloud is to note the direction of the wind given by a pilot balloon just before it disappears into it.

4. Speed of Motion

(a) Relative measurements

The observations with nephoscopes and theodolites dealt with in the last section can be extended to provide a measure of the relative speed of clouds, if a watch is added to the equipment. The quantity actually measured is the *angular speed* of the motion.

Let us develop the very simple theory for the mirror nephoscope, leaving it to the reader to adapt it to other forms. In Fig. 126, let O be the centre of

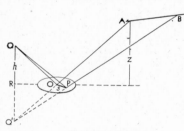

the mirror, Q the tip of the pointer, OP the apparent path of the cloud as it moves from A to B. Since both OP and AB are horizontal, they are also parallel; this can be proved quite easily by means of the construction suggested by the dotted lines. Now let s be the distance OP, h the height of the point Q above the mirror, and Z the elevation (not known) of the cloud. Then clearly

$$AB = Zs/h.$$

FIGURE 126
Theory of mirror nephoscope.

Now let us suppose that P is chosen to lie on the first concentric circle of the nephoscope, and let the image of the cloud move from O to P in t seconds. Then the speed of the cloud is $AB/t = Z(s/ht)$. The quantity

$$\omega = s/ht \qquad \ldots \ldots \ldots (8.1)$$

is the *angular speed* of the cloud. If we know, or can safely assume, the height Z, then the *true speed* is

$$v = Zs/ht \qquad \ldots \ldots \ldots (8.2).$$

Another way of expressing the result of (8.1) is to assume a height of 1000 (feet or metres) and calculate the *relative speed*.

$$v_{1000} = 1000 \, s/ht \text{ (ft. sec}^{-1}, \text{ m. sec}^{-1}) \qquad \ldots \ldots \ldots (8.3).$$

(b) *Absolute measurements*

The speed of a pilot balloon just before it enters a cloud is an independent way of measuring the speed, as well as the direction and height, of a cloud layer. Unfortunately this method is not useful for detached, scattered clouds. All other absolute measurements of the speed of clouds depend in one way or another on a knowledge of their height.

5. Measurement of Cloud Height

(a) *By triangulation*

Observations of the same cloud feature by means of two theodolites can be used to give the height of the cloud and its motion, the theory being exactly that given in chapter VII for the computation of the position and speed of a pilot balloon. The capital difficulty of this is to be sure that the two observers are looking at the same part of the cloud, because the same cloud may appear totally different from different aspects. A telephone line between the two theodolites is almost essential. To get over this difficulty, two especially mounted cameras (photo-theodolites) have sometimes been used; but the trouble and expense involved makes the method suitable for special researches only.

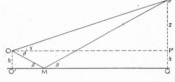

(b) *Bravais' method*

A one-theodolite method, interesting chiefly because of its ingenuity, was devised about a century ago. From a hill or tower the observer

FIGURE 127
Bravais' method.

O (Fig. 127) measures with a theodolite the angular elevation γ of a cloud feature and the angular depression β of its image reflected in a pond. The height h of the observer above the level of the pond being accurately known, we have, in the notation of the figure

$$O'M = h \cot \beta$$
$$MQ = (h+Z) \cot \beta$$
$$OP' = O'M + MQ = (2h+Z) \cot \beta$$
$$\therefore Z = OP' \tan \gamma = (2h+Z) \cot \beta \tan \gamma$$
$$\therefore Z(1 - \cot \beta \tan \gamma) = 2h \cot \beta \tan \gamma$$

and finally

$$Z = \frac{2h \tan \gamma}{\tan \beta - \tan \gamma} \qquad \ldots \ldots (8.4).$$

Obviously this method would be of use only on rare occasions.

(c) *By theodolite and range finder*

The range finder, used chiefly for military purposes, can be used to measure the distance of clouds if they are reasonably sharply defined. If the distance r is thus measured, and the angle of elevation H determined by a theodolite or sextant, the height of the cloud is immediately given by $Z = r \sin H$.

This is not the place to deal with the construction of the range finder, except to say that there are two entirely distinct types, the *coincidence* range finder and the *stereoscopic* one.[3] The latter is probably better for cloud observations unless a sharp boundary is available, but requires a specially qualified observer. Ordinary range finders of either type, however, are not well suited to cloud observation because of their high power and consequent small field. A special low-power stereoscopic range finder was constructed by Zeiss several years ago for this purpose; it had a base of 6 metres. Small infantry range finders (1m base) are of very little use for cloud observations.

(d) *By calculation from surface temperature and dew point*

On occasions when the air may be supposed to be thoroughly mixed from the ground up to the base of the cloud (particularly in the case of thermal cumulus), the height of the cloud base may be calculated with fair accuracy from thermodynamical considerations. The temperature of rising air falls more rapidly than its dew point; the rate of change of each may be calculated[4] and the results compared; the comparison leads to the formula

$$Z = 220(\theta - \theta_D) \text{ feet} \qquad \ldots\ldots\ldots (8.5),$$

where Z is the height of the condensation level above the surface, θ and θ_D the temperature and dew point at the surface in degrees Fahrenheit. The cloud base is usually about 100 or 200 feet higher than the condensation level.

Special psychrometers with built-in nomograms for this relation are made by several firms.

(e) *By means of ceiling balloons*

As mentioned above, a pilot balloon which enters a cloud gives the height of the cloud as a sort of by-product of the observations. In airways practice, however, the height of the cloud base, or *ceiling* as it is called, is required more frequently than it is feasible or desirable to make pilot-balloon observations, especially when the sky is covered by low stratus or nimbostratus. To obtain this information, small balloons known as *ceiling balloons* are inflated and released.

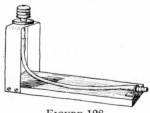

These balloons weigh about 8 to 10 grams and are inflated to rise about 140 or 150 metres per minute (460 or 490 feet per minute). They are filled by means of a device such as that shown in Fig. 128, released, and followed with the naked eye. The elapsed time in minutes until the balloon enters the cloud is noted, and multiplied by the rate of ascent to give the ceiling. Ceilings up to about 2,000 or 2,500 feet can be measured in this way, unless the wind is very strong.

FIGURE 128
Filler for ceiling balloons.

[3]See GLAZEBROOK, *Dictionary of Applied Physics.* London 1923, Macmillan, vol. IV, p. 633, and KLEINSCHMIDT, *Handbuch*, p. 601.

[4]HANN-SÜRING, *Lehrbuch der Meteorologie.* 5th ed., Leipzig 1939, W. Keller, vol. I, p. 345.

(f) By means of the ceiling projector[5]

All the above methods of measuring cloud height are either expensive, time-consuming, or uncertain of success, and can only be used by day.   At night, on the other hand, there is a method of the utmost simplicity and directness, which is by far the most accurate and convenient of all.   This method is that of the ceiling projector.

The ceiling projector is a small searchlight which is used to project a narrow beam of light on to the base of the cloud, the angular elevation of the spot being measured from a station at a fixed distance from the projector and in the vertical plane of the beam.   Small incandescent searchlights for this purpose have been developed to a high degree of perfection.   A typical example, using a 12 volt, 420-watt aeroplane landing-light lamp and a 16-inch primary mirror, projects a beam of about 2° spread with a maximum intensity of about three million candles.   This beam has remarkably sharp edges and presents a very striking appearance; under conditions of good visibility and without a moon, the spot is visible at ceiling heights of at least 15,000 feet.   The angular elevation of the spot is measured by means of an alidade or a clinometer, which may be graduated in degrees, or in ceiling heights if the projection angle and the base line are kept constant.

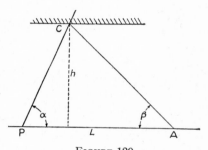

FIGURE 129
Geometry of the ceiling projector.

The geometry of the problem is extremely simple (Fig. 129).   Let Z be the ceiling height, L the base line, α the projection angle, and β the angular elevation of the spot.   Then $L = Z \cot \alpha + Z \cot \beta$, and the ceiling is

$$Z = L/(\cot \alpha + \cot \beta) \qquad \ldots\ldots\ldots (8.6).$$

If the beam is projected vertically, $\cot \alpha = 0$, and in this event

$$Z = L \tan \beta \qquad \ldots\ldots\ldots (8.7).$$

It is here assumed that the projector and alidade lie in the same horizontal plane.   If the alidade is higher than the projector by an amount y, the horizontal distance between the two may be increased in practice to $L + y \cot \alpha$; if the projector is higher, the base line may be decreased to $L - y \cot \alpha$.   If now the calculation is made as before, using the standard base line L, it will yield the height of the cloud above the alidade in each instance.

The accuracy of the measurement is limited by the uniformity of the underside of the cloud, and by the precision with which the alidade can be set on the spot of light.   For a given ceiling height Z_1, this accuracy is a function of the angle of projection α, since

$$[\partial\beta/\partial Z]_{\alpha_1, z} = L \sin^2\beta/Z_1^2$$

---

[5]Called the *cloud searchlight* in England.   The use of the term *ceiling* seems to be confined to North America.

which is clearly a maximum when $\beta = \pi/2$, i.e. when the spot is overhead. Since it is impracticable to alter the projection angle to suit the ceiling to be measured, it is necessary to compromise by choosing an angle which will give reasonable accuracy at the most interesting levels. In the Canadian Service, the standard base line is 1,000 feet and the projection angle $\alpha = \tan^{-1}3.0 = 71°34'$. This gives the maximum possible accuracy to ceilings in the neighbourhood of 3,000 feet. In some other countries, including the United

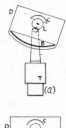

States, the beam is projected vertically, which of course gives somewhat greater accuracy to measurements of very high ceilings.[6] Nevertheless the gain in this direction is slight, and the relative advantages of the two angles depend more on other matters, not the least important of which is the facility of removing precipitation from the glass cover of the projector. The tilted projector has an obvious advantage here, and the design used in the United Kingdom combines the tilted top

with the vertical beam.[7] The advantage of the vertical beam is the ease with which its adjustment can be tested.

The three common types of projector are shown diagrammatically in Fig. 130. The second and third of these are suitable only for the projection of a vertical beam, while the first may be tilted at any angle. All of them have a drum D, a light source L (usually a low-voltage lamp operated from a transformer), and a primary parabolic mirror B. In the forms (a) and (b), a secondary spherical mirror C serves to recover light which would otherwise have been lost to the beam; in the form (c), a number of concentric cylindrical shields, E, absorb the scattered light. A transformer is built into the base of the first two forms, being enclosed in the waterproof box T.

FIGURE 130
Three types
of projector.

The mechanical features of the tilting form of ceiling projector are shown in Fig. 131. The horizontal axis is carried by a substantial U-frame. A quadrant is provided for setting the angle of elevation, but a much more convenient method is afforded by the various faces of the casting P, which are at the correct angles to be horizontal when the projector is at $71°34'$ and $90°00'$. The accuracy of this adjustment can be tested at any time with an ordinary machinist's level.

The U-frame is mounted on the transformer box, which carries a slip-fitting for the 4-inch pipe on which the entire apparatus is mounted. The level of the instrument can be adjusted by means of two pairs of set screws which bear on the pipe.

The same sort of mounting is provided for the second type of projector (Fig. 132). In this instrument, however, the drum is cast integral with the transformer box. This makes a very strong and simple construction where

[6]For further theoretical details, concerning the brightness of the spot, etc., see MIDDLETON, W. E. K., *J.O.S.A.*, **29**:340-349, 1939.

[7]Air Ministry, London, Meteorological Office, *Observer's Handbook*, 1939 ed., p. 76.

only a vertical beam is required, but has the disadvantage that it must be dismounted and laid on its side if for any reason an adjustment of the focus must be performed, unless special auxiliary apparatus is provided.

Full instructions for adjusting projectors are given in the manufacturers' publications, and we shall only indicate general principles here. First of all, the lamp is brought to the focus of the primary mirror. This is best done by projecting the beam horizontally on to a wall at least 100 feet distant, and setting the lamp filament to give the narrowest beam. In projectors with only one mirror this is the entire adjustment, but if there is a secondary mirror it is now installed, and the projector looked at (with the current off, or else through very dark glasses) from a point about 20 feet away and just off the axis. Two images of the filament will be seen, and the secondary mirror will be adjusted until the two are the same size and superimposed.

FIGURE 131
Ceiling projector.

*(Courtesy of The
Canadian Westinghouse Co., Ltd.)*

After the beam has been adjusted it is pointed in the right direction, and the projector is ready for use.

The angular elevation of the spot is measured either by an alidade or by a clinometer. The clinometer is a portable instrument, the principle of which will be immediately evident from Fig. 133. The observer looks through the bottle-shaped sight and centres the spot on the cross-wires. A pendulum, the index end of which may be seen at A, indicates on a scale the elevation of the spot; when the observer is satisfied with his settings he clamps the index by means of the button B, takes the instrument from his eye, and reads the scale.

The alidade (Fig. 134) is a stationary instrument, mounted on a stand and carefully levelled. The plane of the scale contains the centre line of the beam from the projector. In the example shown, a mirror is fitted at an angle of 45°, and performs the same function as the prism in a pilot-balloon theodolite. As it is sometimes difficult to find a faint spot with the mirror, open ring sights are also provided. The scale of this

FIGURE 132
Ceiling projector.

*(Courtesy of
The Crouse-Hinds Co., Ltd.)*

instrument is graduated directly in feet from 0 to 10,000, for use with a given projection angle and base line.

In the above form, the ceiling projector can be used only at night. Following a suggestion by the author, and at the request of the United States Weather Bureau, the Bureau of Standards has recently developed a photoelectric method of measuring cloud heights in the daytime,[8] a method which should be of great value to aviation in the future.

FIGURE 133
Clinometer.

(Courtesy of
The Crouse-Hinds Co., Ltd.)

The light spot on the cloud cannot be seen in the daytime because the brightness of the underside of the cloud may be 10^6 times as great as that of the spot. But if a *modulated* light beam is used, it is possible to build a photoelectric receiver which is sensitive to such light and not at all to the steady light of day.

The projector has a 24-inch mirror and uses a quartz water-cooled mercury arc as a source of light. Fed with 60-cycle current, this arc gives "120-cycle light" almost completely (95 per cent) modulated. The receiver is a "photoelectric telescope" with a lens 8 inches in diameter having a photocell behind a diaphragm at its focus. The telescope is mounted so that it may be rotated about a horizontal axis and in the plane containing the beam from the projector, the base line being 1,000 feet.

The output of the photocell is fed into a special resistance-capacitance amplifier circuit, tuned to 120 cycles. The output of this is rectified by an ingenious electronic synchronous commutator which is phased with the signal, and finally measured by means of a vacuum-tube voltmeter.

Ceilings of 9,000 feet have been measured with this apparatus in the daytime.

FIGURE 134
Alidade.

(Courtesy of The
Canadian Westinghouse Co., Ltd.)

6. The Structure of Clouds

(a) *Size of cloud particles*[9]

There are three principal methods of measuring the size of cloud or fog droplets. Which of these is used depends somewhat on the conditions of the experiment. The microscopic method and the sedimentation method can be employed only if the observer is within the cloud or fog; the optical method also if he is outside it, provided a suitable light-source is available.

---

[8]LAUFER, M. K., and L. W. FOSKETT, *J. Aeron. Sc.*, 8:183-187, 1941.

[9]Critical discussion and bibliography in HOUGHTON, H. G., and W. H. RADFORD, *M.I.T. Papers in Physical Oceanography and Meteorology*, vol. VI, no. 4, 1938.

(a) *The optical method*,[10] used most extensively by H. Köhler, depends on the measurement of the bright rings (coronas) produced around a light source by diffraction.   The relations between the radius r of the predominating cloud droplets and the angular radius θ_n of the nth interference minimum are, for the first three rings,

$$\left.\begin{array}{l} \sin\theta_1 = 1.220\lambda/2r \\ \sin\theta_2 = 2.233\lambda/2r \\ \sin\theta_3 = 3.238\lambda/2r \end{array}\right\} \qquad \ldots\ldots\ldots(8.8).$$

When white light is being used, λ is set equal to 0.571μ, and the outside of the red ring is considered the minimum.   When an extended light source, such as the moon, is employed, its angular radius should be subtracted from that of the corona.   Generally only the first ring will be seen, sometimes the second, rarely the third.

The measurement of the angles involved may be done very simply.   A stick about 2 feet long (Fig. 135) is fitted at one end with a diaphragm about 2 inches square with a $\frac{1}{8}$-inch hole in the centre.   A slider carries two sharp points about $\frac{1}{2}$ inch apart in a plane at right angles to the stick. The angle subtended by the points at any distance from the eye-hole may be calculated, and a scale may be drawn on a flat side of the stick.

FIGURE 135
Instrument for measuring the angles of coronas.

Such an apparatus is amply accurate enough for the purpose.   The method is useful for measuring the predominant drop size in alto-stratus, or mountain fog, but not very successful in fogs near sea-level, because of their inhomogeneity.[11]   The simple formula (8.8) is of doubtful validity for drops smaller than 20 microns in diameter.[12]

(β) *Sedimentation method*.[13]   Measurements of the rate of fall of fog particles through still air should give a measure of their sizes, the two quantities being related by Stokes' law, so that

$$\frac{4}{3}\pi r^3(\sigma - \rho)g = 6\pi\eta rv \qquad \ldots\ldots\ldots(8.9).$$

The right-hand side of this equation is the air resistance, η being the viscosity of the air and v the speed of fall; the left-hand side is the net force on the drop, g being the acceleration due to gravity, σ the density of the drop, and ρ that of the air.

In the apparatus used by Kneusel, a sample of fog was collected in a box which could then be closed, and the drops fell through a double tube and finally through a cubical chamber, where they were observed in dark-field illumination by a microscope.

[10]See Köhler, H., *Medd. fr. Stat. Met.-Hydr. Anstalt*, vol. II, no. 5, Stockholm 1925.
[11]Houghton and Radford, *l. c.*
[12]Wilson, J. G., *Proc. Camb. Phil. Soc.*, **32**:493-498, 1936.
[13]See Kneusel, S., *Met. Zeits.*, **52**:64-67, 1935.

The weakness of this method lies in the unknown effect of evaporation, and it is probable that the results are a good deal affected. It would also seem improbable that a true sample of a heterogeneous fog would reach the observation chamber, and more likely that the smaller drops would be greatly favoured.

(γ) *Microscopic method.* The most generally successful method of observing the sizes of the particles in fog or *accessible* cloud is the microscopic method. In this method, fog or cloud droplets are caught on a surface of oil[14] or of vaseline,[15] and photographed under a dark-field microscope. The apparatus of Houghton and Radford is shown diagrammatically in Fig. 136. In a sheet-metal case D, mounted on a tripod N, are contained a lamp P, a water-cell and condenser M, a dark-field condenser L_2, and a microscope tube H with a focussing mechanism J. The optical parts of the microscope are a 16 mm objective L_1 and a 6× eyepiece G. A camera shutter is at F. The "stage" of the microscope is at K, so mounted that it can be swung out into the fog and the slides, which are only 5 mm square, removed and replaced. The upper portion of the case, E, removable for visual observations, carries a light-tight fixture B with a focussing screen and a film pack C. The hood A facilitates focussing in daylight.

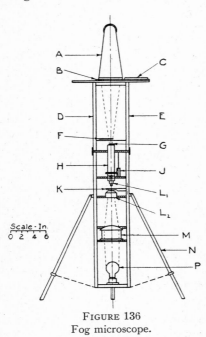

FIGURE 136
Fog microscope.

(after Houghton and Radford, 1938)

A standard method has been developed for coating the slide with vaseline, exposing it to the fog, and measuring the photographs. A correction for the slight flattening of the drops as they rest on the vaseline surface is also applied. Since it is inconceivable that anyone would attempt work in this interesting field without reading the paper in question, further details will be omitted, except that it should be observed that while the sedimentation method discriminates against the larger particles, the microscopic method tends to favour them. Probably neither method gives a completely correct idea of the size distribution.

(b) *Number of cloud particles, and liquid water content of clouds and fogs*

(α) *Chemical methods* have been used by many workers[16] to determine the water content of clouds. A known volume of fog-laden air is passed through

[14]Bricard, J., *La Meteorologie*, 15:83-92, 1939.
[15]Houghton and Radford, *l. c.*
[16]Bibliography in Kleinschmidt, *Handbuch*, p. 268, and in Houghton and Radford, *l.c.*

an appropriate absorption tube, and the total amount of water measured. The amount which entered in the form of vapour can be determined from observations of the vapour-pressure, and the liquid water content obtained by subtraction. The difficulty of such methods is in the sampling, it being practically impossible, according to Radford, to cause foggy air to flow into a tube without some loss of liquid water.

(β) *The evaporation method* suffers from the same difficulty. In this method, all the cloud particles are evaporated by heating, for example in a chamber added to the intake of an Assmann psychrometer.[17] The absolute humidity of the air before heating, d_1, and that after heating, d_2, can be determined from the relations

$$d_1 = \frac{e_1}{R_1 T_1}, \ d_2 = \frac{e_2(P - e_1)}{R_1 T_1(P - e_2)} \qquad \ldots \ldots (8.10),$$

in which e_1 and e_2 are the corresponding vapour-pressures, P the atmospheric pressure, R_1 the gas-constant for water-vapour, and T_1 the temperature of the air before heating. The method suffers from the sampling error mentioned above; this and other errors have been exhaustively investigated by Eriksson, who concludes that its accuracy depends more on the possible accuracy of humidity measurement than on any other factor.

(γ) *The separation method*[18] is the simplest method, and probably the most nearly free from sampling error, but it requires rather large apparatus. Fairly good results have been obtained by merely exposing one or more wire screens facing the wind, but the improved fog sampler described by Radford appears to be a final solution. This instrument depends on the principle that for a good sample, the direction and speed of the air should be practically unchanged before entering the separator.

The scheme of the apparatus is shown in Fig. 137. Air is drawn through a tube A, 2 feet in diameter and 3 feet long, by a motor-driven fan B. At the intake end is a detachable unit C consisting of a stainless-steel tube 8 inches long with seven screens of the same material, $\frac{3}{8}$ inch apart. The central part is removed to admit a short coaxial tube D, 5 inches in diameter, with seven screens of the same type as those in the outer section. The outer screens act as a guard-ring for the central section, which is used as a measuring unit, being easily removed for weighing. An "air-meter" anemometer (see page 124) is installed at E for the measurement of the air speed. The water collected by the outer section drains into a flask F, and may be subjected to chemical analysis.

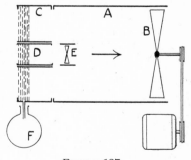

FIGURE 137
Fog sampling instrument.

[17]The latest form of this apparatus, originally due to KÖHLER (*Medd. fr. Stat. Met.-Hydr. Anstalt*, vol. V, no. 2) is described by G. L. ERIKSSON, *Geograf. Annaler.*, **20**:276-307, 1938.

[18]HOUGHTON and RADFORD, *l.c.*

If the size distribution of the drops is measured as described in the previous section, and the liquid water content per unit volume is known, it is obvious that the number of drops can be calculated.

7. Cloud Photography

In so far as the observation of the *form* of clouds is related to instruments at all, it concerns the photography of clouds. It is not likely that a complete tyro in photography will begin by making successful cloud pictures, and detailed instructions would therefore be out of place in this book, being more appropriate to a photographic manual. It is our purpose merely to direct the attention of the reader to the use of the motion-picture camera in this field.

One of the chief difficulties in observing the metamorphoses of clouds is the slowness with which they take place. The motion-picture camera affords a means of speeding up these changes to any desired degree, by spacing the exposures appropriately. Some very beautiful and interesting results have been obtained in this manner.

For serious work, some automatic means of making exposures, at uniform intervals of any desired length, is almost essential. With this, and an adequately sturdy tripod, the details may be left to the meteorological camera-man with the assurance that, after some little practice, he cannot fail to produce results of beauty, possibly of scientific interest.

CHAPTER IX

SUNSHINE RECORDERS

1. General Considerations

(a) *Purpose and classification*

Sunshine recorders are supposed to measure "the duration of bright sunshine." As to just what constitutes "bright" sunshine there is room for disagreement; but the sunshine recorder at least measures only the duration, not the brightness, of the direct light from the sun.

All such instruments fall into two main classes, according to whether they make use of the heat energy from the sun, or of only the shorter wavelengths that affect photographic materials. In the first class, besides the almost ubiquitous Campbell-Stokes recorder, we have the Marvin sunshine recorder, standard in the United States. In the second are the photographic instruments of Jordan and of Pers.

(b) *The sunshine recorder as a sundial: Time in meteorology*

With the exception of the Marvin recorder, every one of these instruments is effectively a sundial. As we shall see later, in order to adjust such recorders it is necessary to be able to calculate the LOCAL APPARENT TIME at any moment. Local apparent noon, in particular, is the time when the sun is due south, and a knowledge of how to find this useful instant is also of service in adjusting wind vanes and in other ways.

The interval between two successive transits of the sun over the meridian is a TRUE SOLAR DAY, and time based on the length of this day is called APPARENT SOLAR TIME. This is the time indicated by a sundial (or sunshine recorder) when correctly adjusted.

Unfortunately, the true solar day varies in length in a rather complicated manner throughout the year; and for convenience a fictitious heavenly body, the MEAN SUN, is assumed. This revolves around the earth, completing each revolution in the *average* length of a true solar day. Time based on the transits of the mean sun is called LOCAL MEAN TIME.

Four times a year, about April 15, June 13, August 31, and December 24, the apparent solar time is the same as the local mean time. At other times a certain amount, known as the EQUATION OF TIME, has to be added (algebraically) to the local mean time to obtain the apparent solar time. In other words,

Local mean time + equation of time = apparent solar time.[1]

---

[1]This is perhaps the most useful definition for our purpose. The equation of time is sometimes defined as the correction to the sundial to give local mean time. Before using any tables one should always be sure which definition is being used.

The following table gives the equation of time for every third day throughout the year to a sufficient degree of precision ($\frac{1}{2}$ minute) for our purpose.[2]

Day	January	February	March	April	May	June	July	August	September	October	November	December
1...	−3½	−14	−12½	−4	+3	+2½	3½	−6	+½	+10½	+16½	+10½
4...	−5	−14	−12	−3	+3½	+2	−4	−6	+1½	+11½	+16½	+9½
7...	−6½	−14½	−11	−2	+3½	+1½	−4½	−5½	+2½	+12½	+16	+8
10...	−7½	−14½	−10½	−1	+4	+1	−5	−5	+3½	+13	+16	+7
13...	−9	−14½	−9½	−½	+4	0	−5½	−4½	+4½	+14	+15½	+5½
16...	−10	−14½	−8½	+½	+4	−½	−6	−4	+5½	+14½	+15	+4
19...	−11	−14	−8	+1	+3½	−1	−6	−3½	+6½	+15	+14½	+2½
22...	−11½	−14	−7	+1½	+3½	−2	−6	−2½	+7½	+15½	+13½	+1
25...	−12½	−13½	−6	+2	+3½	−2½	−6½	−2	+8½	+16	+12½	−½
28...	−13	−13	−5	+2½	+3	−3	−6½	−1	+9½	+16	+11½	−2
31...	−13½		−4		+2½		−6	0		+16½		−3½

The civil time used in everyday life, known as *standard time, summer time, daylight saving time,* etc., is the mean solar time for some standard meridian, such as Greenwich (0°), 75°W, etc. In most countries the standard time is based on a meridian which is some multiple of 15° west or east of Greenwich, but in others the meridian of a principal observatory is used. The meteorologist has only to know what meridian his standard time is based on, and the longitude of his station, to calculate the mean solar time for the place from the standard time.

The mean sun revolves around the earth at the rate of 360° in 24 hours, or 1° in 4 minutes. Therefore if the station is n degrees west of the standard meridian, the mean sun will cross the meridian of the station $4n$ minutes later than it crosses the standard meridian. Similarly if the station is n degrees east of the standard meridian, the mean sun will cross the meridian of the station $4n$ minutes before noon standard time. The following rules may be deduced:

In the western hemisphere

Local mean time = standard time + $4(\lambda_s - \lambda)$ minutes,

or Standard time = local mean time − $4(\lambda_s - \lambda)$ minutes,

where λ_s is the longitude of the standard meridian, λ that of the station, in degrees.

In the eastern hemisphere

Local mean time = standard time − $4(\lambda_s - \lambda)$ minutes,

or Standard time = local mean time + $4(\lambda_s - \lambda)$ minutes.

However, it is so easy to make an error in the application of such formulae that the meteorologist is advised to think each problem through from first principles, until the process becomes second nature, and even after that.

---

[2] It varies a little from year to year. See *The Nautical Almanac* or *The American Ephemeris* for accurate values.

Example: Find the Eastern (75th meridian) standard time of local apparent noon at Toronto ($\lambda = 79°30'$W.) on June 4.

$$\text{Local mean time} = 12^h00^m - \text{equation of time}$$
$$= 12^h00^m - 2^m = 11^h58^m$$
$$\text{Standard time} = 11^h58^m - 4(75 - 79\tfrac{1}{2})^m$$
$$= 11^h58^m + 18^m = 12^h16^m.$$

2. The Campbell–Stokes Recorder

(a) Description

For the sake of brevity, the early history of the Campbell-Stokes sunshine recorder will be omitted here,[3] and the instrument will be described as it is today (Fig. 138), the particular type illustrated being that approved by the Meteorological Office (London).

The instrument consists fundamentally of a portion of a spherical bowl, having a glass sphere placed concentrically within it. The diameter of the bowl is such that the sun's rays are focussed as sharply as possible on a card held inside it.[4]

Three sets of slots are milled in the bowl, as shown in Fig. 139, making it possible to hold either a straight card or one of two curved cards, which latter are developments of frustra of cones having 16° semi-angle. The long curved cards, which fit in the lower slots, are used from April 12 to September 2; the short curved cards are used from October 15 to the last day of February, and fit in the upper slots; the straight cards are used in the middle slots during the two remaining periods near the equinoxes.

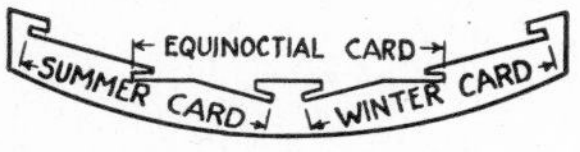

FIGURE 138
Campbell-Stokes sunshine recorder.

(Courtesy of Negretti and Zambra)

FIGURE 139
Cross-section of bowl of Campbell-stokes recorder.

It is possible to rotate the bowl around a horizontal axis about its centre, in order to make the centre line of the equinoctial card lie in the plane of the celestial equator. Adjustments are also provided for the glass sphere, so that it may be precisely concentric with the bowl. Finally a sub-base with three levelling screws makes it possible to level the instrument with accuracy.

[3]See Curtis, R. H., *Q.J. Roy. Met. Soc.*, **24**:1-30, 1898.

[4]The full specification is given in an appendix to *M.O. Prof. Notes* no. 45, London 1926.

In this form the instrument cannot be used in the tropics, because the support for the glass sphere would interfere with the bowl. A tropical form of the instrument is available, which can be used in all latitudes less than 45°. In this, the sphere has two short holes at opposite ends of a diameter, into which pivots enter. The pivots are on the ends of screws carried by a heavy frame.

(b) Method of operation

The radiant heat of the sun, concentrated by the spherical lens, burns a narrow track in a specially prepared card, which is printed with blue ink, white lines and figures being left to mark the hours. Naturally the width and depth of the burn depend on how brightly the sun is shining. With a clear blue sky, the card will be burned clean through; but towards sunset or just after sunrise only a faint burn will be seen under the same conditions. Exact rules for evaluating the traces must therefore be followed, and these will be found in the Observers' Handbooks of the Services using these instruments.

(c) Exposure and adjustments

It need scarcely be said that the sunshine recorder, of whatever type, should, if possible, be exposed in such a location that no terrestrial objects cast shadows on it at any time of year. Because of the feeble burning power of the low sun, objects rising not more than 3° above the horizon can be disregarded; but in mountainous regions or in cities it is well to survey the horizon and to determine the duration of possible sunshine cut off by the obstacles in each month of the year. This may be done by means of a transit instrument, the results being converted by the standard methods of spherical astronomy. A much more convenient instrument for the purpose (*Tagbogenmesser*) has been described by W. Schmidt,[5] and consists essentially of a small telescope mounted equatorially, the polar axis being movable to suit various latitudes. The optical axis of the telescope coincides with the polar axis, and the observer looks downward at a mirror inclined at an angle of $45° \pm \delta/2$. As the hour circle is rotated, the direction of view follows the path which the sun would have when its declination is the particular value of δ for which the mirror is set. Such an instrument might well form part of the kit of a meteorological inspector.

The location for the recorder having been selected, and a firm base built for it, it must be set up and adjusted. Assuming that the instrument is properly constructed, and has its parts in the correct relative position, three adjustments are necessary:

(1) The base must be level,
(2) The bowl must be adjusted so that the centre line of the equinoctial card lies in the plane of the celestial equator,
(3) The vertical plane containing the noon mark on the bowl and the centre of the glass sphere must be in the meridian.

The first of these adjustments may be made with an ordinary carpenter's level, using the levelling screws. When this has been done, the second adjustment

---

[5]SCHMIDT, W., *Met. Zeits.*, **50**:328-331, 1933.

may be made simply by reference to the scale of latitudes engraved on the bowl adjustment bracket, if the instrument is of reliable manufacture.

The third adjustment must be made on a sunny day, preferably at local apparent noon. The standard time of local apparent noon having been determined as in section (1)b, the recorder is turned until the burn comes exactly on the noon line at this moment. The level should then be checked, and readjusted if necessary.

(d) Errors of the Campbell-Stokes recorder[6]

Besides the errors due to faulty *orientation*, there will be errors if (4) the centre of the sphere does not coincide with the centre of the bowl, or (5) the distances between the hour lines of the cards are incorrect. There is no good reason for lack of concentricity, since this may be checked with calipers to a sufficient degree of precision. As to the cards, their manufacture has been standardized for a long time.

A good idea of the state of adjustment of a Campbell-Stokes recorder may be obtained by examining a series of records. If the burn is in its correct position at the equinoxes, but not parallel to the central white line at other times, it indicates that the centre of the sphere is displaced in the plane through the celestial equator. If the burn is not parallel to the line at any time, but is symmetrical, the latitude adjustment is at fault. If the burn crosses the card at an angle, the recorder either is not level in an E-W direction, or is not set in the meridian.

3. The Jordan Sunshine Recorder

The Jordan recorder in its present form (Fig. 140) consists of two semi-cylinders each having a short, narrow slit in its flat side. A piece of sensitized paper (blue-print paper) lines the curved side of each cylinder, and the sunlight coming through one of the slits makes a trace on this, one chart covering the morning hours, the other the afternoon, with a little overlap. When the sensitized paper is removed, it need only be washed briefly in water to render the record permanent. A quadrant is available for setting the instrument for latitude; like the Campbell-Stokes recorder, it also must be level and in the meridian.

FIGURE 140
Jordan sunshine recorder.

(Courtesy of Negretti and Zambra)

[6]For a full treatment see GLAZEBROOK, *Dictionary of Applied Physics*. London 1923, Macmillan, vol. III, p. 511.

Comparisons[7] of the Jordan and Campbell-Stokes recorders have shown that though the total amount of sunshine recorded by them is not greatly different, "the records of the Jordan instrument afford room for much greater difference of opinion as to what ought to be tabulated, and consequently measurements of the Jordan curves are open to considerably more uncertainty than are measurements of the Campbell-Stokes curves." The sensitivity of the photographic paper is also difficult to maintain constant from year to year, and this is probably the chief reason that the instrument is not more widely used.

4. The Pers Sunshine Recorder

If the photographic method be admitted, the most ingenious recorder on this principle would appear to be that of Pers, shown diagrammatically in

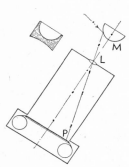

Fig. 141. The optical axis of a lens L and a hemispherical mirror M is directed to the celestial pole. The lens L throws the image of the sun, reflected in the mirror, on to a sheet of blue-print paper at P, tracing out part of a circle 35 to 44 mm in diameter as the sun moves round the sky. The hemispherical mirror is really polished and silvered *inside* a block of glass, as shown in the inset. One of the principal advantages of this instrument is that it can be used at any latitude, even at the poles, with no loss of record.

FIGURE 141
Pers sunshine recorder.

5. The Marvin Sunshine Recorder

In contrast to the instruments we have been describing, the Marvin electrical sunshine recorder, used for many years by the United States Weather Bureau, is not a sundial, but requires a chronograph to provide a time scale.

The Marvin recorder is essentially a differential air thermometer, with a clear bulb and a black bulb, mounted in such a position that the sun can shine about equally on the two bulbs. The general arrangement will be seen from Fig. 142, A being the clear bulb, B the black one, and C a narrow tube joining the two and extending nearly to the bottom of B. Part of B and C is filled with mercury, and there is a little absolute alcohol in the system, so that the instrument actually functions partly as a vapour-pressure thermometer. Two platinum wires are sealed through the tube C at D. The whole instrument is enclosed in an evacuated jacket E, to protect the bulbs from wind.

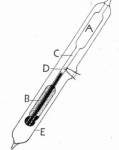

FIGURE 142
Marvin sunshine recorder.

When radiation falls on the instrument, the black bulb will absorb more than the clear one, the air in it will expand (and the vapour-pressure of the

---

[7]CURTIS, *l. c.*

alcohol will increase), and the mercury will rise in C until it closes the electrical circuit at D.   This circuit usually includes one pen magnet of a chronograph which also records wind, rainfall, and sometimes other quantities.

The adjustment of the recorder is effected by shaking it in various positions, an operation which would appear to demand a good deal of practice.[8]   It seems very unlikely that different recorders can be set in exactly the same way.   The final adjustment is made by changing the inclination of the recorder in the plane of the meridian, until "the mercury column will just close the electrical circuit during times when the disk of the sun can be just faintly seen through the clouds."[9]

Although, like the Campbell-Stokes instrument, the Marvin recorder operates with the *heat* radiation from the sun, it differs from the former in that its bulbs are equally sensitive to radiation from the whole sky.   Now there may be more energy coming from a complete overcast in the middle of the day than from the unobstructed sun in the early morning.   The Campbell-Stokes recorder would not be sensitive to this diffused energy, and it is not probable that a comparison between the two instruments could lead to any significant results.

The advantage of the Marvin recorder (and in the opinion of the writer, the sole advantage) is that it gives an easily deciphered record at a distance. Against this slight gain in convenience may be set the following serious defects:

(1) It is sensitive to diffuse radiation as well as to the direct radiation from the sun.

(2) There is no *objective* standard for its adjustment, so that instruments adjusted by different observers, or different instruments adjusted by the same observer, could not be expected to give comparable results.

(3) It is very fragile.

The second of these defects could be eliminated by adjusting the instrument *in situ* by direct comparison with an instrument for *measuring* solar radiation; but such instruments are not everywhere available, and the other defects would remain.   In addition, one would expect the sensitivity to depend to some extent on the temperature of the air, as is indeed stated in the official instructions.[10]

---

[8]U.S.W.B., *Circular G, Instrument Division.* 5th ed., Washington 1923.
[9]*Ibid.*, p. 4.
[10]*Ibid.*, p. 5.

CHAPTER X

INSTRUMENTS FOR THE INVESTIGATION OF THE UPPER AIR

1. Introduction

The history of the investigation of the upper air, apart from pilot-balloon observations (see chapter VII), begins with the work of Hermite and Besançon in 1892. The half-century that has elapsed since then has seen one method after another come to its zenith, and then decline into a position of minor importance because of the advances of technology.

Limitations of space make it impossible to recount the brief but crowded history of upper-air measurements.[1] We shall therefore be contented with the shortest of references to techniques which are no longer in general use, and shall emphasize instead the principles of the apparatus used at the present time. Anything which may be written here may be rendered out of date at any moment by some startling technical discovery, for the investigation of the upper air is a subject still almost in its infancy.

There are four methods of carrying instruments aloft:

(*a*) by means of captive balloons,
(*b*) by means of free balloons,
(*c*) by means of kites,
(*d*) by means of aircraft;

and each method has its appropriate instruments. For our purpose we shall classify these instruments as follows:

(1) Instruments for use with free balloons, without radio transmitters,
(2) Instruments for use with captive balloons or kites,
(3) Instruments for use with aircraft,
(4) Radio-meteorographs for use with free balloons (radiosondes).

A few years ago it would have been advisable to devote a good deal of space to each of these classes of instruments. Now, the first two are almost entirely obsolete, the third uncommon, because of the recent improvements in the construction of radiosondes. Under present conditions there seems to be no purpose served by a discussion of kites or captive balloons and their related instruments, especially since there is a very long and authoritative article on the subject in Kleinschmidt,[2] which is available in the unlikely event of such ascents being required.

2. Sounding Balloons

The majority of aerological ascents are now made with sounding balloons, manufactured either by the hollow-mould process referred to above (p. 146),

---

[1] For a short account see KLEINSCHMIDT, *Handbuch*, p. 434.
[2] *Handbuch*, pp. 473-538.

or by cementing together gores made of sheet rubber. The hollow-mould balloons are considerably less costly and have largely superseded the built-up type.

The weight of these balloons is about 350 grams, and they will inflate to a
diameter of about 15 feet before they burst. Given a free-lift of about 900
grams they will ascend at a rate of about 360 metres per minute. The relation
between free-lift and rate of ascent is probably not very well known for these
large balloons; but this is not usually of much importance, since the height of
the balloon is determined from the records of pressure, temperature, and
humidity furnished by the instrument attached to it.

These balloons are inflated with hydrogen (or helium in the United States),
using a filling nozzle of known weight. Frequently it is desirable to make the
balloon ascend more slowly in the first part of the flight than it does at greater
altitudes. The means used by the United States Weather Bureau to attain
this end is simple and interesting. A small pilot balloon has a measured quantity of fine sand placed in it, and is then suitably inflated with air or helium
and attached to the main balloon. When a certain roughly calculable height
is reached, the small balloon bursts, releasing its sand ballast.

3. Sounding-Balloon Meteorographs (without radio)[3]

The success of a sounding-balloon ascent depends on the meteorograph
coming to earth intact (or at least with its record undamaged) and being found
and returned to the sender. It may surprise many people to know that even
in Ontario nearly three-quarters of all sounding-balloon meteorographs were
eventually recovered, while in thickly-populated central Germany a loss was
exceptional. Nevertheless the mechanical parts of the instrument are often
damaged, frequently beyond repair, and cheapness, next to lightness and
accuracy, is the quality most greatly to be desired in these devices.

Sounding-balloon meteorographs may be classified into two distinct types,
according to the presence or absence of a clock. The earliest of these instruments were in effect a combination barograph, thermograph, and hygrograph,
modified to make them light enough for use
with balloons. Later it was found satisfactory
to make a record of temperature and humidity
against pressure, and many instruments arranged in this way were devised.

All the instruments having clocks are
fundamentally similar to that of Beck[4] (Fig.
143), which is chosen for illustration because
it shows the necessary features so well. On
a cast aluminium frame are mounted the

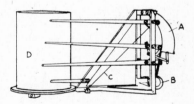

FIGURE 143
Balloon meteorograph of Beck.

Bourdon barometer tube A, the bimetal B, the hair C, and a clock with its
drum D. The four scriber arms make a record on smoked foil wrapped around

---

[3]See KEIL, K., *Über Meteorographen für aerologische Zwecke.* Int. Aerolog. Comm., Berlin
1938.

[4]KEIL, *l.c.*, p. 42.

the drum; the lowest one is fixed, to make a base line, and the other three in order record temperature, pressure, and humidity. When in use the entire instrument is covered by a radiation shield permitting the free flow of air past the sensitive elements.

The difficulty of getting small clocks to function well at very low temperatures led to the development of meteorographs without clocks. The best known of these, and the most interesting and original, is that developed by W. H. Dines.[5] Many thousand ascents were made with these simple instruments.

The meteorograph, without its radiation shield, is shown in Fig. 144. It is built up on a frame ABCD of stiff nickel-silver, stamped out of one piece. The side BC forms a spring tending to separate the longer arms, which tendency is resisted by the pressure of the air on the aneroid chamber E. The end A of the frame is formed into a carrier for the polished, silvered plate F, about the size of a postage stamp, on which the record is made.

Two needle points scratch curves on the plate, one (G) making a record of temperature, the other (H) a record of humidity. These records are drawn as functions of the pressure, since as the pressure decreases, the frame opens out, G and H moving to the left in relation to A.

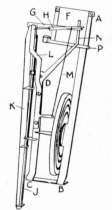

The temperature pen is operated by a bimetallic thermometer of unusual form consisting of an invar rod J and a thin strip of nickel-silver K. The invar rod is held to the frame at D. The relative expansion of J and K causes the point of G to move upwards as the temperature decreases.

The humidity element is a separate attachment, consisting of the frame L, the spring-hinged arm H, and the hair M. An extension of the main frame at N, pushed away from the plate by a spring P, serves to keep the scribers off the plate except when under calibration or in use.

FIGURE 144
The Dines meteorograph.

The instrument is surrounded by a light wire frame, attached only at the edges of the aneroid chamber. This frame consists of three rings and connecting pieces, and fits snugly into a cylindrical aluminium radiation shield. For use, this is placed in the centre of a light wicker frame which protects the instrument when it falls; no parachute is employed.

The record is evaluated by means of a measuring microscope of simple form, magnifying about 80 diameters. The calibration marks appear on the record, so that the working out of the flight is a matter of interpolation only.

A modification of the Dines instrument constructed by Patterson in Canada had a bimetallic thermometer of the usual form, and also an ingenious device for removing the scribers from the plate during the descent of the apparatus *before* it reached the ground, to avoid the obliteration of the lower part of the record.

---

[5]Meteorological Office (London), *M.O. 321*, 1929.

4. Special Applications of Sounding Balloons

(a) Obtaining samples of air from great heights

Various forms of apparatus have been designed to obtain samples of air from aloft, the most successful being those of Regener[6] and of Dines.[7] The essential feature of such instruments is an evacuated glass vessel with some means of opening it for a short time and then closing it. In the instrument of Dines the flask is opened by breaking off a capillary and closed by melting a small pellet of sealing-wax.

(b) Measuring the electric field

Simpson and Scrase[8] have devised an ingenious recording electrometer for use with a balloon, for the details of which the reader must be referred to the original description. Other devices, some of them very complicated, have been sent up with balloons for the study of ionization, and especially cosmic rays. Such instruments are, however, outside the scope of this book.

5. Aeroplane Thermometers and Meteorographs

(a) Thermometers for use on aircraft

As was mentioned on page 67, the practice of mounting large spirit thermometers on the wing struts of aircraft has declined with the cleaning up of aeroplane design. Few modern aircraft have any members to which such thermometers could be fastened if they are to be read from the cabin. Air thermometers are usually mounted on transport planes, but these are generally of the vapour-pressure or liquid-in-metal type, indicating on a dial in the instrument panel. Such instruments are of meteorological interest, as they make it possible for the pilot to perform a "sounding" as he climbs to cruising level, supplementing the information obtained by the use of the more specialized aerological apparatus. The characteristics of these thermometers may be learned from the catalogues of the makers of instruments for aircraft.

(b) Aeroplane meteorographs

Aeroplane meteorographs are much less used than they were only two or three years ago, because of the development of the radiosonde. Nevertheless there will be occasions where their use is convenient. In one respect a meteorological aeroplane flight has advantages over the newer method; namely, observations of cloud, precipitation, visibility and other optical phenomena, and turbulence, can be made by the pilot.

The conventional forms of aeroplane meteorograph were evolved directly from the kite meteorograph, which in turn developed from the small instruments with clocks, used for sounding-balloon ascents. Just as the kite meteorograph could well be larger and heavier than the balloon instrument, so the

[6]REGENER, E., *Luftfahrtforschung*, 12:361-366, 1935.
[7]DINES, L. H. G., *Q.J. Roy. Met. Soc.*, 62:379-386, 1936.
[8]SIMPSON, C. G., and F. J. SCRASE, *Proc. Roy. Soc. London*, A **161**:309-351, 1937.

aeroplane meteorograph could be larger still. It would seem that some manufacturers feared to go far enough in the direction of greater weight and strength, in passing from the kite meteorograph to the type made for use with aircraft.

As it is typical,[9] we shall choose for description the well-known Lindenberg pattern meteorograph, made by J. and J. Bosch[10] and named for the famous aerological observatory. It is shown in Fig. 145.

The record is made by five pens[11] on a piece of smoked aluminum foil wrapped around the drum, which revolves in one to six hours, according to the type and setting of the clock. The five pens shown have the following functions, beginning with the top one: base line (fixed), humidity record, temperature record, pressure record, time marker. The last is operated by a small electromagnet at the discretion of the pilot, in order to identify points on the record corresponding to his written observations.

The pressure record is obtained by a pair of nickel-silver aneroid chambers, compensated for temperature at about 500 mb. The temperature is measured by a bimetal in the form of a ring, actually about three-quarters of a circle, placed in a ventilation tube of polished aluminum, of which half is removed (as for inspection) in the figure. The bundle of hairs which constitutes the hygrograph is in the same tube. A conical entrance to this tube cuts down the speed of the air stream.

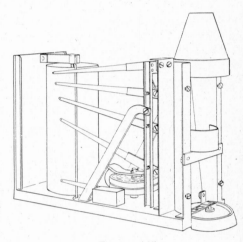

FIGURE 145
The Bosch aeroplane meteorograph.

The meteorograph is not mounted on the aircraft in the position shown but with the ventilation tube beneath and horizontal, that is to say, parallel to the chord of the wing. An outer case, somewhat streamlined, has rings for attaching shock cords; but special arrangements would have to be made on a modern monoplane.

Before the ascent, the instrument is allowed to run for a few minutes, preferably in a special ventilating tube, while the pressure, temperature and humidity are measured to obtain reference points. The drum is then turned completely round once. After the flight, the record sheet is taken off the drum, dipped in a thin alcoholic solution of shellac, allowed to drain a little, and the remaining alcohol burned off, making the record permanent. The reason for turning the drum around is to make lines of known and constant pressure, temperature, and humidity from which the trace can be measured. We shall

---

[9]For other types see KEIL, *l.c.*

[10]At one time a similar instrument was also made in the United States.

[11]So called; really steel points.

not go further into the evaluation of these records, as the use of these instruments is no longer general.

6. Radiosondes—General Remarks and Classification

The idea of transmitting meteorological information to a distance automatically is not new,[12] having been strongly advocated by Buys-Ballot in 1868 and carried out, over telegraph lines, by Olland in 1875. The first application to aerology was made by F. Herath and M. Robitzsch in 1917, using a kite-wire to transmit signals from a meteorograph attached to the kite, but no great use seems to have been made of this apparatus. It was not until the development of the vacuum-tube oscillator that there was any possibility of transmitting signals from an instrument attached to a free balloon, and the history of the subject really begins in 1927, when Idrac and Bureau[13] received signals from a small transmitter which reached the stratosphere. In the succeeding fourteen years a very large number of radiosondes have been designed and constructed, some of which have been much more successful than others. Compared to balloon meteorographs they have the very great advantage that the results of the ascent are immediately available, so that they may be used in actual forecasting. *Ballon-sonde* results were never useful for this purpose because it was days or weeks, sometimes a year or two, before the meteorograph was recovered and returned.

It is not our intention to describe or even to catalogue all these instruments,[14] but rather to discuss the principles on which they operate, using as illustrations, where possible, types that are likely to come to the attention of English-speaking readers.

Radiosondes fall naturally into four classes:

(1) Those transmitting *signals spaced in time*, the values of the meteorological elements being deduced from the intervals between signals.

(2) Those making use of *a change of audio-frequency*, the radio carrier-wave being modulated, and the values of at least some of the meteorological elements being related to the audio frequencies sent out by the transmitter.

(3) Those making use of *a change of radio-frequency* in a manner similar to class (2), the carrier-wave being unmodulated.

(4) Those transmitting signals in Morse or other codes, which can be interpreted as values of the meteorological elements.

The various types will be discussed in the above order.

Certain features are common to all radiosondes. The assembly that is sent up with the balloon consists usually of a parachute and the radiosonde proper. (The parachute is omitted when ascents are made at sea or on small

---

[12]For a historical summary see DUCKERT, P., *Beitr. z. Phys. d.f. Atm.*, **18**:68-80, 1932.

[13]IDRAC, P., and R. BUREAU, *Compt. Rend.*, **184**:691, 1927.

[14]A brief description of most of the instruments designed up to March 1939 is to be found in the publications of the International Aerological Commission, *Über Radiosonde-Konstruktionen*, Berlin 1937, and Supplement, Berlin 1939.

islands.) The radiosonde instrument, although it may be all together in a box or carton, consists of three parts: (1) the meteorological assembly which keys or modulates the transmitter or varies its frequency; (2) the radio transmitter; (3) the battery or batteries that supply the electrical energy to operate the instrument.

The meteorological assembly consists of an aneroid barometer, some form of thermometer, and a hygrometer,[15] together with the special mechanisms necessary to the particular type of radiosonde. Provision is made for exposing the thermometer and hygrometer to the air and at the same time shielding them from radiation. The radio transmitter consists usually of one vacuum tube and a few small circuit elements; rarely two tubes, or more. The batteries are highly specialized dry batteries developed for the purpose by several firms, and characterized by light weight and reasonable shelf-life.

A few remarks on the term *radiosonde* may be of interest. Until recently, there seemed to be a tendency to call these instruments *radio-meteorographs*, a good sound term, but too long. The term *radiosonde* stems from *ballon-sonde*, French for "sounding balloon," which has been an international word for at least thirty years, in the company of many other aeronautical terms, such as *longeron* and *hangar*. The United States Weather Bureau has now officially adopted "radiosonde" in preference to "radio-meteorograph," and we may consider the term established.[16]

7. The Time-Interval Radiosonde

(a) *General principles—The Olland cycle*

The fundamental principle of the time-interval type of radiosonde was worked out by Olland in 1875, and may be represented by some such diagram as Fig. 146. Suppose an arm OM, carrying an electrical contact at the end M,

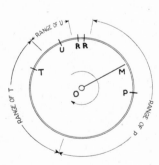

FIGURE 146
The Olland cycle,
fundamental form.

to be rotating at a uniform speed about O. On a circle with O as centre, let there be at least five contacts so arranged that M touches each of them for a moment once in each revolution. Let the contact P be connected to a barometer of some sort, in such a way that it moves over the arc indicated for the entire range of pressures to be transmitted. In a similar way let T be connected to a thermometer and U to a hygrometer. Finally, let us provide two fixed reference contacts RR, identifiable by the invariable interval between them and forming a zero of time to which the signals corresponding to contacts P, T, and U may be referred.

Now if a radio transmitter is caused to send out

---

[15]Radiosondes for special purposes may have a photocell, a Geiger counter, etc. We are dealing here with the usual instrument for measuring pressure, temperature, and humidity.

[16]SAMUELS, L. T., *Bull. Amer. Met. Soc.*, **19**:407-408, 1938.

a signal each time the moving contact M touches one of the five contacts R, R, P, T, and U, a series of intervals can be measured at a distant receiving station, and these measurements converted into values of pressure, temperature, and humidity by referring to a previous calibration.

The precision with which this can be done depends on how small a part of a revolution can be distinguished. If, for instance, OM is driven by an ordinary watch at the rate of one r.p.m., the watch will give 300 ticks per revolution, and therefore OM will move around the circle in only 300 discrete motions. Let us suppose, now, that the contact P moves over 60 per cent of the circle, and covers a range of 900 mb in pressure. Sixty per cent of the circle is 180 ticks; therefore the precision of a pressure reading is ±2.5 mb. If, however, the arm be driven continuously, as by an electric motor, the precision depends on the resolving power of the receiving apparatus.

A system such as that of Fig. 146 is mechanically awkward. To simplify the mechanism and to improve the precision of reading, the schemes shown in Fig. 147 were devised. In Fig. 147a, the moving arm has been replaced by a rotating helix, such as a thin wire wound in a screw thread cut on an insulating cylinder.[17] The contacts attached to the meteorological apparatus (only one is shown in the figure), and the reference contacts, each touch the helix once in a revolution, the time interval between the resulting signals being a linear function of the height of the meteorological contact above the base. The advantage of this scheme is that any or all of the meteorological elements may occupy more than one complete cycle, indeed any number of

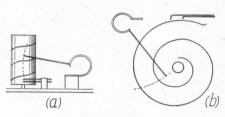

(a)　　　　　　　　　　(b)

FIGURE 147

Two modifications of the time cycle arrangement.

cycles except that there is a limit to the amount of overlapping that can be tolerated. In practice 2 or $2\frac{1}{2}$ cycles is sufficient for the pressure contact, 2 for the temperature, one quarter of a cycle or less for the humidity.

A contact sliding over a cylinder in a curved path of this sort does not remain in one plane, and so will press harder when it is opposite its axis of rotation than when it is near the ends of the cylinder. In order that the motion of the contacts may lie in one plane, an equiangular spiral may be substituted for the helix, as in Fig. 147b, with the further advantage that an insulating cylinder is not required. Again any desired number of cycles can be obtained by choosing an appropriate pitch for the spiral.

The *accuracy* of all these arrangements depends chiefly on the uniformity of the speed of revolution over the entire cycle from one reference contact to the next. Features of design may influence the attainable accuracy for good or bad, but a uniform rate of revolution must, within the required limits, be obtained.

[17]LANGE, K. O., *Bull. Amer. Met. Soc.*, **18**:107-126, 1937.

The time-cycle type of radiosonde will be illustrated by reference to the form developed by R. C. Jacobsen of the Canadian Service, with the collaboration of the Sangamo Company, Ltd., and the Stromberg-Carlson Telephone Manufacturing Company, Ltd., of Toronto.

(b) *The Canadian radiosonde*

The meteorological part of this instrument is shown in Fig. 148, and the scheme of the spiral and contacts in Fig. 149.

FIGURE 148
The Canadian radiosonde, meteorological part.

The spiral A is driven at about $4\frac{1}{2}$ r.p.m. by an electric motor of special construction, consisting of a permanent bar magnet B rotating inside a rectangular coil C. An eccentric on the shaft of the magnet vibrates a spring against an adjustable contact; this spring is weighted to have a natural frequency of about 1,500 vibrations per minute, and the motor revolves at this number of r.p.m. with great accuracy, its speed being practically independent of the voltage and changing only slowly with temperature. It is run from the 4.5 volt battery which supplies the filament of the transmitting tube, and develops ample power on approximately 0.12 watts.

The spiral is insulated from the frame of the instrument. This frame carries an aneroid bellows E, a bimetal F, and a hygrometric hair G, each with its contact arm, which moves over the spiral as shown in Fig. 149. Once in each revolution, the end of the spiral makes contact with the reference contacts H and J. The pressure and temperature arms are provided with special quick-break devices as shown at K; the thin wire is fastened to the arm by insulating cement, and completes the circuit through the spiral only for the moment after contact but before the lateral pressure pushes it away from the arm.

An excellent feature of this instrument is that there are no pivots in any of the meteorological elements, hence no opportunity for lost motion.

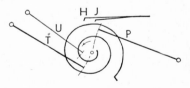

FIGURE 149
The Canadian radiosonde, scheme of contacts.

The transmitter operates on a frequency of 65 megacycles and consists of one tube (type 1H4G), a small inductance, a resistance and a mica condenser. The circuit is shown in Fig. 150. During the first part of a flight the filament is of course greatly over-loaded, but the tube will oscillate down to a voltage of 3.5 volts with 60 volts on the plate. Actually there is an ample reserve of power with three medium-size flashlight cells and the smallest obtainable "B" batteries.

The entire instrument—meteorograph, transmitter, and batteries—is contained in a special case of corrugated cardboard covered with bright metal foil. Suitable radiation shielding and ventilation are provided. For shipment the cardboard case contains the entire assembly,[18] and packs economically. For the ascent, the aerial is attached below, and a silk parachute between the radiosonde and the balloon.

The signals are received on any short-wave receiver of adequate range and sensitivity (1 microvolt per metre), amplified and fed to a relay. This relay operates a chronograph[19] of special design, which will be described by reference to the diagram, Fig. 151.

A roll of wax-surfaced record paper 11 inches wide is fed at a speed of $\frac{1}{2}$ inch per minute from a roll A over a drum B on to a horizontal table C, being finally re-rolled at D. Just above the surface of the paper travels an endless chain, carrying four styli, and so dimensioned that the distance between the styli is equal to 4/3 of the pitch diameter of either of the sprockets F. The axes of

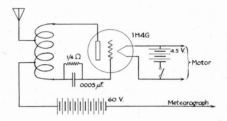

FIGURE 150
The Canadian radiosonde, transmitter circuit.

these sprockets are horizontal, and the entire assembly is mounted on a frame which can be displaced by an electromagnet through about 1/16 inch in the direction indicated by the arrow G, and returned by a spring. The electromagnet is controlled by the relay mentioned above.

When no signal is being received, the styli pass across the paper in constant succession, taking about 13 seconds (the time of a cycle in the radiosonde) to travel about 6 inches, the succeeding stylus coming on to the chart before the preceding one has left, and each drawing a fine straight line nearly at right angles to the direction of motion of the paper. Because of the constant motion of the paper, these lines are about $\frac{1}{8}$ inch apart. Each signal produces a rectangular jog in the line, the beginning of the jog being an accurate indication of the time at which a contact was made on the radiosonde.

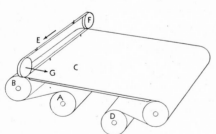

FIGURE 151
The Canadian radiosonde, recording chronograph.

The speed of the styli can be regulated with accuracy, in order to synchronize their travel with the length of the radiosonde cycle. The phase rela-

[18]This is essential if a large programme is contemplated.
[19]Developed from that described by LANGE, K. O., *Bull. Amer. Met. Soc.* **18**:107-126, 1937.

tion between the two motions is chosen so that the double reference contact comes in the interval between the entry of one stylus and the lifting of the preceding one, and therefore the double line of jogs shows at both sides of the sheet.   The appearance of the record is shown schematically in Fig. 152, in which the lines produced by the undeflected styli have been left out.

It may not be possible to keep the reference marks exactly parallel to the edge of the paper, but this does not matter, because the times of the pressure, temperature, and humidity contacts are measured as a fraction of the length of the cycle in which they occur.   Only if there is an unusually great difference between the length of a cycle and of those preceding need it be discarded.

This method of recording has the advantage that the significant points (changes in lapse-rate, etc.) of the record can be picked out on the chronograph, making it unnecessary to evaluate all the available points.

The meteorological part of each radiosonde must be calibrated, but the radio transmitter need take no part in this.   For this reason, and because of

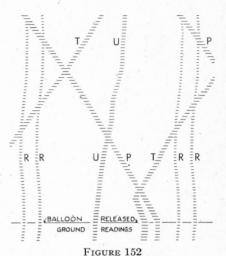

FIGURE 152

The Canadian radiosonde, appearance of record.   R—reference, P—pressure, T—temperature, U—humidity.

the small size of the instrument, it is possible to calibrate twenty-four of them at a time in a baro-thermostat of reasonable dimensions.   The number of points which need be taken on the pressure and temperature curves depends largely on the accuracy with which the spiral is made and centred.

8. The Variable-Audio-Frequency Radiosonde

(a) *General principles*

The possibility of having a variable audio-frequency controlled by meteorological elements depends on a low-frequency vacuum-tube oscillator circuit, some element of which is controlled by a meteorological instrument.   Numerous designs are possible; for example, the radiosonde[20] developed at the National Physical Laboratory uses iron-cored coils, the inductance of which is varied by an aneroid or a thermometer.   Another scheme uses a relaxation oscillator, its frequency controlled by a resistance varying with temperature or humidity.   Whatever scheme is used, a continuous radio-frequency signal is sent out, modulated to the variable audio-frequency or frequencies desired, which may be used simultaneously or one after the other.   These principles will be illustrated by reference to the radiosonde used in the United States so largely at

[20]THOMAS, H. A., *Proc. Roy. Soc. London, A* **167**:227-250, 1938.

present, and originally developed by Diamond, Hinman, Dunsmore, and Lapham[21] at the Bureau of Standards.

(b) The Bureau of Standards audio-modulated radiosonde

(i) General scheme

The general scheme of this radiosonde is as follows. The transmitter sends out a continuous signal, modulated to one of four audio-frequencies: (1) a frequency determined by the resistance of a thermometric element, (2) one depending on a resistance controlled by the relative humidity, (3) a high fixed reference frequency, and (4) a low fixed reference frequency. The change from one audio-frequency to another is effected at known values of the pressure by a barometric switch.

(ii) The transmitter

The electrical circuit is shown in Fig. 153. It should be noted that the two triodes constitute only one vacuum tube (type 19). The triode C generates

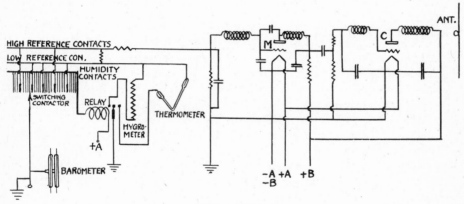

FIGURE 153
The Bureau of Standards Audio-modulated radiosonde, circuit diagram.

oscillations at 65 megacycles per second; the triode M oscillates at one megacycle per second and has a special grid circuit which causes it to block at a frequency depending on the total resistance between grid and cathode. This resistance is furnished either by the thermometer or the hygrometer, except when the reference resistors are connected, as explained below. The range of blocking frequencies is 10 to 200 cycles per second.

(iii) The barometric switch

The barometric switch, like all the other parts of the instrument, is arranged for production in very large quantities. As will be seen from Fig. 154,

[21]DIAMOND, H., HINMAN, W. S., and F. W. DUNMORE, Bur. Stds. J. Res., 20:369-392, 1937; Bull. Amer. Met. Soc., 18:73-99, 1937. DIAMOND, H., HINMAN, W. S., DUNMORE, F. W., and E. G. LAPHAM, Bur. Stds. J. Res., 25:327-367, 1940.

an aneroid causes a contact to move over a series of eighty conducting strips, separated by thicker insulating washers. Every fifth strip is twice as thick as the rest. The entire contact assembly can be moved a short distance parallel to its length, for adjustment. In the circuit every fifth strip is connected either to the high or the low reference resistor, the remaining strips being connected to the humidity resistor, except near the low-pressure end, where all the strips are connected to the reference circuits. When the moving contact is on an insulating washer, the signal corresponding to the temperature is sent out.

FIGURE 154
The Bureau of Standards Audio-modulated radiosonde, barometric switch.

(Courtesy of Julien P. Friez and Sons)

(iv) *The thermometer*

The thermometer element is special to this radiosonde. It consists of a glass capillary bent into a V-shape (Fig. 155), having a bulb on each end, and filled with a special electrolyte which will not freeze at any atmospheric temperatures. Electrolytes have a large negative temperature coefficient of resistance, much larger than the (positive) coefficient of any metal. By careful manufacture, these elements are made interchangeable, thus avoiding a great deal of calibration, and the variations that do occur are taken care of by the use of a special circular slide rule in working out the records. The lag coefficient[22] is low, only about 8 seconds with a ventilation of 500 feet per minute at sea level.

(v) *The humidity element*

Two entirely different forms of hygrometer may be used with this type of radiosonde, (1) a hair hygrometer, and (2) an electrical absorption hygrometer.

(a) *Hair hygrometer*. A "cage" of hairs (Fig. 156a) is connected by levers to a specially-shaped contact which moves along a resistor wound with fine wire. The arrangement has all the usual defects of hair hygrometers at low temperatures, but is preferred by some people because its calibration is relatively simple and certain.

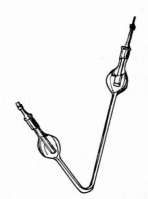

FIGURE 155
The Bureau of Standards Audio-modulated radiosonde, electrolytic thermometer.

(Courtesy of Washington Institute of Technology)

---

[22]See p. 56.

(β) *The electrical hygrometer.*[23] In its present form the electrical hygrometer of Dunmore consists of a thin aluminum tube about $\frac{3}{8}$ inch diameter and $1\frac{11}{16}$ inch long.   The outer surface of this is covered with an insulating, water-resistant varnish, on which is wound a *bifilar* coil of palladium wire. A moisture-sensitive film, containing a suitable amount of lithium chloride, is put on over the palladium wires, and it is the resistance of this film between the wires that is used to determine the frequency at which the signal from the radiosonde is modulated.

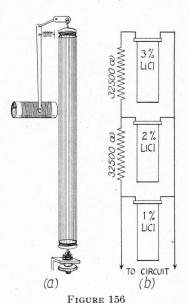

The relation between resistance (or frequency) and relative humidity depends on the amount of LiCl. For use in the radiosonde, three such tubes, with 3, 2, and 1 per cent LiCl respectively, are used in a parallel circuit (Fig 156b) to give a fairly uniform relation.   The resistance also depends on the temperature, making a large correction necessary; but it is claimed that with careful manufacture a standard correction may be used.

There is no doubt whatever that this type of hygrometer is much more responsive than the hair at low temperatures. The large temperature corections are a disadvantage, and the future success of the method will probably depend on how closely the manufacture of the tubes can be standardized.

FIGURE 156

Hygrometers of the Bureau of Standards Audio-modulated radiosonde, (*a*) hair hygrometer, (*b*) electrical hygrometers in parallel circuit.

(vi) *The case*

The outer case of the radiosonde is made of corrugated cardboard covered with foil, arranged so that the various adjustments can easily be made before the flight.   Inner shields in a ventilation tube protect the thermometer from radiation and the hygrometer from rain.

(vii) *The receiving equipment*

The signals from the radiosonde are received on a sensitive receiver of suitable characteristics, and the audio-frequency output fed to an electronic frequency-meter. This device furnishes a D.C. output proportional to the frequency of the A.C. input, but independent of its voltage or wave form.   In order to make a record, a special high-speed recording meter is used; this may take several forms, which will not be described here, except to say that a continuous line is obtained on a roll chart, giving almost instantaneous values of the audio-frequency.

[23]DUNMORE, F. W., *Bur. Stds. J. Res.*, **20**:723-744, 1938; **23**:701-714, 1939. *Bull. Amer. Met. Soc.*, **19**:225-243, 1938; **21**:249-256, 1940.

A short section of such a record is reproduced in Fig. 157. It consists of discrete indications of frequency, the horizontal lines joining them being made by the pen in its rapid motion from one position to another, each time the barometric switch on the radiosonde passed on to a contact or off it. The small fluctuations are due to radio interference. The low reference contacts, adjusted to 160 cycles per second, are shown at L, and the high reference contacts at H; the humidity contacts at U—U and the temperature (intervals between

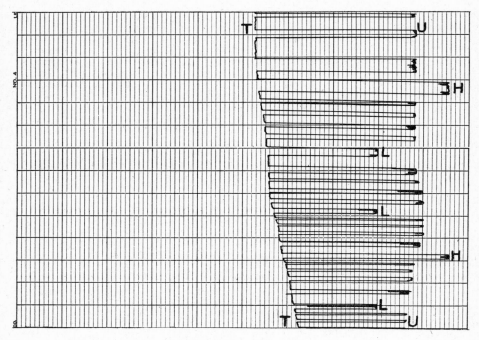

FIGURE 157
The Bureau of Standards Audio-modulated radiosonde, appearance of the record.

contacts) at T—T. Each discontinuity represents a certain pressure, determined by individual calibration and recognizable by its position in the series of short and long contacts, high and low reference frequencies. Corresponding values of pressure and temperature, pressure and humidity, can easily be written down, though it is not quite as easy to locate the significant points as in the time-cycle type of record.

(viii) *Calibration*

The pressure elements are calibrated individually under a bell-jar or in a barostat, the technique varying with the manufacturer. The thermometers are *tested* rather than calibrated, being supposed uniform; the same is true of the electrical hygrometer. The hair elements are of course calibrated, and the radio transmitters are standardized as to the relation between resistance and frequency. The entire process of manufacture is an exceptionally interesting example of mass-production technique; indeed, the instrument could not well be produced otherwise.

9. The Variable-Radio-Frequency Radiosonde

(a) General principles

While the two types of radiosonde described above seem the most promising at the present time, other types have been used with success. One of the first successful radiosondes, associated with the name of Duckert,[24] was of the type in which a variable *radio*-frequency signal is emitted. In Duckert's various instruments the pressure was indicated by discrete contacts, as in the meteorograph just described. We shall therefore illustrate the type by reference to the Finnish radiosonde developed by Väisälä,[25] which transmits all three elements by variations in radio-frequency.

It is obvious that a suitable variation of radio-frequency can easily be produced by a small movement of one plate of a condenser. Actually the difficulty is not to vary the frequency at will, but to avoid variations due to causes which have no simple relation to the meteorological elements which it is desired to measure.

(b) The Finnish radiosonde

An unusual and ingenious solution of the above-mentioned difficulty has been provided by Väisälä, whose radiosonde is shown diagrammatically in Fig. 158. In this, the tank condenser of the oscillating circuit is one of five condensers which are connected in sequence by a rotary switch; the switch is operated by a light anemometer cup wheel (not shown). Three of the condensers are variable, their capacities having a unitary relation to the pressure, the temperature, and the relative humidity; the other two are fixed air condensers, one having a capacity slightly

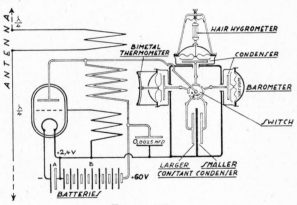

FIGURE 158
The Finnish radiosonde (*after Väisälä*).

less, the other slightly greater, than any values taken by the variable ones.

[24]DUCKERT, P., *Beitr. z. Phys. d.f. Atm.*, **18**:68-80, 1931; **20**:303-311, 1933.

[25]VÄISÄLÄ, V., *Mitt. d. met. Insts. d. Univ. Helsinki*, no. 35, 1937 (*Comm. Phys.-Math. Soc. Scient. Fennica* **9**: no. 9, 1937). This paper (in English) is a delightful account of the growth of an idea.

In this way, the frequency interval between the fixed condensers serves as a unit in which the other frequency variations are measured.

The theory of this is perhaps more interesting than the details of construction. If we let

λ = the wavelength sent with a given "meteorological condenser"
λ_1 = " " " " the larger fixed condenser
λ_2 = " " " " the smaller fixed condenser

C, C_1, C_2 = the capacities of the condensers
C_0 = the plate-to-cathode capacity of the vacuum-tube
L = the inductance of the tank circuit,

then by writing three expressions

$$\lambda^2 = 4\pi^2 L(C+C_0)$$
$$\lambda_1^2 = 4\pi^2 L(C_1+C_0)$$
$$\lambda_2^2 = 4\pi^2 L(C_2+C_0)$$

for the three wavelengths, and eliminating L and C_0, we obtain a relation

$$\frac{\lambda_1^2 - \lambda^2}{\lambda_1^2 - \lambda_2^2} = \frac{C_1 - C}{C_1 - C_2} = y \qquad \dots\dots\dots(10.1).$$

Now since C_1 and C_2 are constant and C is a function of one of the meteorological elements, y is a function of this element only.

Now if the plates of the tuning condenser of the receiver are semi-circular, λ^2 is linear in its scale reading n.

Thus $$y = \frac{n_1 - n}{n_1 - n_2} \qquad \dots\dots\dots(10.2).$$

It will immediately be seen from this equation that the correction for frequency drift, referred to above, is valid. It is further shown[26] by Väisälä that the scale of the receiving condenser will be approximately hyperbolic in pressure, temperature, and the length of the hygrograph hair.

A recording receiver is used, in which a paper-covered drum is rotated with the plates of the tuning condenser. A carriage with an electrically operated stylus is moved parallel to the axis of the drum at a constant rate. The operator tunes each of the five signals in turn, pressing a button to operate the stylus when each is tuned in to his satisfaction. In appearance the record is rather like that of the Canadian radiosonde described above, except that dots are substituted for the jogs in a line. The evaluation is done with a special hyperbolic diagonal scale.

10. The Code-Sending Radiosonde

The idea of a radiosonde which should transmit the indications of the meteorological instruments in the form of code letters (combinations of dots and dashes) was early developed by Moltchanoff.[27] The advantage of such

---

[26]VÄISÄLÄ, *l.c.*, p. 9.
[27]MOLTCHANOFF, P., *Beitr. z. Phys. d.f. Atm.*, **14**:45-47, 1928, and many other papers.

an instrument is that its indications may be received on any suitable wireless set by anyone who can read Morse code.

All such instruments developed so far depend on what has come to be called the "comb" principle; that is to say, one or more contact arms, connected to the meteorological instruments, travel over an assembly of insulated contacts arranged in a row. The indications of such a radiosonde are of necessity discontinuous, and it is probably on this account that the type has found little favour in most countries. There is the further disadvantage that the contacts, which must slide or roll, offer some resistance to the free motion of the meteorological instruments. This may not be serious in the case of the aneroid, but is likely to give some trouble with the bimetal and more with the hair hygrograph.

For these reasons we shall merely refer the reader to two recent and easily accessible papers,[28] illustrating the diversity of schemes that may be used to translate pressure, temperature, and humidity indications into telegraphic code.

11. The Errors of Radiosondes

The time has not yet arrived when it can be said that one general type of radiosonde is better than another. Rather than make comparisons which time (and the ingenuity of engineers) may prove to be ill-considered, we shall deal briefly with the very important question, how far the indications of any radiosonde can be trusted, in view of the properties of the instrumental elements that are built into it.

Similar questions have been in the mind of every honest aerologist since the first *ballon-sonde* was launched. The materials for an answer are to be found in chapter III as to thermometers, and in chapter IV, with less exactitude, as to the hair hygrometer. Numerical applications have been made by Nyberg[29] in a most interesting paper.

For the thermometer, Nyberg derives our equation (3.6), and applies the results to a generalized winter sounding of the form shown by the temperature height curve of Fig. 159 (solid line). A strong inversion extends to 600 metres with a constant lapse rate above this. Assuming a rate of ascent of 300 metres per minute, he calculates the temperatures indicated by thermometers for which λ is 15, 30, and 60 seconds respectively.

Now the lag coefficient of the thermometer in the Finnish radiosonde with this amount of venti-

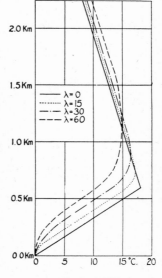

FIGURE 159
Errors due to lag of
radiosonde thermometer
(*after Nyberg*).

[28]PICCARD, J., and H. LARSEN, *Rev. Sci. Inst.*, **10**:352-355, 1939. INSJE, C. M. A., and J. L. VAN SOEST, *Q.J. Roy. Met. Soc.*, **66**:317-322, 1940.

[29]NYBERG, A., *Medd. Stat. Met.-Hydr. Anstalt (Stockholm)*, no. 32, 1940.

lation is about 12 sec., and other types with bi-metals are probably not very different in this regard. Note that the curve is rounded off, and the position of maximum temperature is shifted upwards.

A further point is the excellence or otherwise of the shielding against radiation. This can best be determined by a comparison of ascending and descending records during the daytime. It is well known that many radiosondes, otherwise excellent, are deficient in this regard.

As to the hair, Nyberg does not make use of the equation (4.16) due to Spilhaus, but prefers to make the lag coefficient γ a function of the relative humidity, and to write

$$r_f - r = \gamma \frac{dr}{dt} \qquad \dots\dots\dots (10.3).$$

Measurements showed that γ increased very rapidly when the temperature fell below 0°C., as shown in the following table (γ in seconds):

θ	20	15	10	5	0	−5	−10	−15	−20	−25	−30°C.
γ	32	37	45	55	75	115	175	275	440	710	1050

This is for $r_f =$ about 90 per cent; according to Kleinschmidt[30] the lag is three times as great at $r_f = 40$ per cent, and becomes infinite at $\theta = -40°C.$

The result is that under the conditions prevailing in the upper troposphere the readings of the hair hygrometer are completely unreliable. Fig. 160, after Nyberg, shows the indication of a hair having a lag coefficient of 60 sec. at 0°C. in passing through a hypothetical cloud layer, the actual humidity being shown by the solid line and the indicated humidity by the line of dashes. The indication never reaches 40 per cent, but comes to a standstill at 49 per cent when the radiosonde reaches an elevation of 8,400 m.

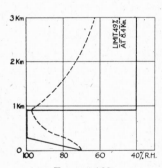

FIGURE 160

Errors due to lag of radiosonde hygrometer (*after Nyberg*).

Curtiss, Astin, Stockmann, and Brown[31] state that goldbeaters' skin is several times as responsive as human hair. If this statement is correct, such a hygrometer will repay study, especially as it can be made to give better control of a pen or contact than the hair can provide. There is no doubt that the electrical hygrometer responds much more rapidly; twenty times as fast at 24°C. and 68 to 35 per cent R.H., according to a recent paper.[32] It is fairly evident that it responds more rapidly in the stratosphere also.

Less is heard about the errors of the pressure element. There seems to be

[30]KLEINSCHMIDT, E., *Beitr. z. Phys. d.f. Atm.*, **2**:99-124, 1908.

[31]CURTISS, L. F., ASTIN, A. V., STOCKMANN, L. L., and B. W. BROWN, *Bur. Stds. J. Res.*, **22**:97-103, 1939. This paper describes a time-cycle radiosonde.

[32]DIAMOND, HINMANN, DUNMORE, and LAPHAM, *l.c.*

no difficulty in obtaining an overall accuracy of 5 mb with the pressure-switch type of radiosonde, without compensation or correction for temperature errors in the aneroid. With corrections such as are applied to the readings of the Canadian radiosonde, an accuracy of 3 mb is probably obtainable, part of this being calibration error and the rest secular change in the aneroid.

12. Special Uses of Radiosondes

In addition to the ordinary meteorological radiosondes in the service of daily forecasting, a number of special instruments have been constructed for physical researches, especially in the measurement of solar radiation, ozone, and cosmic rays in the stratosphere. The familiar circuit in which a photocell discharges a condenser has been used by O'Brien, Steadman, and Stewart[33] to control a transmitter which emits short signals at a rate proportional to the incident flux of solar radiation. A circuit on the same general principles as the Bureau of Standards radiosonde described above, except that a photocell controls the frequency of modulation, has been developed by Coblentz and Stair[34] for the measurement of ultraviolet radiation, and used by them[35] to determine the distribution of ozone in the stratosphere.

Another interesting radiosonde is that of Curtiss, Astin, Stockmann, and Brown,[36] for the measurement of cosmic rays. A high-speed counter with an integrating circuit was employed for this purpose, short signals being sent down to the ground and printed on a tape chronograph. Of course the instrument included a barograph for the transmission of indications from which the height could be estimated.

A possible application which has been the subject of a good deal of research is the radio pilot balloon. Accurate direction-finding from two stations (or else in two planes) is involved, and the difficulties are considerable ; but a successful solution will make it possible to measure upper winds above a continuous cloud layer, an impossibility with ordinary pilot-balloon technique. The importance of this to aviation needs no emphasis.

13. Calibration Apparatus

The sort of calibration apparatus required for radiosondes depends largely on whether the entire mechanism must be calibrated as a unit, or whether the pressure, temperature, and humidity elements can be tested separately. In the latter event, the ordinary apparatus used for calibrating surface instruments needs only to be modified to fit it for mass production.

For radiosondes that must be calibrated as a unit, some form of baro-thermostat is essential if a large-scale programme is in view. This should

[33]Abstract in *Bull. Amer. Met. Soc.*, **18**:352, 1937.

[34]STAIR, R., and W. W. COBLENTZ, *Bur. Stds. J. Res.*, **20**:185-215, 1938. COBLENTZ and STAIR, *Bull. Amer. Met. Soc.*, **18**:345-352, 1937. STAIR, *Bur. Stds. J. Res.*, **22**:295-305, 1939.

[35]COBLENTZ, W. W., and R. STAIR, *Bur. Stds. J. Res.*, **22**:573-606, 1939.

[36]CURTISS, L. F., ASTIN, A. V., STOCKMANN, L. L., and B. W. BROWN, *Bur. Stds. J. Res.*, **23**:585-595, 1939.

permit simultaneous variation of pressure and temperature, if possible at any desired rate, but at least in steps of any desired magnitude, with provision for holding the conditions constant at any point. It is probably too much to ask for controlled humidity while this is going on, but worth considering if a very large programme is being started. The cooling should be by mechanical refrigeration, *propane* being the most suitable refrigerant for the range of temperatures needed. The temperature should be controlled automatically, and it is desirable to be able to pre-set any temperature and have the chamber come down (or up) to this point and stop.

Adequate ventilation should be provided, even at low pressures (40 mb); and thermocouples should be available to determine whether all parts of the working space are at the same temperature. Above all, the chamber should be amply large enough to take the desired number of instruments without crowding.[37]

14. Radio-Wave Soundings

An entirely new method of exploring the atmosphere, and in particular of determining the height of discontinuities (inversions, upper fronts, etc.) has been discussed in a series of papers by A. W. Friend[38] and others. In this method, short pulses of electromagnetic waves (123 metres' wavelength, for example) are sent upwards, just as in the well-known investigations of the ionosphere. It is found that these waves are faintly but adequately reflected from discontinuities in the atmosphere, the strength of the reflected wave being proportional to the rate of change of dielectric constant with height. Since the dielectric constant of the air is a function of both its density and its water-vapour content, discontinuities in these elements will show in the reflection pattern. The method is in its infancy, but shows much promise.

----

[37]A baro-thermostat incorporating as many as possible of these features is under construction at Toronto as this book goes to press.

[38]FRIEND, A. W., *Bull. Amer. Met. Soc.*, **20**:202-205, 1939; **22**:53-59, 1941; *J. Aeron. Sc.*, **7**: 347-352, 1940. FRIEND, A. W., and R. C. COLWELL, *Proc. I.R.E.*, **27**:626, 1939.

INDEX

A

ABBE, CLEVELAND, errors of thermometers, 62
    weight barometer, 19
Absolute humidity, definition, 87
Absolute scale of temperature, 52
Absorption hygrometers, 100
Accuracy, confused with sensitivity, 2
    definition, 2
    special meaning of, in meteorological observations, 4
Aeroplane meteorographs, 189
Aeroplane thermometer, 189
ALBRECHT, F., hot-wire anemometer, 143
Alidade, 173
Air, evaporating power of, 113
Aircraft, thermometers for use on, 189
"Air meter," 124
Anemobiagraph, 139
Anemograph, defined, 123
Anemometer, bridled, 133
    condenser discharge, 129
    contact, 128
    cup, 125
        combined with wind vane, 130
        experiments on, 126
    defined, 123
    DINES, 135
    heated, 131
    helicoidal, 124
    hot-wire, 142
    magneto, 131
    mountain, 131
    normal-plate, 132
    pendulum, 132
    portable, 128
    pressure-plate, 132
    pressure-tube, 134
        distant indication with, 142
        errors of, 141
        mounting of, 140
    propellor, 124
    rotation, special, 131
    windmill, 124
Anemometers, classification of, 123
    exposure of, 143
    rotation, 124
Anemovane, 130
Aneroid, compensation of, for temperature, 42
    PAULIN system, 39
    steel, 40
Aneroid barometer, 11, 37
Aneroids, accuracy of, 45
    elastic errors of, 44
Angular speed of clouds, 168
ASSMANN psychrometer, 54, 92
    heated, 177
ASTIN, A. V., see CURTISS
Atmometers, 113
Atmosphere, water-economy of, 102

B

Ball bearings, 7, 41
    in barograph aneroid, 41
    miniature, 7
Balloons, bursting thickness of, 146
    ceiling, 170
    colours of, 146
    common weights of, 146
    gases used to inflate, 146
    inflation of, 148
        excess pressure during, 151
        safety measures in, 150
    manufacture of, 145
    materials for, 145
    pilot-, 145
    rate of ascent of, 148
    sounding-, 186
Bar, definition, 13
Barograph, aneroid, 41
    photographic, 23
    siphon, 18
    weight, 21
Barometer, aneroid, 11, 37
    elastic, 11, 37
    fixed-cistern, 16
    FORTIN, 14
    "height" of the, 11
    "Kew," 16
    marine, 17
    mercury, 11, 14
        corrections to, 27
    movable-scale, 18
    normal, 23
    siphon, 18
    weight, 19
    theory of, 20
Barometers, comparison of, 32
    installation of, 26
    mercury, errors of, 33
        general accuracy of, 37
        test chamber for, 36
        transportation of, 25
        verticality of, 36
Barometer tubes, filling of, 24
Baro-thermostat, 205
BATE, A. E., capillarity, 34
Bearings, 7
BEAUFORT scale of wind force, 118
BENIOFF, H., and B. GUTENBERG, variograph, 50
BENNDORF, H., and W. ZIMMERMANN, variograph, 49
BILHAM, E. G., response of thermometers, 58
    (and see HIGGINS)
Bi-metal, stiffness of, 71
Bi-metal thermometer, 68
BIRKELAND, B. J., see HESSELBERG
"Bottle thermometer," 81

207